Enlarged Edition

Diagramming Step by Step

One Hundred and Fifty-Five Steps to Excellence in Sentence Diagramming

EUGENE R. MOUTOUX

Butler Books
Louisville

The system of diagramming used in this workbook was introduced by Stephen Clark in 1863, modified by Alonzo Reed and Brainerd Kellogg (*A Work of English Grammar and Composition*, 1877), and expanded by Homer C. House and Susan Emolyn Harman (*Descriptive English Grammar*, 2nd ed., Prentice Hall, 1950).

ISBN: 978-1-953058-67-6

Published by:

Butler Books
P.O. Box 7311
Louisville, KY 40257
(502) 897-9393
Fax (502) 897-9797
www.butlerbooks.com

This book is dedicated to

Mary Joan (Joni) Moutoux,

my wife of 41 years,
who died on February 18, 2006.
Her kindness and optimism inspired those around her.
She was a loving companion to me
and a nurturing mother to our children.

"Put one foot in front of the other
And soon you´ll be walkin´ ´cross the floor."
- Jules Bass, "Santa Claus is Comin´ to Town"

Foreword

Diagramming Step by Step: One Hundred and Fifty-five Steps to Diagramming Excellence is the second of my books on sentence diagramming published by Butler Books of Louisville, Kentucky. The other, *Drawing Sentences: A Guide to Diagramming*, is a compilation of three shorter, previously published books: *A First Book of Sentence Diagramming*, *A Second Book of Sentence Diagramming*, and *A Workbook of Sentence Diagramming*. It is, in effect, two complete courses in Reed & Kellogg diagramming. A third book, *Analyzing the Grammar of Literature: Diagrams of 130 Long Sentences from British and American Writers*, consists of 130 sentences ranging in length from 70 words to 472 words. Its intended audience is people who know diagramming well and are looking for a challenge.

While both *Diagramming Step by Step* and *Drawing Sentences* feature model diagrams, explanatory material, exercises, and answers to exercises, *Diagramming Step by Step* supplements this basic structure with 24 pages of writing tips related to the topics of the lessons in which they appear and with 30 pages, separate from the 24 lessons, of introduction to modern linguistics and tree diagramming. The examples and exercises of *Diagramming Step by Step* are completely different from the examples and exercises in my other books of sentence diagramming.

As the subtitle of *Diagramming Step by Step* implies, this book contains 155 examples of Reed & Kellogg diagrams. Each example is accompanied by an explanation. Each lessons offers, in addition to examples and explanations, an exercise consisting of several sentences to be diagrammed by the student; "answers" (diagrams and explanations) for all 247 sentences in these exercises are in the back of the book. In a section entitled "People in the Park," a storyteller (that's me) tells stories about the lives of people in the park, and the student is asked to diagram the sentences of these stories. Grammar hints are provided for those who need them. This section includes 140 sentences for the student to diagram; again, answers are in the back. A section of ten sentences with more than 100 words each completes the Reed & Kellogg section of this book. Each of these sentences is broken into several parts for ease of diagramming; the student is asked to diagram the parts and then put them together to form a diagram of the whole sentence. My diagrams of the separate parts as well as of the complete sentences are in the back of the book. The final section of the book offers readers a chance to broaden their understanding of syntax. You will perhaps be surprised to learn that modern linguistics has much to offer and that tree diagramming illustrates certain syntactic relationships more accurately than Reed & Kellogg diagramming. I think we need to see these improvements and acknowledge them.

Should you buy this book if you already have *Drawing Sentences*? Not necessarily, but if you are looking for additional diagramming challenges for yourself or your students, you will find plenty in this book. Should you buy this book instead of *Drawing Sentences*? Again, not necessarily. In general, I think *Drawing Sentences* is a better choice for younger learners and *Diagramming Step by Step* a better choice for older teens and adults. Whichever book or books you decide to use, I wish you many pleasant hours of learning about the structure of the English language.

Table of Contents

~ Traditional Grammatical Terms and Diagramming Symbols ~

Absolute phrase - a phrase that has a logical, but not a grammatical, connection to the rest of the sentence. See *nominative absolute*.

Active voice - a characteristic of transitive verbs that indicates the relationship of the verb to the subject as doer or performer. A transitive verb is in the active voice when the subject of the sentence is the agent, i.e., when the subject is doing something.

Adjective - a word that modifies (qualifies, describes, limits) a noun, pronoun, or equivalent expression. One differentiates between *attributive adjectives* and *predicate adjectives* according to their position relative to the modified nouns and pronouns.

Adjective clause - a clause that functions as an adjective by modifying (qualifying, describing, limiting) a noun, pronoun, or equivalent expression. There are two types of adjective clauses: 1) *relative clauses* and 2) clauses linked to nouns in other clauses by means of a *relative adverb*.

Adverb - a word that modifies verbs, adjectives, and other adverbs, as well as prepositions, prepositional phrases, conjunctions, clauses, and sentences

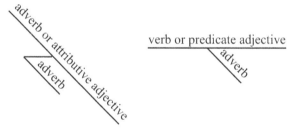

Adverbial objective - a noun or pronoun used as an adverb (indirect objects are included among adverbial objectives)

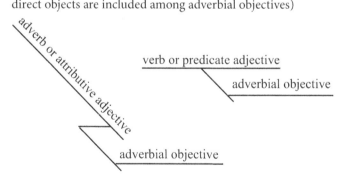

Antecedent - a word, phrase, or clause to which a pronoun refers (for which a pronoun stands)

Appositive - a word or group of words whose purpose is to identify or explain another word or group of words in the same sentence. The appositive usually follows the word(s) with which it is in apposition. Appositives can be restrictive or non-restrictive. An example of a restrictive appositive is the word *John* in the phrase *his brother John* (he has more than one brother; no comma is used between *brother* and *John*); on the other hand, *John* is a non-restrictive appositive in *his brother, John* (John is his only brother;

a comma separates the two nouns).

Article - definite (*the*) and indefinite (*a, an*)

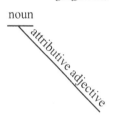

Attributive adjective - an adjective that either precedes the noun or pronoun it modifies (*a pleasant evening, a certain someone*) or comes immediately after it (e.g., *there will be time enough for that tomorrow* or *let's do something different*)

Auxiliary verb - a helping verb. Auxiliary verbs help to form such things as tense, voice, emphasis, and mood. They are underlined in the following examples: the present progressive *am seeing*, *are seeing*, and *is seeing*; the emphatic *do see* and *did see*; the perfect tenses *has seen*, *had seen*, and *will have seen*; the future *will see* and *shall see*, the passive *is seen*, *was seen*, *will be seen*, etc.; and the modal forms *must see*, *can see*, *may see*, etc.

Clause - a group of words with a subject and a predicate

Comparative degree - forms of adjectives and adverbs with the suffix *-(e)r* or with a preceding *more*, e.g., *larger, more beautiful, faster, more abundantly*; also *worse*. Comparisons using the comparative degree and the relative adverb *than* are called unequal comparisons.

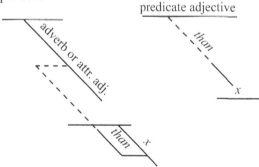

Complement - a term that includes subjective complement (predicate nominative and predicate adjective), direct object, indirect object, objective complement and retained object

Complementary infinitive - an infinitive used to complete certain modal-like verbs. The complementary infinitives are underlined in the following examples: *they ought to study, she used to collect stamps, I have to prepare a speech, he is going to announce the winners, you are to travel to London.*

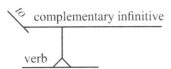

Complex sentence - a sentence containing at least one dependent (subordinate) clause

Compound sentence - a sentence containing at least two independent (main) clauses

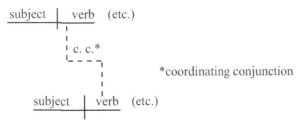

*coordinating conjunction

Compound-complex sentence - a sentence containing two or more independent (main) clauses and at least one dependent (subordinate) clause

Conjunction - a word that connects words, phrases, and clauses. One distinguishes two kinds of conjunctions: *coordinating conjunctions* and *subordinating conjunctions.*

Conjunctive adverb - a word that, like a conjunction, connects and, like an adverb, modifies. There are two kinds of conjunctive adverbs: *transitional adverbs* (*however, moreover, therefore,* etc.) and *relative adverbs* (*when, while, where,* etc.).

Coordinating conjunction - a word that connects words, phrases, and clauses of equal importance. The principal coordinating conjunctions are *and, or, but,* and *nor.* See *compound sentence.*

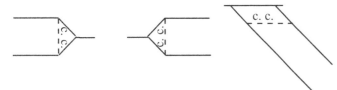

Correlative adverbs - the adverb pairs *as . . . as, so . . . as, so . . . that, then . . . when, there . . . where,* and *the . . . the.* Each of these adverb pairs can be restated as a pair of prepositional phrases, with the second of the two containing a relative pronoun (thus the second adverb is called a relative adverb) and the first containing the antecedent (e.g., *as . . . as* can be restated as *in the degree in which*).

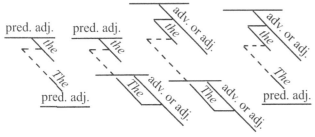

Correlative conjunctions - two-part conjunctions such as *both . . . and, either . . . or,* and *neither . . . nor.*

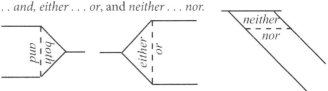

Definite article - English has only one definite article: *the.* It designates the noun it modifies as specific or as previously mentioned.

Demonstrative adjectives - *this, that, these, those.* These adjectives are used to point out someone or something.

Demonstrative pronouns - *this, that, these, those.* Like all pronouns, they are used as noun substitutes.

Dependent clause - also called subordinate clause. A dependent clause functions as an adverb, an adjective, or a noun; it is dependent upon, or subordinate to, an independent (main) clause.

Direct address - a noun or phrase indicating the person(s) spoken to; sometimes called a vocative.

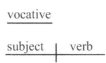

Direct object - a noun, pronoun, or equivalent expression that names the direct recipient of the action of a transitive verb. Not all sentences have direct objects. You can identify a direct object by asking *whom?* or *what?* immediately after a non-linking verb.

subject	verb	direct object

Elliptical clause - a clause with an unexpressed, but understood, word or words. In diagrams, *x*'s represent unexpressed words.

Equal comparison - a comparison using the positive degree of the adjective or adverb and the correlatives *as . . . as* or *so . . . as.*

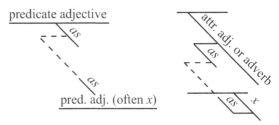

Expletive - a word with a function but with little or no meaning. For example, in the following sentences *there, that,* and *whether* are expletives: *There is a cat on the roof. Did you hear that the game has been canceled? I don't know whether she will be able to attend.*

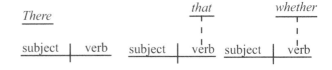

Finite verb - a verb that has person and number. Participles,

~ 2 ~

gerunds, and infinitives are nonfinite verbs.

Future tense - a tense that is formed by combining the auxiliary verbs *shall* and *will* with the present infinitive (without *to*)

Future-perfect tense - a tense that is formed by combining the auxiliary verbs *shall* and *will* with the present-perfect infinitive (without *to*)

Gerund - a verbal noun; a word ending in *-ing* that is both verb and noun

Imperative sentence - a sentence that expresses a command or a request. The subject, *you*, is usually unexpressed.

Indefinite article - English has only two forms of the indefinite article: *a* and *an*.

Indefinite pronoun - a word like *each, every, enough, much, any, either,* and *some*

Indefinite relative pronoun - *whoever, whomever, whosever, whichever,* and *whatever*, as well as *whosoever, whomsoever, whosesoever, whichsoever, whatsoever,* and *what*. Indefinite relative pronouns refer to unexpressed indefinite antecedents such as *anyone* or *anything*.

Independent expression - a word or group of words with no grammatical connection to the rest of the sentence. Independent expressions include vocatives, interjections, nominative absolutes, and pleonasms. Not only nouns, but also adverbs, infinitives, infinitive phrases, participles, participial phrases, and prepositional phrases can be used independently.

Indirect object - a noun or pronoun used with verbs of giving, saying, and showing to indicate *to whom* or *for whom* the direct object is intended. Indirect objects are adverbial objectives.

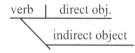

Indirect question - a question expressed as part of a sentence without the use of quotation marks. The following sentences contain indirect questions: *He asked <u>why we were late</u>. She wondered <u>if she had to go to school</u>. The teacher wants to know <u>who said that</u>.*

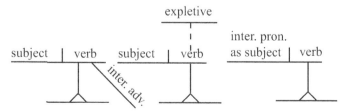

Infinitive - the basic form of any verb (usually preceded by the word *to*). Infinitives have tense and voice (present active, *to call*; present passive, *to be called*; present-perfect active, *to have called*; and present-perfect passive, *to have been called*) as well as progressivity (*to be calling, to have been calling*). Infinitives can function as adverbs (*they are running <u>to win</u>*), as adjectives (*you have nothing <u>to do</u>*), and as nouns (*we all want <u>to succeed</u>*).

Infinitive phrase - an infinitive with its modifiers and objects. Like simple infinitives, infinitive phrases can be used as adverbs, adjectives, or nouns.

Intensive pronouns - pronouns that intensify or identify nouns and other pronouns. In form, they are indistinguishable from reflexive pronouns: *myself, yourself, himself, herself, itself, ourselves, yourselves,* and *themselves.* Intensive pronouns are appositives and are so diagrammed. Examples: *she <u>herself</u> made the dress* (or *she made the dress <u>herself</u>*), *we met with the manager <u>herself</u> to discuss the problem.*

noun or pronoun   (intensive pronoun)

Interjection - a word or group of words with no grammatical connection to the rest of the sentence, used to express feeling or emotion, e.g., *wow, holy Toledo, for crying out loud, hurrah*

interjection

subject | verb

Interrogative adjectives - adjectives used in direct and indirect questions: *which, what*

Interrogative pronouns - pronouns used to ask direct and indirect questions: *who, whom, whose, which, what*

Intransitive verb - a verb that does not need a direct object. Some intransitive verbs are *be, seem, go, sleep, grin,* and *travel.* Many intransitive verbs can also be transitive; for example, a tent can *sleep three people*, a boss can *grin his approval*, and one can *travel the world*.

Linking verb - an intransitive verb that requires a predicate nominative or a predicate adjective for completion. The most common linking verb is *be*, including the participles and gerunds *being* and *having been*, and the finite forms *is, am, are, was, were,* etc. Some other verbs that can be linking verbs are *seem, become, feel, look, remain,* and *taste.* Factitive verbs (*make, call, elect,* etc.) can function in the passive voice as linking verbs: *he <u>was made</u> rich, she <u>is called</u> Kathy, you <u>will be elected</u> president.* Some scholars put the verb *be* in a category of its own and do not include it among the linking verbs.

Modal auxiliary - a verb used with a main verb to add a note of necessity, possibility, permissibility, or the like: *can, could, may, might, must, should, would*

Nominative absolute - a substantive (noun or noun substitute) modified by a participle or a participial phrase and having no grammatical connection to the rest of the sentence. The participle *being* is sometimes unexpressed: *His money [being] safely in the bank, he relaxed at last.*

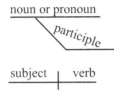

Noun - the name of anything (*Mr. Smith, John, woman, principal, student, Atlanta, country, kindness, hatred, dawn, darkness, sound, loudness, lion, lemur, book, computer, alertness, curiosity, weight, water, wish,* and thousands of others)

Noun clause - a clause that functions as a noun

Noun phrase - a noun and its modifiers (including articles, adjectives, prepositional phrases, relative clauses, and infinitives)

Nouns as adjectives - a noun placed before another noun such that the former modifies the latter, e.g., *wastepaper* basket, *K-Mart* special, *holiday* blues, *cabin* fever

Number - singular or plural. Nouns and pronouns have number (they are singular or plural) and so do verbs. The number of the subject of a sentence must agree with the number of the verb. If one says, "They eats later," one makes an agreement error involving number.

Objective complement - a noun, adjective, or equivalent expression (prepositional phrase, infinitive, infinitive phrase, participle, participial phrase, gerund, or gerund phrase) that completes the action of the verb and in some way either repeats (i.e., is identical with) or describes the direct object. Consider these sentences: *They named their baby daughter Estelle. That makes me angry. We found the book difficult. I saw them leaving. The weather forced him to stay at home. She asked him to help with the groceries.* Most authorities agree that the first four sentences contain objective complements; however, there is significant disagreement concerning the last two. In this book, all underlined words above are considered objective complements. One way to recognize an objective complement, when it is a substantive, is this: If a verb seems to have two direct objects and the first of the two is not an indirect object, then the second is an objective complement.

```
verb  |  direct object  \  objective complement

verb  /  objective complement  |  direct object
```

Object of a preposition - a noun or other substantive that follows a preposition and completes it. Without an object, a particle cannot be a preposition.

Participial phrase - a participle with its objects and modifiers

Participle - a verbal adjective. Transitive verbs have five different kinds of participles: present active (*giving, speaking*), present passive (*being given, being spoken*), present-perfect active (*having given, having spoken*), present-perfect passive (*having been given, having been spoken*), and past (*given, spoken*).

Particle - a subordinate word that is uninflected, i.e., doesn't change its form to reflect changes in tense, number, or the like. In English, prepositions, conjunctions, interjections, articles, and expletives are uninflected. Some scholars limit the set of particles to those words that are added to verbs to form phrasal verbs.

Passive voice - a characteristic of transitive verbs that indicates the relationship of the verb to the subject as receiver of the action. A transitive verb is said to be in the passive voice when the subject of the sentence is acted upon, i.e., when something is done to the subject. See *active voice.*

Past participle - a verb form used with various tenses of the verb *have* to form the perfect tenses, e.g., *driven, called, gone, seen*

Past-perfect tense - the tense in which verbs use *had* as an auxiliary verb, e.g., *had worked, had been reading, had been planted*

Past tense - This tense is subdivided into three groups: 1) simple past, e.g., *saw, gave, hunted, was (were) seen, was (were) given, was (were) hunted;* 2) past progressive, e.g., *was (were) seeing, was (were) giving, was (were) hunting, was (were) being seen, was (were) being given, was (were) being hunted;* 3) emphatic past, e.g., *did see, did give, did hunt.*

Person - an expression used to distinguish among the speaker (or writer), the person spoken (or written) to, and the person spoken (or written) about: first person (*I, we*), second person (*you*), and third person (*he, she, it, they*). The person of the subject must agree with the person of the verb. If one says, "I likes him," one makes an agreement error involving person.

Personal pronouns - pronouns that denote person (first, second, third) and, in some instances, number (singular, plural), gender (masculine, feminine, neuter), and case (nominative, objective, possessive): nominative forms *I, you, he, she, it, we,* and *they;* objective forms *me, you, him, her, it, us,* and *them;* and possessive forms *my, mine, your, yours, his, her, hers, its, our, ours, their,* and *theirs*

Phrasal prepositions - prepositions that consist of more than one word, e.g., *out of, because of, instead of, along with, as for, by means of, in addition to, in spite of*

Phrasal verb - a verb-particle combination with an idiomatic meaning such that the meaning cannot be known from the separate meanings of the verb and the particle, e.g., *she looked up the word, he carried out the command.* Notice that one cannot say *the*

word up which she looked or *the command out which he carried*, which shows that *up* and *out* are not prepositions here.

Phrase - a group of words that form a unit but do not have a subject or a predicate

Pleonasm - the deliberate repetition within a sentence of an important element, e.g., *Coney Island, what a magical place it was.*

Possessive - the inflected forms of nouns (*Mary's, the workers', the men's*) and pronouns (*my, mine, your, yours, his, her, hers, its, our, ours, their, theirs*) used to show possession or belonging to

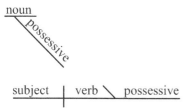

Predicate - the verb together with its modifiers and complements

Predicate adjective - an adjective or equivalent expression that follows a linking verb and refers to the subject

| subject | linking verb \ predicate adjective |

Predicate nominative - a substantive that follows a linking verb and refers to the subject

| subject | linking verb \ predicate nominative |

Preposition - a particle that requires an object (noun, pronoun, or the equivalent) for completion. Prepositions usually precede their objects.

Prepositional phrase - a preposition with its object (including article and adjectives, if any). Prepositional phrases function as adverbs and as adjectives. See *object of a preposition*.

Present participle - a verb form ending in *-ing* that can function 1) both as a verb and as an adjective, e.g., *a woman wearing a blue skirt, lovers holding hands*; 2) as a verb only, e.g., *the deer were running through the woods, we are planning a party*; 3) as an adjective only, e.g., *a sinking ship, the loving mother*

Present-perfect tense - the tense in which verbs use *has* or *have* as an auxiliary verb, e.g., *has (have) held, has (have) woven, has (have) been holding, has (have) been weaving, has (have) been held, has (have) been woven*

Present tense - This tense is subdivided into three groups: 1) simple present, e.g., *see(s), give(s), hunt(s), am (are, is) seen, am (are, is) given, am (are, is) hunted*; 2) present progressive, e.g., *am (are, is) seeing, am (are, is) giving, am (are, is) hunting, am (are, is) being seen, am (are, is) being given, am (are, is) being hunted*; 3) emphatic present, e.g., *do (does) see, do (does) give, do (does) hunt*

Progressive verb forms - verb forms in various tenses used to show an action going on or a state continuing. These forms occur in all six tenses of finite verbs (*is showing, was showing, will be showing, has been showing, had been showing, will have been showing*) and in the present and past tenses of the passive voice (*is being shown, was being shown*). Infinitives have progressive forms in the present and present-perfect tenses (*to be showing, to have been showing*)

Pronoun - a word that takes the place of a noun or of a noun phrase. There are various kinds of pronouns: personal pronouns (*I, you, he, she, it*, etc.), relative pronouns (*who, whom, whose, which, that*, among others), interrogative pronouns (*who, whom, whose, which, what*), demonstrative pronouns (*this, that, these, those*), reflexive and intensive pronouns (*myself, yourself, himself, herself*, etc.), indefinite pronouns (*someone, anyone*, etc.), and reciprocal pronouns (*each other, one another*).

Reflexive pronouns - *myself, yourself, himself, herself, itself, ourselves, yourselves, themselves.* A reflexive pronoun can be used as a predicate nominative, a direct object, an indirect object, or an object of a preposition to refer to the subject of the sentence.

Relative adverb - an adverb that can be restated as a prepositional phrase containing a relative pronoun, or as two prepositional phrases, the second of which contains a relative pronoun. For example, *where* in the expression *the hotel where we are staying* can be restated as *in which*, and *when* in the sentence *We can go when the light turns green* can be restated as *at the time at which*. See *correlative adverbs*.

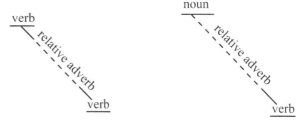

Relative clause - an adjective clause introduced by a relative pronoun. See *relative pronoun*.

Relative pronoun - a pronoun that introduces a dependent clause and has an antecedent (a previously mentioned noun, pronoun, or the equivalent to which it refers) within the same sentence. The principal relative pronouns are *who, whom, whose, which*, and *that*. Additional relative pronouns include the indefinite forms *what, whoever, whomever, whosever, whichever, whatever, whosoever, whomsoever, whosesoever, whichsoever*, and *whatsoever*; these have an unexpressed antecedent. *As* can be a relative pronoun (e.g., *he liked the same songs as his parents had liked when they were young*).

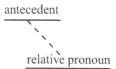

Retained object - a direct object that continues to function as a direct object when the indirect object of a sentence in the active voice becomes the subject of a corresponding sentence in the passive voice. The retained object is underlined in the following

~ 5 ~

example: *Someone gave the youngster a new baseball glove* (active). *The youngster was given <u>a new baseball glove</u>* (passive).

verb in the passive voice	retained object

Sentence - an independent clause that begins with a capital letter and ends with a period, a question mark, or an exclamation point (see *clause*)

Sentence modifier - a word, phrase, or clause that modifies an entire sentence or a major portion thereof, like a clause or an entire predicate

Subject - a noun, pronoun, or equivalent word, phrase, or clause about which the sentence says something

Subjective complement - a noun, adjective, or the equivalent of either, that completes a linking verb. Such substantives are called *predicate nominatives*; such adjectives and equivalent expressions are called *predicate adjectives*.

subject	verb

Subjunctive mood - the modification of verbs used for contrary-to-fact conditions (e.g., *if she were here, if I had a million dollars*), unreal wishes (e.g., *I wish I were an astronaut, he wishes he could fly*), and indirect commands and suggestions (e.g., *she insists that he go along*), among others (e.g., *Be it ever so difficult, . . .*)

Subordinate clause - See *dependent clause.*

Substantive - a noun or a noun substitute (such as a pronoun, adjective, phrase, or clause)

Tenses - present, past, future, present perfect, past perfect, future perfect. Tense has a lot to do with time but is not synonymous with it.

Transitional adverb - an adverb used to join clauses. Examples are *consequently, furthermore, however, moreover, nevertheless, therefore,* among others.

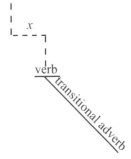

Transitive verb - a verb that needs a direct object for completion (see *intransitive verb*)

Unequal comparison - See *comparative degree, equal comparison.*

Verb - a word expressing action or state. Most verbs end in *-s* in the third person singular of the simple (one-word) present tense. An *-ing* ending is used to express verbs as participles and gerunds. The simple past of most verbs differs in form from the present

tense, as does the past participle.

Verbals - nonfinite verb forms: *gerunds, participles,* and *infinitives*

Vocative - See *direct address.*

Voice - a term that refers to the relation of the verb to the subject as doer of the action of the verb or as recipient of the action. A transitive verb is said to be either in the active voice (when the subject of the sentence is acting) or in the passive voice (when the subject is acted upon).

Lesson 1: Subjects and Verbs

Subjects are difficult to define simply. One incomplete definition is this: *The subject of the sentence is the noun, pronoun, phrase, or clause about which the sentence says or asks something.* Here are some examples:

Susan finished her report and handed it in. The sentence says something about Susan. It tells the reader what Susan did. Susan is the subject of the sentence.

Is patience a virtue? The sentence asks the reader something about patience.

So far so good; nevertheless, this definition has its weaknesses. Let's examine a few more sentences:

Carla's blatant impatience caused everyone in the restaurant to laugh. The sentence tells the reader something about Carla and something about her impatience. Is *Carla's* or *impatience* the subject? *Carla's* is a possessive, which cannot be a subject.

It is raining. It is the subject. But does the sentence really tell something about *it*?

You know that mighty Casey struck out. Is the subject of the sentence *you* or *Casey*? *You know* is the main clause (which always contains the subject of the sentence), and the rest of the sentence is a dependent clause (which never contains the subject of the sentence).

Here are two helpful hints:

1) *The subject of the sentence is the word with which the verb agrees.* This can be more helpful than you may at first realize. Take these sentences:

Our friends' dog is sick. What is the subject: *friends* or *dog*? If *friends* were the subject, the verb would have to be *are*. Since the verb is *is*, the subject is *dog*.

On the lake they see a sailboat. What is the subject: *lake, they*, or *sailboat*? It can only be *they* because *see* does not agree with either of the other words.

Across from the library there will be state-of-the-art tennis courts. If a verb is in the future tense (as this one is), you may want to change it mentally to present tense before looking for agreement. In this case, the change would be from *will be* to *are* (you wouldn't say *is*, would you?). You can see that the verb agrees with *tennis courts*, not with *library*.

2) *In standard prose, the subject of a sentence usually comes before the verb.* There are two exceptions: 1) when the word *there* is used to announce the delayed appearance of the subject (as in the previous example) and 2) in some questions. If you have a hard time finding subjects in questions, mentally change the questions to statements (e.g., change *Have you seen the toys in the attic?* to *You have seen the toys in the attic*).

* * * * *

Let's consider the tenses (present, past, future, present perfect, past perfect, and future perfect), voices (active and passive), and forms (simple, progressive, and emphatic) of two **verbs**: *play* and *sell*.

Active voice of *play*: (simple present) *play, plays*; (simple past) *played*; (simple future) *will play, shall play*; (simple present perfect) *has played, have played*; (simple past perfect) *had played*; (simple future perfect) *will have played, shall have played*; (present progressive) *am playing, are playing, is playing*; (past progressive) *was playing, were playing*; (future progressive) *will be playing, shall be playing*; (present-perfect progressive) *has been playing, have been playing*; (past-perfect progressive) *had been playing*; (future-perfect progressive) *will have been playing, shall have been playing*; (present emphatic) *do play, does play*; (past emphatic) *did play*

Passive voice of *play*: (simple present) *am played, is played, are played*; (simple past) *was played, were played*; (simple future) *will be played, shall be played*; (simple present perfect) *has been played, have been played*; (simple past perfect) *had been played*; (simple future perfect) *will have been played, shall have been played*; (present progressive) *am being played, is being played; are being played* (past progressive) *was being played, were being played*

Active voice of *sell*: (simple present) *sell, sells*; (simple past) *sold*; (simple future) *will sell, shall sell*; (simple present perfect) *has sold, have sold*; (simple past perfect) *had sold*; (simple future perfect) *will have sold, shall have sold*; (present progressive) *am selling, are selling, is selling*; (past progressive) *was selling, were selling*; (future progressive) *will be selling, shall be selling*; (present-perfect progressive) *has been selling, have been selling*; (past-perfect progressive) *had been selling*; (future-perfect progressive) *will have been selling, shall have been selling*; (present emphatic) *do sell, does sell*; (past emphatic) *did sell*

Passive voice of *sell*: (simple present) *am sold, is sold, are sold*; (simple past) *was sold, were sold*; (simple future) *will be sold, shall be sold*; (simple present perfect) *has been sold, have been sold*; (simple past perfect) *had been sold*; (simple future perfect) *will have been sold, shall have been sold*; (present progressive) *am being sold, is being sold, are being sold* (past progressive) *was being sold, were being sold*

Every diagram has at least two lines: a horizontal base line, which is used for subjects, main verbs, direct objects, predicate nominatives, predicate adjectives, and objective complements (more about these things later), and a vertical line that passes through the base line and divides the subject of the sentence from the predicate of the sentence (the predicate is the main verb and its objects or complements).

All finite verbs (verbs that can be used as main verbs), regardless of tense (present, past, future, present perfect, past perfect, and future perfect), voice (active and passive), mood (indicative, imperative, and subjunctive), and form (simple, progressive, and emphatic), including modal auxiliary verbs (introduced on page 10), are diagrammed in the space provided for the verb, namely, right after the subject following a vertical line that passes through the horizontal base line. Excluded are only the so-called verbals: infinitives, gerunds, and participles (more about them later). As you work through this book, you may want to check the definitions section on pages 1-6 for the meanings of words and expressions you do not understand.

Subject	verb

In diagramming, the subject is always placed on the far left of a horizontal line called the base line. A vertical line passing through the base line separates the subject from the verb. Since all sentences on this page consist only of a subject and a verb, they are diagrammed according to the model in the box on the left.

Step 1. Children play.

The noun *children* is the subject of the sentence. The verb *play* is in the present tense.

Children	play

Step 2. They were selling.

The personal pronoun *they* is the subject of the sentence. The past progressive *were selling* is the verb. The nominative (subject) forms of the personal pronouns are *I, you, he, she, it, we, you,* and *they.*

They	were selling

Step 3. It had been played.

The subject of the sentence is the personal pronoun *it.* The verb *had been played* is in the past-perfect tense, passive voice.

It	had been played

Step 4. Sandwiches are being sold.

The subject of the sentence is the plural noun *sandwiches.* The verb *are being sold* is a progressive form in the present tense, passive voice.

Sandwiches	are being sold

Step 5. Have you been playing?

The subject is *you.* Like all subjects, it is placed on the left end of the base line. The verb *have been playing* is a progressive form in the present-perfect tense. In a sentence diagram, the first word of the sentence is capitalized regardless of where it appears in the diagram.

you	Have been playing

Exercise 1: Subjects and Verbs

Now it's your turn to diagram. The "answers" (diagrams and explanations) are on page 239.

1. Ducks quack.

2. Mosquitoes are buzzing.

3. People have been talking.

4. They will be captured.

5. Money had been collected.

6. That will have changed.

7. Do fish fly?

8. What happened?

9. Who was talking?

10. I did study.

Writing Correctly 1

Be consistent in your use of tenses. In general, if you begin writing a story using the past tense, continue using the past tense throughout the story; if you begin with the present tense, stay with the present tense.

* * * * *

Use the present-perfect, past-perfect, and future-perfect tenses to indicate actions or states that are past relative to present, past, and future time, respectively.

> - *On most days, the children have finished their homework* (present perfect) *by the time their father gets home from work* (present time) .
> - *By the time he got home yesterday* (past time), *the children had finished their homework* (past perfect).
> - *By the time he gets home this evening* (future time), *the children will have finished their homework* (future perfect).

* * * * *

When the indefinite pronoun *none* is used as the subject of a sentence, it sometimes takes a singular verb and sometimes a plural verb. When its referent is a singular noun, as in *none of the flour*, it takes a singular verb: *None of the flour is fresh.* When the referent is plural, opinions of grammarians vary. Purists have long held that *none* is always singular, since it is derived from *no one*. Martha Kolln says that its number should be determined by the number of the referent. Most grammarians, however, take a position between these two. My own opinion is that *none*, when it has a plural referent, usually sounds best with a plural verb. Instead of using a singular *none* with a plural referent, why not use *not one*, which is of course singular?

* * * * *

Do compound subjects using *or* or *nor* take singular or plural verbs? It all depends. If the noun closest to the verb is singular, the verb is singular; if the closest noun is plural, the verb is plural. *Either two cans of soup or one can of stew is needed for admission to the game. Neither the coach nor the players are expected to speak at the banquet. Does the coach or the players play the game?* When the verb is divided, as it is in the last sentence, number is determined by the position of the helping verb (in this case, *does*).

* * * * *

Compound personal pronouns joined by *or* or *nor* sometimes sound awkward no matter which verb form is chosen. You probably would not want to write any of the following sentences: *He or I am going, He or I is going; Either you or he was there, Either you or he were there; Neither you nor I am listening, Neither you nor I are listening.* In these cases, rewording is in order: *He or I will go; Someone was there--either you or he;*

You aren't listening, and neither am I.

* * * * *

Both of the following sentences are incorrect: *Standing on stage is Norman Jones, John Taylor, and an unidentified third person. Norman Jones, along with John Taylor and an unidentified third person, are standing on stage.* Both sentences violate the important rule that the number of the verb is determined by the subject of the sentence. Here are the same sentences expressed correctly: *Standing on stage are Norman Jones, John Taylor, and an unidentified third person. Norman Jones, along with John Taylor and an unidentified third person, is standing on stage.* The subject of the first sentence is plural (*Norman Jones, John Taylor, and an unidentified third person*); the subject of the second sentence is singular (*Norman Jones*).

* * * * *

The indefinite pronouns *each* and *one* are both considered to be third-person singular in expressions like *each of them, each of the fish, one of the cabinets, one of them*. What about expressions like *each of us, each of you, one of us, and one of you*? Should one write *each of us is* or *each of us are*? *one of you is* or *one of you are*? Even in these expressions, *each* and *one* are regarded as third-person singular. Googling turns up ten times more instances of *each of us is* than of *each of us are* and about seven times more instances of *one of you is* than of *one of you are*.

* * * * *

Sometimes collective singular nouns require a plural verb. Examples: *A large number of people were present. A majority of the representatives are expected to vote for the measure.* It is recommended that words like *team, choir*, and *orchestra* be used with plural verbs when the members are acting individually.

* * * * *

Don't overuse the verb *be*, including the following finite forms: present-tense *am, are, is, am being, are being,* and *is being*; the past-tense *was, were, was being,* and *were being*; the future-tense *will be* and *shall be*; the present-perfect *has been* and *have bee*n; the past-perfect *had been*; and the future-perfect *will have been* and *shall have been*. Use action verbs instead, as follows:

> *He is a frequent speaker at the Rotary Club.*
> *He speaks frequently at the Rotary Club.*
>
> *Their meetings were every Thursday evening.*
> *They met every Thursday evening.*

Lesson 2: Modal Auxiliary Verbs

Authorities differ among themselves as to which verbs should be called modal auxiliaries. My own list includes these seven: *can, could, may, might, must, should,* and *would.* Since it is impossible to discuss the modals without reference to the indicative and the subjunctive moods, let's be sure we have a clear idea of those terms.

Actually, English has three moods (or modes): indicative, imperative, and subjunctive. The imperative is the easiest to grasp. It includes the verb forms used to give commands: *Go! Run! Sit! Speak!* In each case, the imperative is the same in form as the present infinitive (*to go, to run, to sit, to speak*) without the particle *to.* This is even true of the infinitive *to be,* whose imperative form is *be* (as in *Be good!* or *Be quiet!*). Imperatives do not have to be followed by an exclamation mark, but they often are. Modal auxiliary verbs cannot be used in the imperative mood.

The indicative mood is used for pointing out, describing, or asking about actual things or happenings. Most verb forms that we use every day are indicative. Here are some sentences whose verbs are in the indicative mood: *It is snowing. That has been my house for the last ten years. When does the movie begin? I had a headache. Will you be my friend?*

Three modal forms, *can, may,* and *must,* are always indicative. *Ronald can run fast* says simply that Ronald has the ability to run fast. *The children may go with us* says that the children have permission to accompany us or that it is possible that they will go with us. *Stella must stay home this evening* tells of a particular obligation incumbent upon Stella. If we want to put Ronald's ability to run fast in the past, we can say *When he was young, Ronald could run fast*; however, we must choose altogether different verbs if we want to place the children's permission and Stella's obligation in the past: *The children were permitted to go with us* and *Stella had to stay home that evening.*

The modal auxiliary verb *could* is used not only in the past indicative but also in the present subjunctive: *If Ronald had not injured his foot, he could run fast.* In this sentence, *could* does not refer to an actual ability but only to an ability Ronald would have if he had not hurt himself. This sentence rules out Ronald's ability to run fast here and now. We have a slightly different situation in the sentence *If Ronald wanted to, he could run fast.* This sentence implies one of two things depending on context: it is impossible for Ronald to run fast because he doesn't want to, or it is improbable that Ronald can run fast because it is improbable that he wants to. You can swing probability to the positive side by choosing the indicative: *Ronald can run fast if he wants to.*

Might is the present subjunctive form of *may.* Note the difference between *If she is here, she may be able to help us* and *If she were here, she might be able to help us.* In the first sentence, her ability to help is possible (because it is possible that she is here), whereas in the second sentence the ability to help is purely speculative (because she is not here).

Would is used in unreal (contrary-to-fact) conditional sentences: *If I had time, I would help you.* Contrast that with a sentence containing a real condition: *If I have time, I will help you. Would* is also used to expresses habitual action in the past, e.g., *Back then people would often sit on their front porch and talk with passing neighbors.*

Should is seldom used these days as a future-tense indicator, e.g., *Next year I should like to visit my cousin in New York.* It is widely used to express obligation (*I really should do my homework*) and expectation (*You should be able to find our house*).

Must has no subjunctive form. If we want to use the verb *must* in an unreal condition, we have to choose another verb: *If he had to work harder, he would.*

All seven modals can be used with basic present-perfect forms (present-perfect infinitives without *to*). Here are some examples:

> *Can* and *could*: *He cannot have finished so soon* and *She could have pouted but she didn't.*
> *May* and *might*: *If she was there, she may have been able to help them* and *If she had been there, she might have been able to help them.* When so used, *may* and *might* retain the distinction between real and unreal, possible and impossible.
> *Would*: *If I had had time, I would have helped you.* This is an unreal conditional sentence in past time.
> *Should*: *I really should have done my homework* and *You should have been able to find our house.*
> *Must*: *They must have left* and *You must have been helped.*

Many grammarians claim that the subjunctive mood is almost dead in English, used only in an occasional expression such as *If I were you.* I disagree. If I asked you for the tense of *gave* and *lived,* perhaps you would say past. And I would say you are half right. They are past indicative forms, but they are also present subjunctive forms: *If we gave him five dollars* (right now), *he would be able to eat; If you lived closer* (right now), *we could get together more often.*

A modal auxiliary verb and the verb it modulates are considered a single verb phrase. In a sentence diagram, this verb phrase is placed in the normal position of the verb, i.e., right after the vertical line that follows the subject.

Subject	verb

Step 6. This must leak.

This	must leak

The demonstrative pronoun *this* is the subject of the sentence. The complete verb consists of the modal auxiliary verb *must* with the present infinitive of the intransitive verb *leak*. Intransitive verbs have no passive voice (more about transitive and intransitive verbs later).

Step 7. Could rewards be offered?

rewards	Could be offered

The subject of the sentence is the noun *rewards*. The complete verb consists of the subjunctive modal auxiliary verb *could* together with the basic present passive form (the present passive infinitive without *to*) *be offered*.

Step 8. They should have hurried.

They	should have hurried

The subject of the sentence is the personal pronoun *they*. The complete verb consists of the modal *should* with the basic present-perfect form of *hurry*.

Step 9. Homes may have been destroyed.

Homes	may have been destroyed

The subject of the sentence is *homes*. The verb phrase *may have been destroyed* consists of the modal *may* plus the basic present-perfect passive form of *destroy*.

Step 10. Who can help?

Who	can help

The subject of the sentence is the interrogative pronoun *who*.

Every sentence has a subject and a predicate. The predicate is everything in the sentence besides the subject, the subject's modifiers, and independent elements (more about modifiers and independent elements later). Up to this point in your study of diagramming, you have been asked to diagram only sentences with unmodified subjects and with predicates that consist only of a verb or verb phrase. Things gradually become more complicated as you proceed through this book; however, it is important to remember that every diagram you do must include the lines with which you are now familiar: a main horizontal line, called the base line, and a vertical line passing through the base line.

Exercise 2: Modal Auxiliary Verbs

11. You may stay.

12. We must go.

13. Can elephants jump?

14. They should be scolded.

15. Should I have asked?

16. Carolyn must have been delayed.

17. That could have been done.

18. She may have been asked.

19. They might be coming.

20. Might we have succeeded?

Writing Correctly 2

Verb forms that are used in unreal (contrary-to-fact) conditions, as well as in noun clauses expressing wishes, suggestions, and commands, are said to be in the subjunctive mood. The subjunctive mood has (1) certain unique forms (*they be, she were*), (2) present-tense forms that are identical with the past indicative (*I had, you wanted*), (3) past-tense forms that are identical with the past-perfect indicative (*he had told, we had seen*), and (4) some forms that are exactly the same as the indicative, tense and all (*they stay, you cancel*).

English has two different present-subjunctive conjugations. Let's call them present subjunctive I and present subjunctive II:

Present Subjunctive I		**Present Subjunctive II**	
I be	*we be*	*I were*	*we were*
you (sing.) be	*you (pl.) be*	*you were*	*you were*
he, she, it be	*they be*	*he, she, it were*	*they were*
I play	*we play*	*I played*	*we played*
you play	*you play*	*you played*	*you played*
he, she, it play	*they play*	*he, etc. played*	*they played*

The present subjunctive I of the verb *be* (*I be, you be*, etc.) is entirely different from the present indicative (*I am, you are*, etc.), whereas the present subjunctive I of the verb *play* differs from the present indicative only in the third person singular (*he, she, it play / he, she, it plays*). The present subjunctive II of the verb *be* differs from the past indicative in the first and third person singular (*I were / I was; he, she, it were / he, she, it was*). The present subjunctive II of *play* is exactly the same as the past indicative.

Past Subjunctive

I had been	*we had been*
you had been	*you had been*
he, she, it had been	*they had been*
I had studied	*we had studied*
you had studied	*you had studied*
he, she had studied	*they had studied*

The past subjunctive is identical with the past-perfect indicative.

The subjunctive mood also has progressive forms such as *I be playing; he, she, it were playing; we had been studying*.

Of importance as well are the so-called conditional forms with *would* and *would have*. *I would hurry, you would wonder*, and *they would listen* are present conditional forms, whereas *I would have hurried, you would have wondered*, and *they would have listened* are past conditional forms.

* * * * *

Here are three sentences that show how the subjunctive mood is used today:

> *She insisted that he take the present.* (pres. I)
> *I wish I were there.* (pres. II)
> *He would have fainted if he had been there.* (past)

What do you think of the sentence *If you were home, I would have helped you*? *Were* is a present subjunctive form whereas *would have helped* is a past conditional; thus, the main clause does not flow logically from the subordinate clause (more about this in Lesson 15).

How about *If they have time, I would help them*? Here the *if*-clause is expressed in the indicative, which makes it a real condition (the verb of an unreal condition would have to be the present subjunctive II *had*), but the main clause is expressed in the conditional, the way it should be expressed when the subordinate clause is unreal (more on this later as well). *If they have time, I will help them* is a real conditional sentence.

I'll bet you get the next one right. Is *I wish she was right* right? When one wishes for something (an object, a situation) that is contrary to what is real right now, one should use the present subjunctive II: *I wish she were right*. If the wish pertains to the future, the conditional is used: *She wishes her mother would hurry*. The same conditional is used if the main verb is in past time: *She wished her mother would hurry*. In the latter sentence, *would hurry* expresses time that is future with respect to a particular point in the past. What do you think of *He wished he were there*? I hope you like it, because it correctly expresses an unreal wish. In such wishes, the present subjunctive II is used to express the same time as that expressed by the main verb. And if the wish refers to the past, as in *I wish I had studied longer* or *I wished I had studied longer*, the past subjunctive II is needed.

The strict mother demands that her son sit up straight at the dinner table. The strict mother demanded that her son sit up straight at the dinner table. You probably approve of the grammar if not the sentiment of each of these sentences, and you are right. The present subjunctive I is used when relating certain commands and suggestions. How does one know this is a subjunctive form? If it's indicative, you should be able to say *Her son sit up straight*, which sounds very bad. Remember, however, with most verbs the third person singular is the only subjunctive form that differs from its corresponding indicative. Example: *The strict mother demands that her children sit up straight at the table.* You certainly can say *Her children sit up straight*, can't you?

The subjunctive can express "no matter if . . .": *Be it ever so humble, there's no place like home. Every person, be he black, white, or brown, is her friend.*

Lesson 3: Imperatives, Vocatives, Contractions, and Coordinating Conjunctions

The **imperative mood** is used to express a command, a request, or a suggestion. The subject of an imperative sentence is usually an unexpressed *you*. Here are some sentences with verbs in the imperative mood (the imperatives are underlined): *Answer! Be still! Do come to the party on Saturday! Tell that to the teacher. Use time judiciously. You go first!* An exclamation point is used at the end of some imperative sentences to convey a sense of urgency or powerful emotion.

* * * * *

A **vocative** is a noun (whether a name or not) or the pronoun *you* used in direct address. Vocatives are independent expressions, which means that they are not connected grammatically to the rest of the sentence. Here are some sentences with vocatives (the vocatives are underlined): *Mr. Abramson, come to Room 214 immediately. What would you do, children, if the lights went out? You, I need your help.*

* * * * *

A **contraction** is a word formed by joining two words and letting an apostrophe replace one or more omitted letters. Here are examples of contractions formed from verbs and the adverb *not*: *isn't, aren't, wasn't, weren't, won't, hasn't, haven't, don't, doesn't, didn't, can't,* and *shouldn't.* Examples of contractions of pronouns and verbs are *I'm, you're, he's, she's, it's, we're, they're, I'll, you'll, he'll, she'll, it'll, we'll, they'll, I've, you've, we've, they've, I'd, you'd, she'd, he'd, we'd, they'd, who's, who'll,* and *who'd.* Examples of contractions involving adverbs and verbs: *there's, here's, where's, where'd, why's, why'd, how's, how'd.*

* * * * *

Coordinating conjunctions connect words, phrases, and clauses of equal importance and almost always of the same kind, i.e., nouns with nouns, verbs with verbs, etc. The principal coordinating conjunctions are *and, but, or, nor*; the correlatives are *both . . . and, either . . . or,* and *neither . . . nor.* In the sentence *Hansel and Gretel marked the trail through the forest,* the coordinating conjunction *and* connects the subjects *Hansel* and *Gretel.* The same coordinating conjunction joins two verbs in the sentence *The children laughed and played.* (compound verb). The stepmother's command, "Hansel and Gretel, wait here until your father and I return," begins with a compound vocative. Here are some additional examples of compound nouns connected by coordinating conjunctions:

> *In which song is America called the land of the free and the home of the brave?* (compound predicate nominative)
> *They have a mountain of money but a thimbleful of time.* (compound direct object)
> *Would you call a tadpole a fish or a reptile?* (compound objective complement)
> *She likes to ride the roller coaster with either her parents or her grandparents.* (compound object of preposition)
> *The meet director gave both the winner and the runner-up a large trophy.* (compound indirect object)

And here are some other words joined by coordinating conjunctions:

> *The project manager was excited but too exhausted to think straight.* (compound predicate adjective)
> *The students were urged to express their ideas clearly and concisely.* (compound adverb)
> *Ours is a government by and for the people.* (compound preposition)

And compound phrases:

> *He could live neither with her nor without her.* (compound prepositional phrase)
> *She yearned to go to Colorado and ski all winter.* (compound infinitive phrase)

Finally, compound clauses:

> *She went shopping but he stayed home.* (compound sentence)
> *If you take Brenda, and Josh rides with Amelie, I'll see to it that Johanna and Natalie find a way.* (compound adverb clause--more about adverb clauses later)

Most imperatives have the unexpressed subject *you*. This is shown in a diagram by an *x* (or by *you* in parentheses) in the position of the subject.

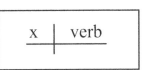

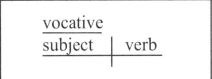

A vocative is grammatically independent of the rest of the sentence. It is diagrammed on a horizontal line above and separate from the subject of the sentence.

Step 11. Listen!

The subject of this imperative sentence is an unexpressed *you*. *Listen* is capitalized because it is the first expressed word in the sentence.

Step 12. Children, we must hurry.

Children
_____

we | must hurry

Children is not the subject of the sentence but a vocative (the noun used to tell those who are being addressed that they are being addressed). The personal pronoun *we* is the subject of the sentence. The verb consists of the modal *must* and the present infinitive *hurry*.

Contractions of a personal-pronoun subject and a verb are broken apart when diagrammed. Contractions involving a verb and *not* are left together in a diagram.

Step 13. We're leaving.

We | 're leaving

To show that the second half of the contraction *we're* is a verb (in this case, a helping verb) and not part of the subject, it is separated in a diagram from the subject *we* and placed in the position of the verb.

Step 14. They aren't leaving.

They | aren't leaving

When diagramming a compound subject, place the individual subjects on parallel horizontal lines and put the coordinating conjunction on a broken vertical line between the two horizontal lines. Do the same, *mutatis mutandis*, with compound verbs.

Step 15. Jack and Jill are falling.   Step 16. Did they win or lose?

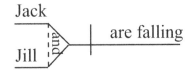

Jack and Jill is a compound subject, while *win or lose* is a compound verb with a shared helping verb, *did*. *And* and *or* are coordinating conjunctions.

To diagram a compound sentence, diagram the first main clause above the second, and put the coordinating conjunction on a broken-line step-down between the verbs of the two diagrams.

Step 17. We are working but you are playing.

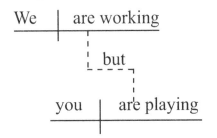

We are working is an independent clause (it can stand alone as a complete sentence), and the same can be said of *you are playing*. These two clauses are joined in this compound sentence by the coordinating conjunction *but*.

Exercise 3: Imperatives, Vocatives, Contractions, and Coordinating Conjunctions

21. Run!

22. Dave, hurry!

23. Don't worry.

24. I'm trying.

25. Gentlemen, we cannot leave.

26. Doctors and nurses are scurrying.

27. Buses come and go.

28. Deer were running and jumping.

29. Children run, jump, and play.

30. Teachers, travel and learn!

31. Listen, boys and girls!

32. Bombs fell and people died.

Writing Correctly 3

Asked to give some imperative (command) forms, many people would provide infinitive forms like *Go! Be [good, patient,* etc.]*! Take [the medicine, your time,* etc.]*! Run!*--and they would be right; however, their answer is incomplete. There is another way of expressing imperatives in English. Do you know what it is? It's the two-word form, whose first word is *do: Do go! Do be [good, patient,* etc.]*! Do take [the medicine, your time,* etc.]*! Do run!* So, there you have it. Do remember this alternate form when you're writing!

* * * * *

What do you think of email salutations like *Hi Jerry* and *Hi friend*? Does anything about them bother your punctuation conscience? Well, something should, because commas have traditionally been used to set off nouns of direct address; in other words, there should be a comma before *Jerry* and a comma before *friend*. O well, you say, and I tend to agree. We may just have to accept this email usage as a fait accompli; nevertheless, in general, use commas before (if possible) and after (if possible) direct address, as follows:

> *Brian, what do you think?*
> *Well, Isabel, I don't know.*
> *Draw me a picture, Katie.*

The use of commas will be discussed later in conjunction with such things as appositives, relative clauses, and adverb clauses. In this lesson, we will look at three ways of using commas: in addresses, in dates, and in expressions involving coordinating conjunctions.

Commas are used to set off the individual parts of addresses: *He lives at 1206 Pheasant Ridge, Goshen, Kentucky, and works at a sporting goods store.* If the zip code is included, put a comma after the zip code but not after the name of the state: *He lives at 1206 Pheasant Ridge, Goshen, Kentucky 40026, and works at a sporting goods store.*

With dates, put a comma after both the day and the year if you use the following form: *Their first child was born on May 2, 1906, in Mt. Vernon, Indiana.* Use no comma at all if you use this form: *Their first child was born on 2 May 1906 in Mt. Vernon, Indiana.*

* * * * *

Now let's examine the use of the comma with coordinating conjunctions. As you know, the principal coordinating conjunctions are *and, or, but*, and *nor*.

In compound sentences, put a comma before the coordinating conjunction joining clauses. In short compound sentences, this comma may usually be omitted. Examples: *They arrived at the airport two hours before scheduled departure, but their flight*

had been canceled. They arrived on time but their friends were late. Don't omit the comma, however, if the omission could cause the reader to stumble: *They saw Bill and Betty appeared soon* (a comma before *and* would make the sentence easier to read).

You probably know that the elements of a series are separated from each other by commas. But what do you think of the Oxford comma? "The what?" you say. The Oxford (Harvard, serial) comma is the comma situated before the *and* or the *or* joining the last two elements of a series. The question here is whether one should use this comma. And the short answer, for Americans, is yes. American writers (journalists excluded) tend to use it, whereas the British do not. There are good arguments on both sides of the Atlantic. Those who oppose the use of the Oxford comma maintain that commas in a series merely represent missing *and*s and *or*s; thus, according to them, when the final *and* or *or* is expressed, the comma before it should be omitted. Advocates of the Oxford comma point out that using it can prevent ambiguity, which is true. Here is an example: *Bids were submitted by the firms of Smith and Johnson, Peterson and Allen and Edwards.* Are the names of the last two firms (1) Peterson and (2) Allen and Edwards or (3) Peterson and Allen and (4) Edwards? The Oxford comma would clear things up. *Bids were submitted by the firms of Smith and Johnson, Peterson, and Allen and Edwards* is consistent with appellations 1 and 2, while *Bids were submitted by the firms of Smith and Johnson, Peterson and Allen, and Edwards* gives us 3 and 4. Okay, say the opponents of the controversial comma, use it only when needed to avoid ambiguity. For better or for worse, most of us in the United States are stuck with the Oxford comma.

Use semicolons to separate comma-laden elements of a series. Here are two examples:

> *Troloppe, an Englishman; Flaubert, a Frenchman; Lessing, a German; and Gogal, a Russian, all arrive at the Pearly Gates at the same time.*
> *She wondered when the media-mail package, which had been shipped two weeks earlier, would arrive; why Professor Bates, who had prepared the package, hadn't sent it first class; and how she would finish her thesis in time for spring graduation.*

* * * * *

Some contractions drive students (and their teachers) crazy. The principal culprits seem to be *you're, it's, they're*, and *who's*. If you don't mean *you are*, don't write *you're* but *your*; if you don't mean *it is*, don't write *it's* but *its*; if you don't mean *they are*, don't write *they're* but *there* or *their* (another can of worms); and if you don't mean *who is*, don't write *who's* but *whose*. (By the way, did you notice the serial semicolons?)

Lesson 4: Articles, Attributive Adjectives, and Direct Objects

Not all languages have **articles**. English has three: *the* (called a definite article), *a* and *an* (called indefinite articles).

* * * * *

Adjectives are said to modify nouns; that is, they describe or limit nouns in some way. If we call something *a house*, we do not differentiate it from any other house. If we call a house *a beautiful house*, we restrict the house to the subset of houses that are beautiful; that is, we exclude from the subset houses that are not beautiful. In this sense, *beautiful* modifies *house*. And if we call the house *a beautiful white house*, we further modify it by the addition of the adjective *white*: we restrict the house to the subset of houses that are both beautiful and white.

* * * * *

Attributive adjectives usually come right before nouns or pronouns, either following an article (*a beautiful house, the beautiful house*) or not preceded by an article (*beautiful houses*). Sometimes a noun is modified by two or more attributive adjectives (*the beautiful white house; a tall, dark, and handsome stranger*). Attributive adjectives are distinguished from predicate adjectives, which come after linking verbs, e.g., *white* in the sentence *The house is white* (more about predicate adjectives later). Occasionally an attributive adjective follows its noun, as in *time enough* and *something else*.

* * * * *

Direct objects receive the action of the verb directly; however, not all verbs take direct objects. Verbs that do are called transitive verbs; verbs that do not are called intransitive verbs (e.g., *come, aspire, squirm, rest*). Linking verbs (e.g., *be, become, remain, seem*) have traditionally been called intransitive verbs; however, many grammarians restrict them to a category of their own. Some verbs are transitive in one or several meanings and intransitive in another or others. It is necessary that the student be able to identify direct objects, which are a basic component of language.

To find a direct object, ask *whom?* or *what?* immediately after a non-linking verb. Take this sentence: *That is a tree.* If you ask *what?* immediately after the verb *is*, you get the answer *tree*; however, *tree* is not a direct object since it follows a linking verb. Now take the sentence *They saw a tree.* If you ask *what?* immediately after the verb *saw*, you get the answer *tree*, which is a direct object. Let's practice:

    In college she studied economics. Is there a direct object in this sentence? To find out, ask *whom?* or *what?* immediately after the verb, which is *studied*. Of course, it makes no sense to ask *whom?* here, but it does make sense to ask *what?* She studied what? Economics. Since *economics* is the answer to this question, it is a direct object.

    Try this one: *In college she sometimes studied until two in the morning. She sometimes studied whom?* makes no sense, and *She sometimes studied what?* has no answer in this sentence; therefore, the sentence has no direct object. As you see, not every non-linking verb has a direct object.

    They like Amy but dislike her friend. The question *They like whom?* points to *Amy* as the direct object of *like*, and *They dislike whom?* gives *friend* as the direct object of *dislike*.

    He has been an accountant for nine years. *He has been what?* does indeed have an answer in the sentence; however, *has been* is a form of the verb *be* and cannot have a direct object. The answer provided by this sentence, *accountant*, is a predicate nominative (more about this later).

    They hiked out into the country and enjoyed the sights. There are two verbs in this sentence: *hiked* and *enjoyed*. Neither *hiked whom?* nor *hiked what?* has an answer; however, *enjoyed what?* does. *Sights* is the direct object of *enjoyed*.

    We planted flowers and vegetables in our garden. The question *We planted what?* yields the answer *flowers and vegetables*, a compound direct object.

    She can read and write French, but she does not speak the language well. She can read and write what? The compound verb *read and write* has a direct object, *French*. *She does not speak what well?* gets us *language* as the direct object of *speak*.

An article is diagrammed on a slanted line below the noun it modifies. The top of the slanted line touches the horizontal line of the noun.

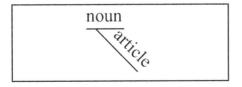

Step 18. The flowers are blooming.

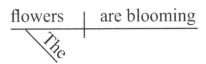

An attributive adjective is diagrammed on a slanted line below the noun it modifies. It is placed to the right of an article.

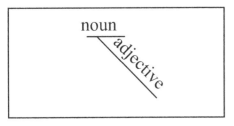

Step 19. Wonderful things are happening.

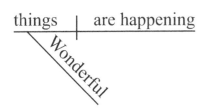

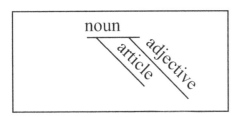

Step 20. A full moon shone.

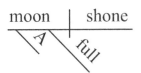

A direct object is diagrammed after its verb. A vertical line touching the base line from above separates the verb from the direct object.

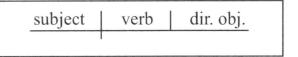

Step 21. Most people saw the comet.

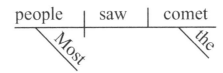

Step 22. They have a cat and a small dog.

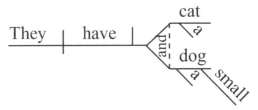

Step 23. The agency feeds unwanted dogs and cats.

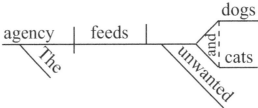

Unwanted modifies both *dogs* and *cats*. It must therefore be placed on a segment of the direct-object line that pertains to both direct objects.

Step 24. They splurged and bought a house.

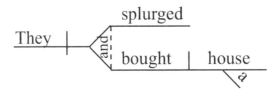

Step 25. Barbara mowed and watered the lawn.

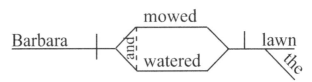

Both verbs have the same direct object.

Exercise 4: Articles, Attributive Adjectives, and Direct Objects

33. I see you.

34. Do you see me?

35. The family is buying a house.

36. Norman must consider a different plan.

37. The city should build a new basketball arena.

38. Do the workers want higher pay or better benefits?

39. Either the county or the city must assume primary responsibility.

40. The new store sells athletic clothing and equipment.

41. Debbie buys and restores old furniture.

42. Do they nurture the children or neglect them?

43. What does he want?

44. Whom can we send?

45. Employers appreciate honest and diligent employees.

Writing Correctly 4

How is it possible that people who would never say *I think they were talking about I* have no trouble at all saying *I think they were talking about you and I*? I have a theory. When I was a kid, back in the Middle Ages, kids who said things like *Me and Jerry caught a frog* were relentlessly corrected by teachers, parents, neighbors, and anyone else who could get in on the act. "No," the pedagogues and would-be pedagogues said, "Not *me and Jerry*. It's *Jerry and I*." Well, when you've heard that forty thousand times, it's indelibly carved in the brain, and you never again say *me* as part of a compound subject, period. Now fast forward fifty years to a generation that has been deprived by enlightened pedagogy of all knowledge of grammar, and it's easy to see how the proscription against *me* in a compound subject could broaden into an all-out war against *me* in any compound situation: direct object, object of a preposition, what have you. Of course, it doesn't stop with *I* and *me*, but by a process of misguided grammatical analogy, the disease is spreading to other personal pronouns as well, especially *he* (*him*) and *she* (*her*), above all when these pronouns are used with *I* in compounds: *That's between he and I*, someone may say. A few years ago, I googled *between he and I* and got 28,700 hits. Interestingly, *between him and I* (also incorrect, of course) brought 26,300 hits. Still, the case is far from hopeless. The correct form, *between him and me*, yielded the most hits, 97,700. The numbers for *between she and I*, *between her and I*, and *between her and me* were 959, 21,000, and 35,000, respectively. Isn't it strange that significantly more people are willing to say *between he and I* than *between she and I*? Almost no one likes *between they and I*, which brought only 70 hits, but *between them and I* is alive and kicking (47,600). It was nosed out by the correct form, *between them and me*, by only 100 hits. Those of us who like logic in our language can take heart in knowing that *between him and her*, which is correct, easily defeated its incorrect rivals. It seems that *I* is the most abused personal pronoun, with *he* second, and *she* a distant third. We can still win this one. Here is the rule (simplified for now): Use *I, he, she, we,* and *they* for subjects, and *me, him, her, us,* and *them* for objects (more about this later).

* * * * *

When two or more attributive adjectives precede the same noun, a comma or commas are sometimes used to separate them from each other. The rule is this: A comma is needed between two attributive adjectives if they could be joined by *and*. For example, *and* could be used to join *old* and *empty* in the sentence *An old, empty house stood on the corner*; therefore, a comma is placed between the two adjectives. On the other hand, in the sentence *Our school offers an unusual academic environment*, *and* could not be placed logically between *unusual* and *academic*; therefore, no comma should be used. In the first sentence, the two adjectives modify *house* independently, whereas in the second sentence *unusual* modifies the noun phrase *academic environment*. This box diagram may help:

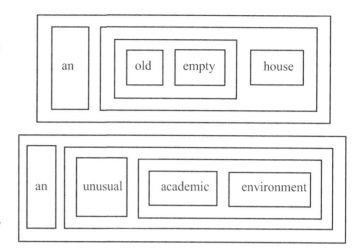

In both box diagrams, *an* can be seen to modify the entire noun phrase, which is what it logically does. Unfortunately, Reed & Kellogg diagramming (the kind of diagramming you are learning in this book) does not do a perfect job of showing the modification of articles that modify noun phrases or, for that matter, of attributive adjectives that do the same.

* * * * *

Speaking of the article *an*, do you know when to use it? Don't you sometimes wonder if *a* or *an* is preferable in particular cases? I do; and when I do, here is the rule I apply to resolve the issue:

> - Use *an* before words beginning with a vowel (in this case *a, e, i, o, u* only) and *a* before a word beginning with a consonant. Exceptions: (1) If a word beginning with a vowel sounds like it begins with a consonant, use *a* before it; (2) If a word beginning with a consonant, or consisting of a numeral or a letter, sounds like it begins with vowel, use *an* before it.

Let's look at a few examples: *European* and *universal* begin with vowels; however, they sound like they begin with the consonant *y*. If you need the indefinite article before them, use *a*: *a European agreement, a universal law*. On the other hand, *FBI* and the letter *m* may follow *an* but not *a*: *an FBI informant, an m*. *An* is usually used before the adjective *historical*: *an historical accord*. Some authorities allow *a* with *historical*; *history* definitely needs an *a*.

* * * * *

Transitive verbs take direct objects; intransitive verbs do not. Many verbs are both transitive and intransitive according their meanings. In the sentence *She spoke softly*, *spoke* is intransitive, whereas the same verb is transitive in the sentence *She spoke German*. One needs a conceptual understanding of *transitive* and *intransitive* to be able to use the verbs *lie* and *lay* correctly.

Lesson 5: Adverbs

You may already know that adverbs modify verbs, adjectives, and other adverbs. Perhaps you will be surprised to learn that they can also modify prepositions, prepositional phrases, conjunctions, clauses, and sentences (these uses will be considered later). Furthermore, there are adverbs called transitional adverbs, which function both as conjunctions and as adverbs. They too are a topic for later consideration. Finally, there are independent adverbs; they modify nothing at all.

How does one recognize an adverb? "They end in *-ly*," says Brian in the back row. He's right, of course, but he's also wrong-- well, more right than wrong. Indeed, most words that end in *-ly* are adverbs. Think of *thoroughly, pleasantly, helpfully, dearly, horribly, astutely*, etc. The list extends into the thousands; however, some words that end in *-ly* aren't adverbs at all, but adjectives: *manly, costly, ugly*, for example. And what would you call *also, too, quite, very, here*, and *there*? Although they don't end in *-ly*, they are adverbs. What's more, there are quite a few adjectives without *-ly* that also serve as adverbs. Think of *fast, high, low, long, right, left, late*, to name several. *Early* is both an adjective and an adverb.

Consider the following sentences in support of some of the observations of the preceding paragraph:

You can say . . .
He is a surly person.
They admire his manly qualities.
Santa had a jolly laugh.

But you can't say . . .
He speaks surly to everyone.
He smiles manly.
Santa laughed jolly.

You can say . . .
Only racecar drivers need fast cars.
It was a long wait.
She made a right turn.
The early bird gets the worm.

You can also say . . .
He drives too fast.
They had to wait long.
She turned right.
That bird arrives early.

Here is an example of adverbs modifying a verb:

The assistant principal spoke softly, patiently, and supportively to the troubled student.

The adverbs *softly, patiently*, and *supportively* modify the verb *spoke*. They tell how the assistant principal spoke. She might have felt like speaking loudly or thunderously, angrily or threateningly, patronizingly or insultingly; however, she chose to speak softly, patiently, and supportively.

The following sentence contains adverbs that modify adjectives:

The motives of the exceedingly gracious hostess were quite political.

The adverb *exceedingly* modifies the attributive adjective *gracious*, while the adverb *quite* modifies the predicate adjective *political.*

In the following sentence, there are two adverbs modifying other adverbs:

Ray answered the question quite hastily and altogether incorrectly.

The adverbs *quite* and *altogether* modify the adverbs *hastily* and *incorrectly*, respectively.

The following sentence contains an independent adverb:

Honestly, I don't care.

Honestly is an independent adverb.

Every adverb is diagrammed on a slanted line. If the adverb modifies a verb or a predicate adjective (predicate adjectives are introduced in the next lesson), the slanted line is extended down from the horizontal line of the verb or of the predicate adjective. To diagram an adverb that modifies an attributive adjective or another adverb, one hooks its slanted line onto the slanted line of the word modified, as shown on the next page.

Every adverb is diagrammed on a slanted line. If the adverb modifies a verb or a predicate adjective (predicate adjectives are introduced in the next lesson), the slanted line is extended down from the horizontal line of the verb or of the predicate adjective.

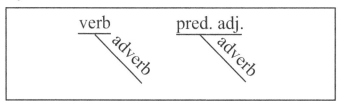

Step 26. The neighbor talks incessantly.

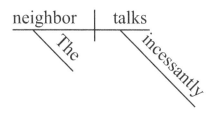

If the adverb modifies an attributive adjective or another adverb, the slanted line of the adverb is placed on the left of and parallel to the slanted line of the attributive adjective or of the adverb and is hooked at the top onto this line.

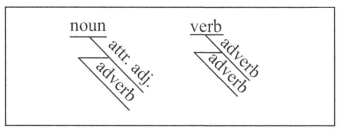

Step 27. The thoroughly bored students were fidgeting.

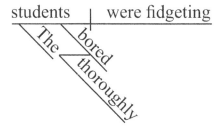

Step 28. Chris awoke very early.

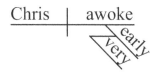

Step 29. Mary walked swiftly and silently.

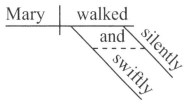

Step 30. The strikingly but superficially beautiful antagonist entered.

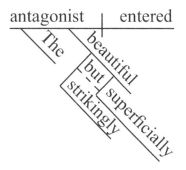

Step 31. Quickly he showered and dressed.

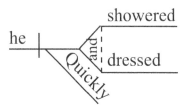

Some adverbs are independent words, modifying nothing at all. Such an adverb is placed on a horizontal line above and separate from the rest of the sentence.

Step 32. Not surprisingly, the fatuous man loves a diffident woman.

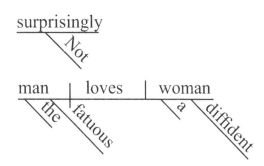

Interrogative adverbs (*when, where, why, how*) modify verbs.

Step 33. How do you know that?

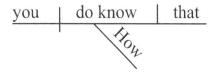

Exercise 5: Adverbs

46. We were speaking clearly.

47. Jenny was telling very scary stories.

48. I cannot run so fast.

49. Angrily and inexorably the storm devastated the coastal regions.

50. Should we put the piano here or there?

51. This subdivision has about fifty residences.

52. Not all Americans favor bigger and more expensive cars.

53. I did the assignment fast and inattentively.

54. She wrote an exceedingly but unexpectedly beautiful poem.

55. Why did you order the books, and when will they arrive?

56. Well, we should try harder.

Writing Correctly 5

In the following pairs of sentences, notice how the meaning changes when the adverbs *only, just,* and *even* are repositioned:

> *William only seems to succeed when opportunity slaps him in the face. William seems to succeed only when opportunity slaps him in the face.*

> *She just doesn't want to go to one game. She doesn't want to go to just one game.*

> *Did you hear about the professor who just died yesterday? Did you hear about the professor who died just yesterday?*

> *His family even ignores him. Even his family ignores him.*

How easy it would be to say or write the first sentence in each of the above pairs while intending to convey the meaning expressed in the second sentence. Take care in the placement of adverbs. Be sure your sentences say what you want them to say.

* * * * *

Have you ever looked up the word *friendlily*? If *friendly* is an adjective, the adverb must be *friendlily*, right? And it is. How about *sillily*? Yep, that's a word, too. *Scholarlily? Heavenlily?* Nope, neither is an acceptable word. So what can you do if you want to express *in a scholarly manner* with one word? You can use *scholarly*, which is accepted not only as an adjective but also as an adverb. I found *ghastlily, holily, jollily, surlily,* and *uglily* in at least one authoritative source. I did not find *timelily, sicklily,* or *mannerlily*. *Timely, sickly,* and *mannerly* are not only adjectives but also adverbs, as are *daily, early, hourly,* and *likely*. My dictionaries do not show *heavenly* as an adverb; however, it almost certainly is. Who would object to this simple sentence: *The choir sang heavenly?* What if you think the word *sillily* sounds *silly*? Then use *silly* as an adverb; it's altogether acceptable. You can do the same with *friendly* and *ghastly* (but not with *ghostly*, which can be used only as an adjective and has no -lily form). The adjectives *holy, jolly, surly,* and *ugly* are not used as adverbs in the United States; the British have a fondness for the expression *jolly well*.

Exercise caution in using two-form adverbs like *wide/widely, direct/directly, near/nearly, most/mostly, hard/hardly,* and *wrong/wrongly*. One form may be correct in one position but not in another, as follows:

> *They wandered far and wide. That is a widely used expression.*

> *Does this plane fly direct from Louisville to Denver? When you arrive, you must go directly to your hotel.*

> *She answered wrong. The racial slur was wrongly attributed to an equal-rights advocate.*

* * * * *

The words *hither, thither, whither, hence, thence, whence, hitherto,* and *henceforth* are useful adverbs. It's sad to see most of them slipping away into the netherworld of archaic words. But they're not dead yet, and they could be coaxed back into good health if enough of us chose to use them judiciously. Nowadays *hither* probably should be restricted to the first position in sentences (*Hither came the faithful annually on the feast day of St. Anne*), where it means *to this place*; elsewhere, *here* seems a better choice. And *thither* is a good choice when *there* would be ambiguous, e.g., *The trail there is steep*. Does this *there* mean *in that place* or *to that place*? If the latter meaning is intended, why not use *thither*? The phrase *hither and thither* is alive and well in sentences like *The children scampered hither and thither in search of the precious eggs*. *Whence* is at least as good as *from where*; but avoid the oft heard phrase *from whence* (that would be like saying *from from where*). Its counterpart, *whither* often seems a better choice than *where . . . to*. *Whence* and *whither* can also mean *from which* and *to which*, respectively.

> *I live in Boston, whence I have come today and whither I shall return on Friday.*

Hitherto (until this time), *thence* (from that time, from that place), and *henceforth* (from this time on) are still in wide use.

> *"Zaire has hitherto been my homeland," exclaimed the articulate immigrant; "henceforth I will live in America."*

> *I was born in Italy; thence comes my propensity to gesticulate abundantly.*

* * * * *

Try not to overuse adverbs like *very, actually,* and *really*. Actually they really very seldom do very much for very many sentences, really.

Use *farther* only as the comparative form of *far*. In most conversations, you will need *further* more often than *farther*.

* * * * *

Yes, you may begin a sentence with *and* or *but*.

* * * * *

Cannot but plus a verb is perfectly good English: *One cannot but notice her beauty.*

Lesson 6: Subjective Complements:
Predicate Nominatives and Predicate Adjectives

A **subjective complement** is a noun or an adjective (or the equivalent of either) that completes a linking verb. Such substantives are called **predicate nominatives**; such adjectives and equivalent expressions are called **predicate adjectives**. Subjective complements can also follow certain intransitive verbs as well as passive-voice forms of factitive verbs (explained below).

These sentences contain predicate nominatives:

The woman in the blue dress is my sister. The predicate nominative is the noun *sister*, which follows a form of the verb *be*.

It is I. The predicate nominative is the personal pronoun *I*.

Have you ever been a lifeguard? The predicate nominative is *lifeguard*. The verb *have been* is a present-perfect form of the verb *be*.

This could be an important clue. As you would probably expect, modal forms of the verb *be* (such as *may be, should be, could have been, and must have been*) can take subjective complements.

She was elected president. President, a predicate nominative, follows a passive-voice form of the factitive verb *elect*. Factitive verbs, such as *make, choose, appoint*, and *designate*, are used to make someone something. Predicate nominatives can also be preceded by the expletive *as*, e.g., *He was chosen as leader of the small delegation* (more about this later).

* * * * *

These sentences contain predicate adjectives:

I had been sick for a week. Sick is a predicate adjective. *Had been* is a past-perfect form of the verb *be*.

She felt sad. Sad is a predicate adjective. In addition to *feel*, the verbs *seem, become, look, remain, taste,* and other similar verbs can be followed by predicate adjectives. You can test them with the adjective *good*: *it seems good, he is becoming good, you look good, we want to remain good, the water tastes good.*

Blackberries grow wild along the south edge of the woods. Wild is a predicate adjective. The verb *grow* is intransitive; that is, it does not take a direct object in the sense in which it is used in this sentence ("to thrive; to become larger"). *Grow* is a transitive verb when it means "to cause to grow" (*She likes to grow green beans and tomatoes*).

They left angry but arrived happy. Angry and *happy* are predicate adjectives; each follows an intransitive verb. *Arrive* is always intransitive, while *leave* is often transitive, as in *The thieves took the cheap jewelry but left the expensive clothing.*

Tom was made livid by the derogatory remark about his daughter. The predicate adjective *livid* follows a passive form of the factitive verb *make*.

Prepositional phrases can be used as predicate nominatives and as predicate adjectives. But this is a topic for a later lesson.

In a sentence diagram, a backslash is used to separate verbs from subjective complements (predicate nominatives and predicate adjectives).

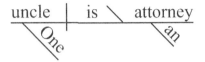

Step 34. One uncle is an attorney.

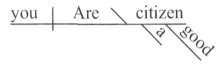

Step 35. Are you a good citizen?

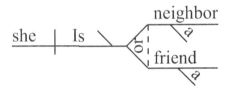

Step 36. Is she a neighbor or a friend?

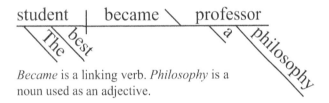

Step 37. The best student became a phiolosophy professor.

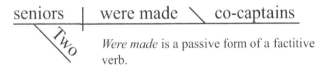

Became is a linking verb. *Philosophy* is a noun used as an adjective.

Step 38. Two seniors were made co-captains.

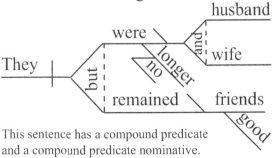

Were made is a passive form of a factitive verb.

Step 39. They were no longer husband and wife but remained good friends.

This sentence has a compound predicate and a compound predicate nominative.

Step 40. The stranger was tall, dark, and handsome.

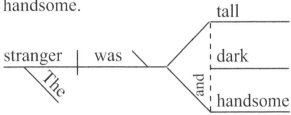

Note the tripartite predicate adjective.

Step 41. He feels good, but he doesn't look good.

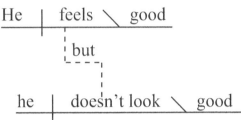

Step 42. I am getting sick.

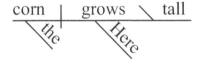

When *get* means "become," as it does in this sentence, it is a linking verb.

Step 43. Here the corn grows tall.

corn | grows \ tall

The intransitive verb *grows* is followed in this sentence by a predicate adjective, *tall*.

Step 44. She is just playing stupid.

She | is playing \ stupid

When *play* means "pretend to be," it can be followed by a subjective complement.

Step 45. How can the fence be made stronger?

Even when accompanied by modal auxiliary verbs, factitive verbs in the passive voice can take subjective complements.

Exercise 6: Predicate Nominatives and Predicate Adjectives

57. Bloomington is a college town.

58. English has long been my favorite subject.

59. She was feeling happy, but he was feeling sad.

60. They quickly became close friends.

61. He is a truly remarkable scholar but a lousy poet.

62. Our waiter was both efficient and courteous.

63. Who was elected class president?

64. Be good and stay healthy.

65. He became angry and silent and left the room.

66. She has been, is, and will be a very effective mayor.

Writing Correctly 6

What do you think of the following sentence?

> *Each day we hear tragic stories of the unfortunate*
> *death of innocent men, women, and children at the*
> *hands of misguided terrorists?*

Of the four adjectives, are not three unnecessary, even tautological? Of course, the death of innocent men, women, and children is unfortunate; of course, stories that relate such happenings are tragic; and, of course, terrorists are misguided. The only useful adjective is *innocent*. Here is the same sentence devoid of redundancy:

> *Each day we hear stories of the death of innocent*
> *men, women, and children at the hands of terrorists.*

That's a lot better, right? Here is another sentence:

> *I found the tale about the good fish, the weird*
> *fisherman, and his stupid wife interesting.*

It contains four weak adjectives, doesn't it? So let's replace them with stronger ones, as follows:

> *I found the tale of the kindhearted fish, the simple-*
> *minded fisherman, and his greedy wife inspirational.*

If you need attributive adjectives, choose them carefully.

* * * * *

Asked how they feel, most people respond with *I feel good* or, in elliptical form, *Good*. Grammarians have long defended this response by pointing out that *feel* is a linking verb and, as such, can be followed by a predicate adjective. (Yes, you can also say *I feel well* because, in that sentence, *well* is an adjective, not an adverb.) Then, just as things were going along smoothly, along came young people who began saying--in response to the question *How are you?--I'm good*. Just a minute, we old fogies objected, *good* when used after *I'm* has always said something about morality, i.e., *I am morally good*. The way to say you are in good health is *I'm well*, we insisted. Well, we can argue that the new *I'm good* is unidiomatic; and indeed it is, or was. But grammar is on the side of the young upstarts. If one can say *I feel good*, there's no grammatical reason why one can't express the same thing with *I'm good*.

* * * * *

When does one place a hyphen between an adverb and an attributive adjective? Take a look at these sentences:

> *The newly appointed commissioner spoke out*
> *fearlessly. She did not take offense at the politely*
> *worded criticism. She accepted or rejected widely*
> *held beliefs on their own merit.*

Should there be a hyphen between *newly* and *appointed*, between *politely* and *worded*, and between *widely* and *held*? The answer is no; adverbs ending in *-ly* and the adverb *very* are not joined by a hyphen to the adjectives they modify. On the other hand, putting a connecting hyphen between other adverbs and their attributive adjectives can facilitate reading. This is especially true when the adverb could be read mistakenly as an adjective, resulting in an unintended meaning. Here are a few examples: *a well-established engineer, a fast-acting salesman, her best-known novel.* In cases like these, hyphens are mandatory. And even though misunderstanding would not result from the omission of the hyphen in a phrase like *a seldom-used word*, why not use it anyway for consistency? You will have many careful writers on your side. If an attributive adjective is a noun (yes, nouns can function as adjectives) modified by an adjective or another noun, use a hyphen to connect that word with the attributive adjective, as follows: *the middle-school principal, the short-term interest, a quality-control expert, a pet-protection agency.* Compound modifiers are hyphenated, for example, *a win-or-lose situation, a hide-and-seek approach.* Additional guidelines for hyphenation are too numerous to enumerate here; nevertheless, do note the following phrases, and extrapolate: *a ten-kilometer run, a sixteenth-century painting, cross-country results, an all-inclusive account, my four-year-old granddaughter, seventy-six trombones, his off-the-record comments, an up-to-the-minute report, the carefully worked-out plan.*

* * * * *

Certain adjectives (*reticent,* for example) are in danger of losing their primary meanings; and the adjective *fewer* seems to be in danger of disappearing completely. It seems that we hear from all sides and venues these days things like this:

> *Less and less people are showing up each week.*
> *I lost less golf balls than you did.*
> *There were less than ten soldiers killed in Iraq today.*
> *The losing team had less attempts from the free-throw*
> *line.*

In each case, replace *less* with *fewer. Less* is singular; *fewer* is plural. It's almost that simple. An exception is made with blocks of time and money.

> *I have less than ten dollars.*
> *Most Americans work less than fifty years.*

Less is correct in both sentences.

* * * * *

We nerds works in the nominative case; however, it should not be used as the object of a preposition. *Of us nerds* is correct.

Lesson 7: Possessives, Appositives, and Expletives

Possessives are nouns and pronouns used to show various kinds of possession or belonging (ownership, authorship, relationship, and other kinds of attachment). Most singular possessive nouns (including names ending in *s*, *z*, or *x*) end in *'s*, and most plural possessive nouns end in *s'*. Exceptions to the latter rule are plural nouns that do not end in *s*; for example, the possessive of *children* is *children's*.

Possessives can be subjective or objective. An example of a subjective possessive is *Tom's* in *Tom's car* (Tom owns the car). An example of an objective possessive is *student's* in *the student's expulsion* (someone expelled the student). Some possessives can be either subjective or objective depending on context. *The manager's reward*, for example, can be a reward given by the manager (the manager rewards someone) or a reward given to the manager (someone rewards the manager).

Possessive pronouns are *my, mine, your, yours, his, her, hers, its, our, ours, their,* and *theirs. My, your, her, its, our,* and *their* always precede the nouns they modify (*my hat, your computer, our house*). *Mine, yours, hers, ours,* and *theirs* are called absolute possessives. These possessives don't precede nouns but are used absolutely, i.e., separately (*That hat is mine, That computer is yours, That house is ours*). *His* can be an absolute possessive; however, it can also be used in the attributive position (*his book, That book is his*). Absolute possessives not only show possession; they also function as subjects, objects, and predicate nominatives. Examples: (as a subject) *I don't know where your coat is, but <u>mine</u> is right here;* (as a direct object) *Pam has my ruler, and I have <u>yours</u>;* (as an object of a preposition) *I don't care what you do with your own toys, but be careful with <u>ours</u>;* (as a predicate nominative) *Those books are <u>hers</u>.*

* * * * *

An **appositive** is a word, phrase, or clause that identifies or explains another word or other words in the same sentence. Appositives are said to be in apposition with the words they identify or explain. Most appositives are nouns in apposition with preceding nouns; however, appositives can also be pronouns, verbs, adjectives, adverbs, prepositions, phrases, and clauses. They occasionally precede the word or words with which they are in apposition. Here are examples of various kinds of appositives:

> *We planned to travel (fly) to Seattle.* (a verb in apposition with a verb)
> *These flowers are for my best friend, you.* (a personal pronoun in apposition with a noun)
> *She regrets the disappearance of many feral (wild) animals.* (an adjective in apposition with an adjective)
> *He removed the books clandestinely (secretly).* (an adverb in apposition with an adverb)
> *We live on (beside) a river.* (a preposition in apposition with a preposition)
> *The office workers were told to be less officious (to mind their own business).* (an infinitive phrase in apposition with an infinitive phrase)
> *On Friday evenings we go out to eat (the only excitement of the week), and then we work all weekend.* (a noun phrase in apposition with a clause)

In English, when a proper name is in apposition with a possessive noun, only the proper name has a possessive ending, e.g., *my friend Melvin's car.*

One distinguishes restrictive (necessary for identification) and nonrestrictive (unnecessary for identification) appositives:

> restrictive: *My cousin Alan broke his arm.* (noun in apposition with a noun)
> nonrestrictive: *My father, a skiing instructor, broke his arm.* (noun in apposition with a noun)

The pronouns *myself, yourself, himself, herself, itself, ourselves, yourselves,* and *themselves* are both reflexive (more about them later) and intensifying. As intensifying pronouns, they are appositives.

> *The author herself will be there to sign copies of her new book.* (an intensifying pronoun in apposition with a noun)
> *They themselves will be there.* (an intensifying pronoun in apposition with a personal pronoun)

* * * * *

An **expletive** is a word that has a function but little or no meaning. The word *as* is an expletive when its function is to introduce a predicate nominative: *She was chosen as her school's representative.* The expletives *or, such as, namely, for example, actually,* etc. are sometimes used to introduce appositives: *Siamese fighting fish, or bettas, are fun to breed. She plays four musical instruments, namely, piano, cello, clarinet, and flute.*

Most possessives are diagrammed like attributive adjectives.

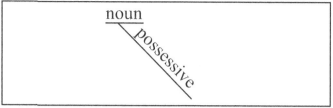

An absolute possessive is diagrammed according to its function as subject, direct object, indirect object, object of a preposition, or predicate nominative.

Step 46. Have you seen Anna's scooter?

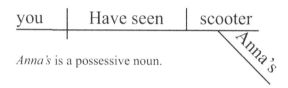

Anna's is a possessive noun.

Step 47. Those are your CDs, and these are mine.

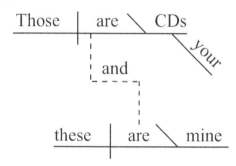

Your is a regular possessive pronoun. *Mine* is an absolute possessive used as a predicate nominative.

Step 48. Mine is over there.

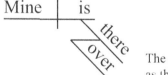

The absolute possessive serves as the subject of the sentence.

Step 49. They can't read the teacher's handwriting.

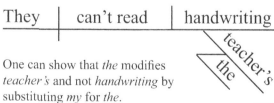

One can show that *the* modifies *teacher's* and not *handwriting* by substituting *my* for *the*.

Appositives are placed in parentheses immediately after the word or words with which they are in apposition.

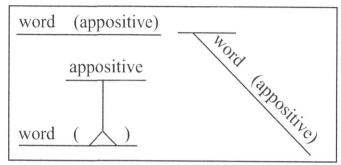

You can disregard the appositive on a pedestal for now. It is a topic for later consideration.

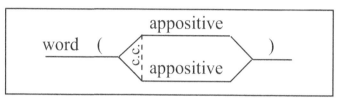

The *c.c.* stands for a coordinating conjunction that joins the two parts of the compound appositive.

Step 50. Everyone likes my friend Jacob.

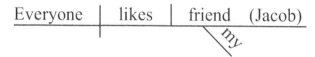

Jacob is in apposition with the direct object, *friend*.

Step 51. That's her son Jay's car.

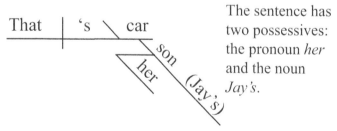

The sentence has two possessives: the pronoun *her* and the noun *Jay's*.

If the appositive *Jay's* is omitted, one says *her son's car*.

Step 52. Two seniors, namely Isabel and Katie, were chosen as co-captains.

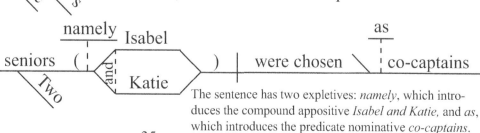

The sentence has two expletives: *namely*, which introduces the compound appositive *Isabel and Katie,* and *as,* which introduces the predicate nominative *co-captains.*

Exercise 7: Possessives, Appositives, and the Expletive *As*

67. That book is mine, and this one is yours.

68. Who has been appointed as their representative?

69. Dave's friends are also her friends.

70. The councilman always writes down his constituents' complaints and suggestions.

71. Have you met my friend Marcy?

72. Her cousins Alan and Jay climbed a mountain.

73. Nathan, a four-year band member, was chosen as the most outstanding musician.

74. Do you know her daughter Pam's address?

75. The renters altered, that is, nearly destroyed, the apartment.

76. They have strength, speed, and mental toughness--the right qualities.

Writing Correctly 7

An appositive that is not necessary for sufficient identification (a nonrestrictive appositive) is set off by a comma or commas.

> *She invited her daughter's fiancée, Fred Morris, for dinner.*
> *Have you read "The Grapes of Wrath," a novel by John Steinbeck?*
> *Isabel couldn't find her favorite food, salmon, on the menu.*
> *The school's principal, Mr. Williams, has removed "The Beloved" from the approved reading list.*

An appositive that is necessary for sufficient identification (a restrictive appositive) is not set off by commas.

> *My friend Wes likes water skiing.*
> *I'm looking for a present for my sister Ellen.*
> *Claire likes the color red.*
> *Bruce will introduce the famous architect Michael Graves.*

A colon is sometimes used to introduce lists. Is it used correctly in the following sentence?

> *Some of theBrethauers' favorite farm animals are: horses, cows, goats, and geese.*

The answer is an emphatic no. Unless you are introducing one or more clauses, a colon should not be used after forms of the verb *be* (*am, is, are, was, were,* etc.), *for example, namely,* and *that is.* Let's stay with the farm-animal sentence. Here are some of the ways in which it could be successfully rewritten:

> *Some of the Brethauers' favorite farm animals are horses, cows, goats, and geese.*
> *Some of the Brethauers' favorite farm animals are these: horses, cows, goats, and geese.*
> *Among farm animals, the Brethauers favor horses, cows, goats, and geese.*
> *Among farm animals, the Brethauers favor these four: horses, cows, goats, and geese.*

This sentence uses *for example* followed by a list:

> *In this book, you will be introduced to exciting elements of grammar, for example, adverbial objectives, objective complements, infinitive phrases, and noun clauses.* (Notice that a comma, not a colon, is used after *for example.*)

If we omit *for example,* we can use a colon, as follows:

> *In this book, you will be introduced to exciting elements of grammar: adverbial objectives, objective complements, infinitive phrases, and noun clauses, among others.*

We come now to a topic to which Lynn Truss devotes more than thirty pages of her popular book *Eats, Shoots and Leaves*: the use of the apostrophe. Truss bemoans the fact that the apostrophe is becoming an object of neglect or misuse. Here is what you need to know: 1)The apostrophe can be used to show the person or thing to which someone or something belongs (as a possession, a part, an aspect, a right, etc.), for example, *Jay's coat, the kids' teacher, the people's rights, Betsy Ross's opinion.* 2) The apostrophe is used for certain plural forms. Usage varies here; the safest course is to use *'s* for the plural forms of lower-case letters and of abbreviations requiring periods: *three r's, two Ph.D.'s.* All other plurals may be written without apostrophe. 3) The apostrophe is used to replace missing letters or numerals, for example, *I'm* (I am), *you're* (you are), *don't* (do not), *let's* (let us), and *the class of '96* (the class of 1996).

To form the possessive of most singular nouns, add *'s*, as in *Johanna's mother, a car's surface,* and *a friend's house.* This rule applies even to the singular forms of most proper nouns ending in *s*: *Chris's career, Tess's piano, Gus's sorrow.* Ancient names ending in *s* tend to form the possessive by adding only an apostrophe: *Ramses' tomb, Archimedes' principle, Moses' commandments, Jesus' disciples.* In general, if a possessive is pronounced without a voiced *s*, use the apostrophe only, e.g., *Mr. Sanders'.*

If two or more people possess something jointly, put *'s* on the last name only, for example, *Katie, Anna, and Jake's sandbox.* The apostrophes in the expression *Brian's and Alan's bicycles* tell the reader that the boys own separate bicycles.

To form the possessive of plural nouns ending in *s*, add only an apostrophe: *the teachers' classrooms, her classmates' interests, the customers' wishes.* Plural proper nouns do the same: *the Smiths', the Humphreys', the Joneses'.* If the plural ends in a letter other than *s*, its possessive is formed by adding *'s*: *the deer's mothers, the fish's mouths, the children's attitude.*

Do not use an apostrophe to form the plural of proper nouns. Here are several examples: *the Watsons, two Courtneys, three Charleses, the Dubois* (French names ending in *s, x,* or *z* are usually left unchanged in the plural).

Do not use absolute possessives, appropriate as predicate nominatives, as attributive adjectives. Note these expressions:

> *her* [not *hers*] *and his house*
> *our* [not *ours*] *and your friends*
> *their* [not *theirs*] *and my classmates*
> *my* [not *mine*] *and your teacher*
> *your* [not *yours*] *and my pet*

Lesson 8: Prepositional Phrases

A **preposition** is a particle (a small, uninflected word) that shows a relationship between its object and another word or other words. As many students have learned, one can name many prepositions by thinking of any place a mouse can go: *in, into, around, up, down, over, under, through,* etc.; however, many prepositions have nothing to do with place: *with, without, for, except, besides, since, of,* etc. When used in a sentence, a preposition must have an object. If a particular word does not have an object, it is not a preposition. It may look exactly like a preposition (i.e., be spelled the same), but without an object it is either an adverb, a conjunction, or a part of a so-called phrasal verb (more about phrasal verbs later). Here are some examples of prepositions, adverbs, and conjunctions that have the same spelling:

> *Jack Horner was sitting in a corner.* (The preposition *in* has the object *corner.*)
> *They just walked in.* (Here *in* is an adverb. Adverbs do not have objects.)

> *Poor Jethro had to stay after school.* (The preposition *after* has the object *school.*)
> *He stayed for an hour after the other students had left.* (Here *after* is a subordinating conjunction. It introduces an entire clause--more about this later.)

> *The dog chased the cat around the house.* (The object of the preposition *around* is *house.*)
> *The flu is going around.* (Here *around* is an adverb.)

> *There is no one here but us.* (The object of the preposition *but* is the pronoun *us.*)
> *Pam went to school but her brothers stayed home.* (Here *but* is a coordinating conjunction.)

For now, only nouns and pronouns will be used as objects of prepositions; later, however, you will see how gerunds and gerund phrases, infinitives and infinitive phrases, as well as noun clauses can be objects of prepositions. It is even possible for a prepositional phrase to be used as the object of a preposition.

Some prepositions consist of more than one word. Examples of these phrasal prepositions are *out of, along with, as for,* and *by means of.*

Adverbs can modify prepositions and prepositional phrases. Examples: *The fireworks display will begin right after the game.* (The adverb *right* modifies the preposition *after.*) The food arrived just in time for the party. (The adverb *just* modifies the prepositional phrase *in time.*)

* * * * *

Most prepositional phrases are adverbial or adjectival. Adverbial prepositional phrases modify verbs, adjectives, and adverbs. Adjectival prepositional phrases modify nouns and pronouns. Here are some examples of **adverbial prepositional phrases**:

> *Isabel and Jay strolled through the park.* (The prepositional phrase *through the park* modifies the verb *strolled.* It tells where Isabel and Jay strolled.)

> *Transparent in the middle, the glass is increasingly opaque as it approaches the frame.* (The prepositional phrase *in the middle* modifies the adjective *transparent.*)

> *Everyone moved closer to the storyteller.* (The prepositional phrase *to the storyteller* modifies the adverb *closer.*)

Here are examples of **adjectival prepositional phrases**:

> *All eyes were focused on the woman on the tightrope.* (The prepositional phrase *on the tightrope* modifies the noun *woman.*)

> *Someone in the corner stood up.* (The prepositional phrase *in the corner* modifies the pronoun *someone.*)

> *As far as anyone knew, he was in good health.* (The prepositional phrase *in good health* functions as a predicate adjective.)

To diagram a prepositional phrase, place the preposition on a diagonal line connected to the horizontal or diagonal line of the word or words modified. From a point near the bottom of this diagonal line, draw a horizontal line to the right, and put the object of the preposition on this line. Any modifiers of the object are diagrammed in the expected manner.

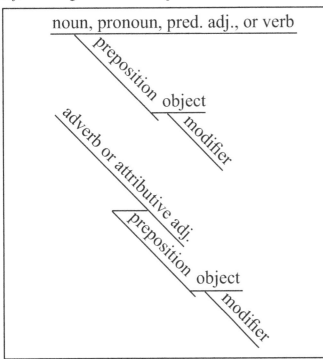

Step 53. A porter carried our baggage to the car.

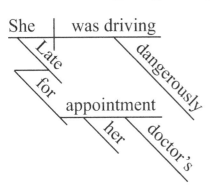

The prepositional phrase *to the car* is adverbial; it modifies the verb *carried*.

Step 54. Late for her doctor's appointment, she was driving dangerously.

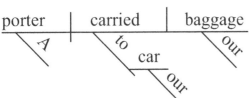

The adverbial prepositional phrase *for her doctor's appointment* modifies the attributive adjective *late*.

Step. 55. He is of sound mind and body.

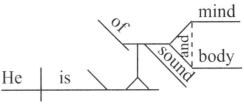

Of sound mind and body, a prepositional phrase with a compound object, serves in this sentence as a predicate adjective.

Step 56. Beth eats too fast for the rest of us.

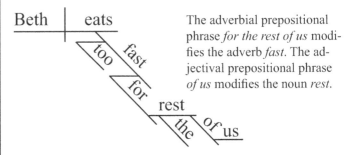

The adverbial prepositional phrase *for the rest of us* modifies the adverb *fast*. The adjectival prepositional phrase *of us* modifies the noun *rest*.

Step 57. In the evening, Joe went out for a ride.

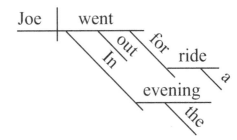

In the evening and *for a ride* are prepositional phrases modifying the verb *went*. *Out*, which looks like a preposition, is an adverb in this sentence.

Step 58. I can live with or without television.

The adverbial prepositional phrase *with or without television* features two prepositions and a single prepositional object.

Step 59. Everyone but Stacy ran right out of the house.

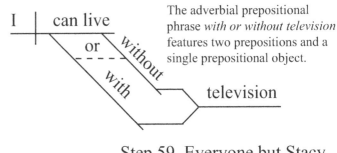

In this sentence, *but* is a preposition. *Out of* is a phrasal preposition. The adverb *right* modifies the prepositional phrase *out of the house*.

Exercise 8: Prepositional Phrases

77. Your cup is on your desk.

78. My uncle is the man with the red tie.

79. Early in the week, friends of ours are coming for dinner.

80. They approach every new challenge with enthusiasm and determination.

81. We can go through the narrow tunnel or over the narrow bridge.

82. This country has a government by and for the people.

83. Because of the cold weather, the pool is not in use.

84. The principal is taking a group of teachers out for lunch.

85. Kathy acted in accordance with the express wishes of her clients.

86. Didn't you leave the house just before dawn?

87. The park is open only on weekends.

Writing Correctly 8

One way of varying sentence structure is to move prepositional phrases around. For example, instead of writing *Mary went to a play on Thursday evening*, one can write *On Thursday evening Mary went to a play*. In general, adverbial prepositional phrases of time can be readily moved, whereas some adverbial prepositional phrases of place refuse to be relocated. It sounds downright bad to say *To a play Mary went on Thursday evening*. Still, other such phrases can be moved without a problem; for instance, *They will build a bank on the corner* can be rewritten as *On the corner they will build a bank*. As for other adverbial prepositional phrases (phrases like *for her boss, with their associates,* and *because of the rain*), most can come first without a problem (*without a problem, most can come first*). Adjectival prepositional phrases, on the other hand, are bound to the noun they modify. Try moving the prepositional phrase in the sentence *He didn't like the color of the tie*. It just doesn't work.

* * * * *

Read the following sentence and ask yourself if it is well written: *The class did the assignment in the allotted time, accurately, and without complaining.* It could be better, right? The writer has violated the rule of parallelism, which prescribes that each element of a series (be it a series of words, of phrases, or of clauses) be of the same grammatical type. The series *in the allotted time, accurately, and without complaining,* consists of two prepositional phrases and one adverb. One way to improve the sentence is to rewrite the series correctly, as *in the allotted time, with no mistakes, and without complaint.* Notice that I have replaced the adverb *accurately* with the prepositional phrase *with no mistakes.* That gives us three prepositional phrases. To make all three objects regular nouns, I changed the gerund *complaining* to *complaint.* Of course, the series could be changed to *punctually, accurately, and uncomplainingly,* also a parallel series.

* * * * *

The object of a preposition is never the subject of a sentence; therefore, in sentences like *One of the participants comes from Peru, One of the courses being offered this semester has caught my eye,* and even *One of the many foreigners who are studying at our university is my roommate,* the main verbs are singular (*comes, has, is*) because the subject, *one,* is singular.

On the other hand, in the expressions *any of* and *a number of, any* and *number* are considered plural when they have plural referents; used as subjects, they require plural verbs, as follows:

> *Do any of the applicants have the necessary credentials?*
> *A number of her friends were already there.*

On the other hand, *number* in the expression *the number of* is usually singular:

> *The number of accused witches executed in Salem, Massachusetts, was under twenty.*

* * * * *

Is there anyone in the twenty-first century who still insists that a sentence not end in a preposition?

> *What are you talking about?*
> *They told us where they came from.*
> *The hunter didn't know what he was aiming at.*

When did you last hear even the most pedantic professor say *About what are you talking?* And if you heard *They told us from where they came*, you could bet the speaker (a) learned English as an adult or (b) just fell from the moon. Let's hope that all hunters know what they are aiming at, but let's also hope that this is not expressed as *All hunters know at what they are aiming.*

You may have heard the story of how Winston Churchill reprimanded a civil servant who had gone to ridiculous lengths to avoid ending a sentence with a preposition. Churchill wrote to him: "This is nonsense up with which I will not put." Churchill's idea, of course, was to demonstrate the absurdity of insisting that prepositions not be placed at the end of sentences but before their objects. Unfortunately, the "prepositions" that Churchill chose, *up* and *with*, are, in this context, not prepositions at all but parts of a phrasal verb (please refer to page 4 of this book for a definition of *phrasal verbs*). Another phrasal verb is *try on.* Since *on* is not a preposition here, we cannot say *On what do you want to try?* (but *What do you want to try on?*) or *That's the jacket on which you just tried* (but *That's the jacket that you just tried on).*

On the other hand, one cannot simply pile up prepositions at the end of a sentence. The third edition of H. W. Fowler's *Dictionary of Modern English Usage*, referred to simply as *New Fowler*, cites a brief dialog that drives home this point:

> Child: *I want to be read to.*
> Nurse: *What book do you want to be read to out of?*
> Child: *Robinson Crusoe*
> (The nurse brings a copy of *Swiss Family Robinson*.)
> Child: *What did you bring me that book to be read to out of for?*

Aside from the fact that the word *to* in the first sentence of the dialog is not a preposition (prepositions need objects, and *to* does not have one in *I want to be read to*), this is a useful illustration of the folly of terminal prepositional overload (pun intended).

Lesson 9: Indirect Objects and Objective Complements

An **indirect object** tells to whom or for whom a direct object is given, said, or shown. In the sentence *He showed them the picture*, the direct object is *picture* and the indirect object is *them* (the people to whom the picture was shown). An indirect object is not preceded by a preposition. Although *He showed them the picture* means the same thing as *He showed the picture to them*, the latter sentence expresses the recipient of the giving as the object of a preposition, not as an indirect object. Here are some more sentences with indirect objects:

> *Chris gave his sister Debbie a present.* (*Present* is a direct object. The indirect object is *sister*.)
> *Will you lend me a dollar?* (*Dollar* is a direct object. The indirect object is *me*.)
> *She is telling her students a story.* (*Story* is a direct object. The indirect object is *students*.)

Remember, not every sentence that has a direct object has an indirect object as well. Indirect objects are found only in sentences that have verbs of giving, telling, or showing, including verbs like *offer, hand, teach, lend, promise, bring*, and *get*. Even verbs like *sing* and *find* can take indirect objects if they imply a kind of giving or offering, as in *Will you sing us a song?* and *Find me a pretty flower!* The indirect objects are *us* and *me*. *Do* doesn't seem to be a verb of giving, but it is in a sentence like *Please do me a favor*.

* * * * *

An **objective complement** is a noun or an adjective (or the equivalent of a noun or an adjective, like a pronoun or a participle) that completes a verb with respect to a direct object. The verb in a sentence with an objective complement is often factitive; that is, it makes someone or something someone or something else. For example, verbs like *elect, appoint, choose, render, name, call, entitle, color, dye*, and the verb *make* itself (but not when it means "to create") are factitive verbs. Here are some sentences containing factitive verbs and objective complements:

> *They called their mascot Herbie.* (The noun *Herbie* is an objective complement.)
> *The summer job will make him strong.* (The adjective *strong* is an objective complement.)
> *The shock of standing in front of the class has rendered the poor boy speechless.* (The adjective *speechless* is an objective complement.)
> *The parents named their daughter Aphrodite.* (The noun *Aphrodite* is an objective complement.)
> *One of my classmates dyed his hair purple.* (The adjective *purple* is an objective complement.)

Like predicate nominatives, objective complements can be introduced by the expletive *as*. Here is an example: *The European travelers chose a bilingual woman as their spokesperson.*

Objective complements appear only in active sentences. To change a sentence with an objective complement into its corresponding passive sentence, one takes the direct object of the sentence and makes it the subject (by the way, the word *subject* in this sentence is an objective complement). The passive factitive verb acts as a linking verb, and the objective complement of the original sentence becomes a subjective complement (either a predicate nominative or a predicate adjective). To see how this works, let's change the sample sentences above into their corresponding passive forms:

> *Their mascot was called Herbie.* (*Herbie* is a predicate nominative.)
> *He will be made strong by the summer job.* (*Strong* is a predicate adjective.)
> *The poor boy has been rendered speechless by the shock of standing in front of the class.* (*Speechless* is a predicate adjective.)
> *Their daughter was named Aphrodite.* (*Aphrodite* is a predicate nominative.)
> *The hair of one of my classmates was dyed purple.* (*Purple* is a predicate adjective.)
> *A bilingual woman was chosen as spokesperson by the European travelers.* (*Spokesperson* is a predicate nominative.)

This rule holds when the objective complement is a noun, a pronoun, or an adjective. We will see in Lesson 11 that it does not apply when the objective complement is an infinitive.

An indirect object is diagrammed like an object of a preposition, on a horizontal line that extends to the right from a point near the bottom of a diagonal line whose top touches the base line under the verb. Leave the diagonal line empty.

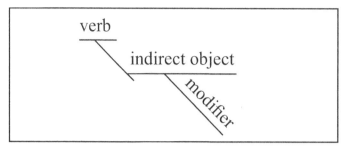

Step 60. Show Jack the letter from Melvin.

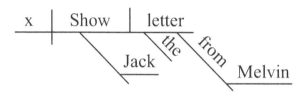

The noun *Jack*, which indicates the person to whom something is to be shown, is an indirect object. The *x* represents the unexpressed subject *you*. The prepositional phrase *from Melvin* is adjectival.

Step 61. She gave Jim her phone number.

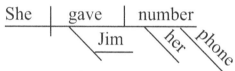

The noun *Jim* is an indirect object.
Phone is a noun used as an adjective.

Step 62. I told Dorothy and Clayton the news.

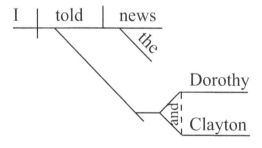

Dorothy and Clayton is a compound indirect object.

Step 63. Play me my favorite melody.

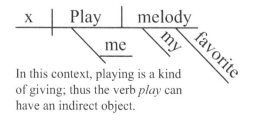

In this context, playing is a kind of giving; thus the verb *play* can have an indirect object.

There are two acceptable ways of diagramming objective complements. The one has tradition on its side, while the other is more appealing to most people today.

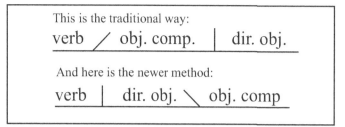

This is the traditional way:

And here is the newer method:

In my first books of sentence diagramming, I gave preference to the traditional manner; however, in this book, as a concession to modernity and because I recognize that the newer way has a certain logic on its side, I will use it primarily and show the traditional method secondarily.

Step 64. What makes you so healthy?

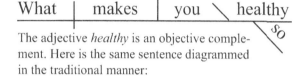

The adjective *healthy* is an objective complement. Here is the same sentence diagrammed in the traditional manner:

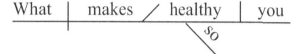

Step 65. The class elected him treasurer.

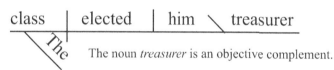

The noun *treasurer* is an objective complement.

Step 66. I chose you as my friend and confidante.

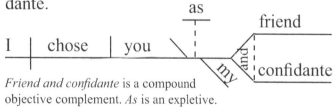

Friend and confidante is a compound objective complement. *As* is an expletive.

Step 67. Why should we keep the rope taut?

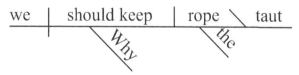

In this sentence, *keep* is a factitive verb even though it doesn't strictly speaking make the rope something else; instead it preserves a state brought about by a loose rope having been made something else, namely taut. The adjective *taut* is an objective complement.

Exercise 9: Indirect Objects and Objective Complements

88. Joe gave Betty an engagement ring.

89. The kindly woman showed her very curious nephew the attic.

90. The governor gave each distinguished student and his or her mentor a monetary award.

91. Debbie told Johanna, her next-door neighbor, the news about their friend Amelie.

92. Don't call me a liar.

93. Donnie considers his wife his best friend.

94. We made the twins Jim and Joe club president and vice-president, respectively.

95. The rescue team found the campers alive and declared them extremely fortunate.

96. Humpty-Dumpty was found in pieces, and neither the king's horses nor the king's men could make him whole again.

97. The nominee chose a local woman as his campaign manager.

Writing Correctly 9

Unlike adverbs and adverbial prepositional phrases, indirect objects and objective complements resist being moved around in sentences. Indirect objects come before direct objects; objective complements follow direct objects. Sentences like *Him they called Navigator* are possible but rare in prose. If we wish to vary the structure of a sentence containing an indirect object, we have to change the indirect object to a prepositional phrase with *to* or *for*, as follows:

> *I have two friends: Jack and Jill. I gave him a pail and her some water.*
> *I have two friends: Jack and Jill. To him I gave a pail, and to her I gave some water.*

To review how sentences containing objective complements can be rephrased as sentences containing subjective complements (predicate nominatives and predicate adjectives), please refer to page 44.

* * * * *

If you often use the coordinating conjunctions *and* and *but* to join two clauses, try something different: perhaps a semicolon to replace *and* (you may want to use a transitional adverb like *moreover* to introduce the second clause) or a semicolon followed by *nevertheless* or *however* to replace *but*. Another alternative to *and* is a subordinating conjunction like *while* (more about subordinating conjunctions later). To replace *but*, you may want to use a clause introduced by *although*. Here are examples:

> *Skip could scarcely afford the weekly flights, and the travel disrupted his sleep.*
> *Skip could scarcely afford the weekly flights; moreover, the travel disrupted his sleep.*
>
> *Kay waved every day as she passed the old couple, and sometimes they waved back.*
> *Kay waved every day as she passed the old couple; sometimes they waved back.*
>
> *Jenny finished a conversation in the hotel restaurant, and her sister relaxed in the lobby.*
> *While Jennyy finished a conversation in the hotel restaurant, her sister relaxed in the lobby.*
>
> *The children presented valid tickets, but admission was denied them.*
> *The children presented valid tickets; nevertheless, admission was denied them.*
> *Although the children presented valid tickets, admission was denied them.*

* * * * *

If I wrote *In conversation, she is occasionally guilty of com-*

mitting the sins of redundancy and ambiguity, which most of her friends understand, you would rightly point out that my sentence contains both redundancy and ambiguity. The phrase *guilty of committing sins* is unnecessarily repetitive, and the referent of *which* is uncertain. *Most of her friends are understanding when, in conversation, she is redundant or ambiguous* is one of several ways of improving the sentence.

Conversation is one thing, formal discourse another. Here is a sentence that, if it appeared in a travelogue, would leave you unimpressed, if not nonplussed:

> *During the flight, the pilot made liberal use of the intercom to point out places below on the ground to the passengers on the plane that he found interesting.*

This lovely sentence features (hits us over the head with) both redundancy (often called tautology) and ambiguity. *Places below on the ground* is redundant as is *passengers on the plane*. As for ambiguity, the relative pronoun *that* has an uncertain referent: Does the pilot find the places, the passengers, or the plane interesting? The sentence could be rephrased as follows:

> *During the flight, the pilot made liberal use of the intercom to point out to the passengers places below that he found interesting.*

* * * * *

To write correctly and to evaluate accurately the writing of others, one must be able to recognize logical errors. Here are several, defined and illustrated:

- *circular reasoning*: the conclusion is presupposed in one of the premises. Example: *God exists because God says so in the Bible.*
- *begging the question*: a premise is no more certain than the conclusion. Example: *We must go to war because it is the right thing to do.* The conclusion begs the question: Is it the right thing to do?
- *non sequitur*: the conclusion does not follow from the premises. Example: *Too much carbon dioxide makes the world warmer. We are producing too much carbon dioxide. Therefore Louisville's summer will be warmer this year than it was last year.*
- *post hoc ergo propter hoc*: a conclusion based on the reasoning that, if A follows B, B must be the cause of A. Example: *Every time I have worn my red sweater the Cardinals have won. Therefore, their winning must depend on my wearing my red sweater.*
- *undistributed middle*: conclusion based on the unwarranted universalizing of a non-universal term in a premise. Example: *Overexposure to the rays of the sun causes cancer. I have been overexposed to the rays of the sun. Therefore, I will get cancer.*

Lesson 10: Adverbial Objectives, Retained Objects, and the Expletive *There*

Adverbial objectives are nouns and pronouns that function as adverbs. Adverbial objectives can express time when (at what time), extent of time (how long), location (place where), destination (place to which), direction, manner (how), value, weight, and quantity, among other things. They modify verbs, adjectives, adverbs, and even prepositions. Here are examples of adverbial objectives that modify verbs (adverbial objectives are underlined):

> time when (at what time): *It is snowing this morning.*
> extent of time (how long): *I hope it snows all day.*
> location (place where): *Students can stay home.*
> destination (place to which): *Teachers want to go home.*
> direction: *He went this way, and she went that way.*
> manner (how): *He always wants to do things his own way.*
> value: *Gasoline costs a fortune.*
> quantity: *It costs three dollars a gallon.*
> weight: *Dumbbells were selling for a dollar a pound.*

Here are some adverbial objectives that modify words other than verbs:

> *A football field is 160 feet wide.* The adverbial objective *feet* modifies the predicate adjective *wide*.
> *A bird in the hand is worth two [birds] in the bush.* (The unexpressed noun *birds* is the adverbial objective; it modifies the predicate adjective *worth*.)
> *You arrived ten minutes late for your lesson.* (The adverbial objective *minutes* modifies the adverb *late*.)
> *I plan to leave about an hour after dinner.* (The adverbial objective *hour* modifies the preposition *after*.)
> *Our new house is near a good school.* (The adverbial objective *school* modifies the predicate adjective *near*.)

Indirect objects are adverbial objectives; as you know, they tell to whom or for whom something is given, said, or shown, and they modify verbs.

* * * * *

In general, one can make a sentence in the active voice passive only if it has a direct object; in fact, it is the direct object of the active sentence that becomes the subject of an equivalent sentence in the passive voice. Surprisingly, the English language allows also the indirect object to be used as the subject of a passive sentence. Here is an example: (active) *For graduation her parents will give her a computer.* (passive equivalent) *For graduation she will be given a computer by her parents.* Notice that *her*, the indirect object in the active sentence, has become the subject *she* of the passive sentence. The question is this: What is the function of *computer* in the passive sentence? The direct object of the active sentence is retained in the passive equivalent and is called a **retained object.**

* * * * *

There is only one "there" there? Wow, three *there*s! What is going on? Well, the last *there* is an adverb; it tells where the lone *there* is. The middle *there* is a word used as a word, and such a word is a noun. The first *there* is the one that interests us especially in this lesson. It's an **expletive**. Remember, an expletive is a word that has a function but little or no meaning. In this sentence, the first *there* tells the reader that the appearance of the subject, whose normal position is before the verb, will be delayed until after the verb; other than that, the first *there* does not do or mean anything at all. Here are several examples of *there* used as an expletive:

> *There is pie in the refrigerator.* (The subject of the sentence is *pie*.)
> *There hasn't been any news this morning.* (The subject of the sentence is *news*. By the way, *morning* is an adverbial objective.)
> *Are there any fish in your pond?* (The subject of the sentence is *fish*.)
> Over there there is an old wheelbarrow. (The expletive is the second *there*. The first *there* is an adverb. The subject of the sentence is *wheelbarrow*.)

Every adverbial objective is diagrammed like an indirect object (that is, like the object of a preposition, but with the position of the preposition left empty).

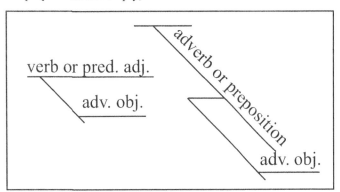

Step 68. It has rained every day this week.

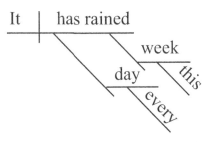

Both *day* and *week* are adverbial objectives modifying the verb *has rained*. They express time when.

Step 69. Which way should we go?

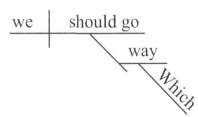

Way is an adverbial objective. It expresses direction. Like *day* and *week* in the previous sentence, it modifies the verb.

Step 70. A haircut costs thirty dollars.

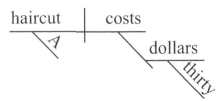

Dollars, an adverbial objective, seems at first to be a direct object. After all, *costs* is not a linking verb, and *dollars* answers the question *what?* Or does it? Does it not more properly answer the question *How much?* Also, a direct object is able to become the subject of a corresponding sentence in the passive voice. One simply cannot say *Thirty dollars are cost by a haircut.* But this gets tricky. What if the sentence were *His recklessness cost him his life*? *Life* really does answer the question *what?* And still one cannot say *His life was cost by his recklessness.* It turns out that there are several verbs that, although transitive, cannot be made passive (cf. Lesson 24).

Step 71. Their new baby weighed almost nine pounds at birth.

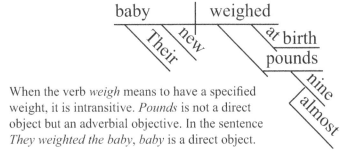

When the verb *weigh* means to have a specified weight, it is intransitive. *Pounds* is not a direct object but an adverbial objective. In the sentence *They weighted the baby*, *baby* is a direct object.

Step 72. This plane can go 500 miles an hour.

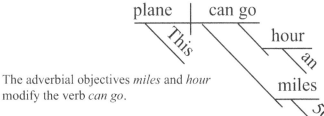

The adverbial objectives *miles* and *hour* modify the verb *can go*.

Step 73. The Statue of Liberty is 93 meters tall.

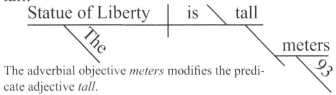

The adverbial objective *meters* modifies the predicate adjective *tall*.

Step 74. This dessert is not worth two cents.

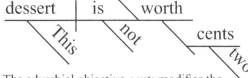

The adverbial objective *cents* modifies the predicate adjective *worth*.

Step 75. John will get there an hour early.

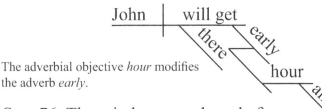

The adverbial objective *hour* modifies the adverb *early*.

Step 76. The rain began an hour before sunrise.

The adverbial objective *hour* modifies the preposition *before*.

Exercise 10: Adverbial Objectives,
Retained Objects, and the Expletive *There*

98. Doug had gone the wrong way.

99. I cannot wait two hours for the doctor.

100. Children, come home immediately!

101. Scott arrived Saturday and will stay at least a week.

102. Does gasoline really cost three dollars a gallon?

103. The physics test is the day after tomorrow.

104. That painting is worth a fortune.

105. A week later a large package arrived.

106. Pat mailed her tax forms two days after the deadline.

107. Sandy was given an engagement ring.

108. There is a mouse in the pantry.

109. There is no one there.

Writing Correctly 10

Avoid using the passive voice. Is that good advice? No, it isn't. There are times when the passive voice is exactly right. *Minimize your use of the passive voice by using it only when it is more effective than the active voice.* Now that's good advice.

Let's examine briefly what the passive voice is and isn't. A verb in the passive voice consists of a form of the verb *to be* (for example, *am, are, is, was, were, will be, has been, had been*) and a past participle (for example, *seen, understood, featured, injured, manufactured, withheld*). Sentences like *The air show will be seen by thousands, The instructions had not been understood, Derby hats are featured in this morning's paper, Ten miners were injured in the accident, The new cars will be manufactured in Mexico,* and *Identification has been withheld* are in the passive voice. In the passive voice, the object of an action is the subject of the sentence. Remember: (1) the passive voice is not the past tense (tense and voice are entirely different things), (2) not all sentences using forms of *to be* are in the passive voice, and (3) the passive voice is not a grammatical error.

The passive voice is often weaker than the active voice. Consider these two sentences:

> *The boys carried the piano into the house.* (active)
> *The piano was carried by the boys into the house.* (passive)

I think you will agree that the former sentence is stronger than the latter.

The passive voice is often less precise than the active voice. Compare these two sentences:

> *Johnny was overheard to say that he hated school.* (passive)
> *The sixth-grade teacher overheard Johnny say that he hated school.* (active)

Of course, the passive-voice sentence could include the agent: *Johnny was overheard by the sixth-grade teacher to say that he hated school*; however, we now have a sentence that is weaker than its corresponding active form.

We should use the passive voice when the object of an action is more important that the doer of the action.

> *Today we learned about x-rays. They were discovered accidentally in 1895 by a German scientist.* (passive)
> *Today we learned about x-rays. A German scientist discovered them accidentally in 1895.* (active)

The focus established by the first sentence in each pair of sentences is x-rays. Use of the passive voice keeps the focus on x-rays.

We should use the passive voice when the doer of an action is either unknown or unimportant.

> *One by one, cancer genes are being identified.* (passive).
> *Researchers are identifying cancer genes one by one.* (active)

The passive voice is often desirable in scientific writing, in which the object of research is more important than the identity of the researcher.

An author may want to conceal the identity of the doer of an action in order to create suspense. With this in mind, he or she may begin a paragraph with *The jewels were stolen late on the 25th or early on the 26th.* The reader isn't even told if there was one thief or more than one, which may be just what the suspense doctor ordered.

In reading this morning's paper (*The Courier-Journal*, April 23, 2007), I found several sentences using the passive voice. Here are three of them:

> *Bangladesh's former prime minister was blocked from boarding a flight home from London yesterday after her country's military-backed interim government banned her from returning.* Clearly the woman's identity is more important than the identity of the one or ones who blocked her.

> *Eight Ethiopians held hostage for 52 days after they were kidnapped along with five European tourists have been released unharmed, government officials said yesterday.* It is clear from the rest of the article that the kidnappers are unknown.

> *Eighty-two members of The Women of Zimbawe Arise group were arrested Thursday in the city of Bulawayo at the protest against power outages.* Of course, they were arrested by the police, so nothing is accomplished by mentioning that fact.

* * * * *

Be careful to use a singular subject with *there is, there's, here is,* and *here's.* This sentence has an agreement error: *There's a man and a woman at the door.*

* * * * *

Awhile, an adverb, cannot be the object of a preposition; thus, the sentence *They stayed for awhile* is incorrect. Use instead the two-word form *a while*: *They stayed for a while.* If you omit *for,* you may choose either *They stayed a while* or *They stayed awhile.*

Lesson 11: Infinitives

The basic form of a verb--the form that is usually preceded by the particle *to*-- is called an infinitive. All infinitives have tense, and transitive infinitives have voice (present active, *to find*; present passive, *to be found*; present-perfect active, *to have found*; and present-perfect passive, *to have been found*) as well as progressivity (*to be finding, to have been finding*); however, they do not have person and number. Infinitives can function as adverbs (*they are playing to win*), as adjectives (*you have nothing to do*), and as nouns (*who doesn't want to succeed?*).

An infinitive with its modifiers and objects is called an infinitive phrase. Like simple infinitives, infinitive phrases can be used as adverbs (*we drove fifty miles to see the performance*), adjectives (*I am looking for something to read on vacation*), or nouns (*the children are learning to write correctly*). When used as nouns, infinitives can be subjects, direct objects, predicate nominatives, appositives, objects of prepositions, and objective complements. Here are several sentences in which infinitives and infinitive phrases are used . . .

. . . as subjects:

> *To die is our common destiny.*
> *To fly is fun for a while.*
> *To stand up for the rights of the underprivileged is admirable.*
> *To drive a car properly requires practice and a respect for the rights of others.*

. . . as direct objects:

> *Do you want to rest?*
> *Children like to run and play.*
> *She tried to read a good book.*
> *Would you prefer to go to a movie today or to eat out tomorrow?*

. . . as predicate nominatives:

> *Their goal will be to survive.*
> *Don's job was to hire the best people available.*
> *To strive is to succeed.*

. . . as appositives:

> *It was not my idea to leave early.*
> *Sometimes it is necessary to stand and fight.* (In both examples, the infinitive phrase is in apposition with the subject *it*.)

. . . as objects of the prepositions *except* and *but*:

> *Nothing remained except to fold our tents and go home.*
> *The waiter did everything but pay the bill.* (an infinitive without *to*)
> *Do you really have nothing to do except disturb others?* (another "*to*-less" infinitive)

. . . as objective complements (the infinitive is often "*to*-less"):

> *She made them stay after school.*
> *Jim heard someone come in the back door.*
> *We watched the red sun sink below the horizon.*

Susan Emolyn Harman maintains that *to be honest* is an objective complement in the sentence *I believe him to be honest*. It seems to me that *him to be honest* is better analyzed as an objective-case subject with a verb in the infinitive form (a construction akin to the subject accusative with infinitive in Latin). The sentence can be restated as *I believe that he is honest*, that is, with an indirect statement (underlined), which is precisely the kind of construction that is rendered as a subject accusative with infinitive in Latin.

Most infinitives are preceded by the particle *to*; however, some are "*to*-less."

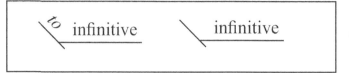

Step 77. To own her own car has long been her desire.

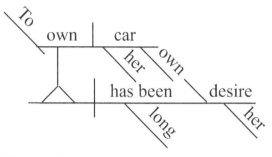

The infinitive phrase *to own her own car* is the subject of the sentence.

Step 78. Bob hates to wash dishes and take out the garbage.

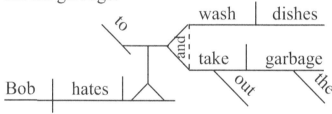

This sentence features a compound infinitive phrase used as a direct object.

Step 79. To love is to live fully.

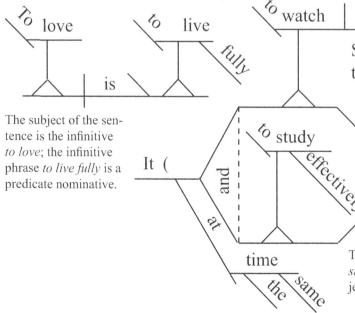

The subject of the sentence is the infinitive *to love*; the infinitive phrase *to live fully* is a predicate nominative.

Step 80. We have nothing to do, we are ready to go, and we can't wait to leave.

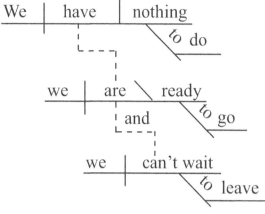

To do is an adjectival infinitive; it modifies the noun *nothing*. *To go* is an adverbial infinitive; it modifies the adjective *ready*. *To leave* is an adverbial infinitive; it modifies the verb *can't wait*.

Step 81. The weather forced Todd to head south.

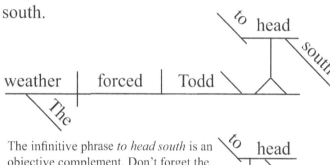

The infinitive phrase *to head south* is an objective complement. Don't forget the other way of diagramming objective complements, as follows:

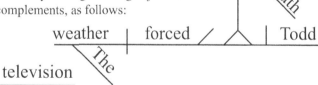

Step 82. It is difficult to watch television and to study effectively at the same time.

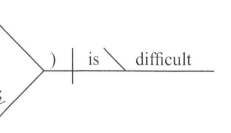

The compound infinitive phrase *to watch television and to study effectively at the same time* is in apposition with the subject of the sentence, *it*.

Exercise 11: Infinitives

110. To pout is childish.

111. We hope to visit Robbie in the fall.

112. It is a pleasure to serve you.

113. Mickey walks three miles every day to stay cardiovascularly healthy.

114. Nothing more could be done except to minimize pain.

115. They did nothing but complain.

116. Their plan was to fly to Seattle and rent a car.

117. That is easy to promise but hard to do.

118. Cathy spoke too softly to be understood.

119. You can't make me watch.

120. Domestic responsibilities compelled them to stay at home.

121. Do you want Lynn to go with you?

Writing Correctly 11

Do you split infinitives? You probably do if you don't know what a split infinitive is. H. W. Fowler divides the English-speaking world, not without humor, into five groups:

> (1) those who neither know nor care what a split infinitive is; (2) those who do not know, but care very much; (3) those who know and condemn; (4) those who know and approve; (5) those who know and distinguish.

What is a split infinitive? Boldly assuming that you don't belong to Fowler's first group, I'll answer. An infinitive is split if there is a word or words between the particle *to* and the remainder of the infinitive (*to*-less infinitives, discussed later in this book, cannot be split). *To seriously discuss* is a split infinitive. *To be seriously discussing* is not. To qualify as a split infinitive, the extraneous word or words must come immediately after *to*.

With one insignificant exception, Shakespeare did not split infinitives, and none is found in the King James version of the Bible, universally lauded for its linguistic excellence. Split infinitives became more common in the 18th and 19th centuries. Today they are said to be in common usage, due no doubt in part to a widespread ignorance of grammar.

In an effort to ascertain the prevalence of split infinitives in 21st-century America, I turned again to *The Courier-Journal*, published daily in Louisville, Kentucky. In the six editorial pages that I examined, I found many infinitives, only several of which were modified by adverbs. And of these infinitives, only one was split by an adverbial modifier:

> *At the same time, there are some folks ranting and raving about the need to virtually recreate the Wild, Wild West by giving guns to anyone who can answer a few standard questions.* (Karyl Ferman, H3, April 22, 2007)

I don't know about you, but I cannot think of a better place for *virtually* than where it is: smack dab in the middle of an infinitive. If current English usage permits the occasional use of a split infinitive, then surely this one is acceptable.

I also found an infinitive whose split occurs between *be* and the participial component of the infinitive (as implied above, it is not a split infinitive):

> *Indeed, under the three-state logic of the ERA sponsors, the amendment making the District of Columbia a state would need only a few more states to be retroactively declared ratified.* (Jonathan Turley, H5, April 22, 2007)

To retroactively be declared is a split infinitive. *To be retro-*

actively declared is not. Here is a similar sentence of my own creation:

> *The head of the tolerance committee expects to be unjustifiably labeled intolerant.*

This sentence does not contain a split infinitive. If someone with an incomplete knowledge of split infinitives thought otherwise, he or she might change the wording to *The head of the tolerance committee expects unjustifiably to be labeled intolerant.* In the process, a perfectly clear sentence would be made ambiguous, for now the reader does not know if the adverb *unjustifiably* modifies *expects* or *to be labeled*. And placing unjustifiably after *labeled*, as in *The head of the tolerance committee expects to be labeled unjustifiably intolerant,* only relocates the source of ambiguity, for now the reader is forced to choose between *labeled unjustifiably* and *unjustifiably intolerant*.

But let's say we really do have a split infinitive, as in the following sentence:

> *Philosophers struggle to irrefutably resolve troublesome issues related to the existence of evil in the world.*

If you are a person who knows what split infinitives are and condemns them, you will try relocating the offending word, the adverb (it's almost always an adverb) *irrefutably*. *Philosophers struggle irrefutably to resolve troublesome issues related to the existence of evil in the world* yields only ambiguity, as does *Philosophers struggle to resolve irrefutably troublesome issues related to the existence of evil in the world*. What's a poor fellow to do? Saving *irrefutably* for the end of the sentence seems awkward at best. Still there's always a way out: start over and express the same thought differently. We could say, for example, *Philosophers struggle to find an irrefutable resolution to troublesome issues related to the existence of evil in the world*. This is at least as good as the original sentence, don't you think? But let's say you don't think so; you like the original sentence better. Do you have to scrap it because it contains a split infinitive? Nowadays the answer of most grammarians is no. It's your choice.

Are there any split infinitives that should be eschewed? Yes, it turns out there are some: those that contain more than one word between the particle *to* and the verb. Here is an example:

> *She admonished the couple to thoughtfully and patiently discuss their differences.*

The infinitive *to discuss* is split by the compound adverb *thoughtfully and patiently*. That's two words too many. In this case a revision is obvious: *She admonished the couple to discuss their differences thoughtfully and patiently.*

Lesson 12: Infinitives (2)

The modal auxiliary verbs *may, might, can, could, should,* and *must* are so closely tied to their complements (the verbs that complete them) that the two (modal auxiliary and complement) are considered single verb forms (*may arrive, can help, should wait, must have seen,* etc.) and are so diagrammed, as you already know. Other verbs achieve this same closeness with their complements (*ought to hurry, am going to meet, used to watch,* etc.). In such a construction, the infinitive that complements the introductory word, is usually preceded by the particle *to* and is called a **complementary infinitive**.

> *Students have to stay in their homerooms until the bell rings.*
> *Students ought to stay in their homerooms until the bell rings.*
> *Students are to stay in their homerooms until the bell rings.*
> *Students are going to stay in their homerooms until the bell rings.*
> *Students used to stay in their homerooms until the bell rang.*

Don't confuse complementary infinitives with direct objects. In general, sentences that contain transitive verbs (i.e., verbs that take direct objects) are able to be restated in the passive voice (more about this later). Even though *have* and *used* can take direct objects, they can't in the above sentences because their meanings there do not allow them to be used passively. If you try to express these sentences in the passive voice, you get nonsense. Example: *To stay in homerooms until the bell rings is had by students.* Nonsense, right?

* * * * *

In the previous chapter, you were introduced to infinitives and infinitive phrases used as predicate nominatives; in this chapter, you will meet **infinitives and infinitive phrases used as predicate adjectives.** The infinitives may be preceded by forms of the verb *to be*, but they can also follow other linking verbs, for example, *seem, appear*, and certain passive verbs. Here are some examples of infinitive phrases that function as predicate adjectives:

> *Donald seemed <u>to have all his ducks in a row.</u>*
> *One contestant appears <u>to lack self-confidence.</u>*
> *The Royal Library of Alexandria is thought <u>to have contained more than 500,000 books.</u>*
> *This is said <u>to be the best Vietnamese restaurant in town.</u>*

* * * * *

In a peculiar construction, the **particle *for*** is used as an expletive to introduce an infinitive phrase used as (1) a subject, (2) a direct object, (3) a predicate nominative, or (4) an appositive. Such infinitive phrases have subjects.

> 1 - *For us to deny our common humanity would be harmful to society.* (subject of infinitive: *us*)
> 2 - *The old man does not like for others to do his work for him.* (subject of infinitive: *others*)
> 3- *The plan was for him to read the script first.* (subject of infinitive: *him*)
> 4 - *It is essential to the success of the company for all employees to contribute their time and talents.* (subject of infinitive: *employees*)

An infinitive phrase can also be used as the object of the preposition *for*: *The salespeople were itching for the last customers to leave the store. The boss bought a second car for the staff to use.* (subjects of infinitives: *customers* and *staff*)

* * * * *

Infinitives and infinitive phrases can be used **as independent expressions**, as they are in the following sentences:

> *To tell the truth, I've never caught a really big fish in my life.*
> *Kay made a good impression, to say the least.*

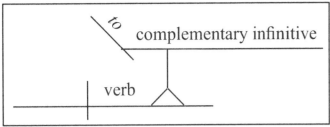

Step 83. The wedding is to be held in an azalea garden

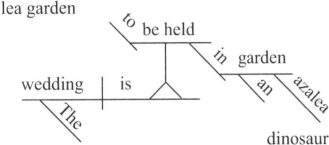

The complementary infinitive *to be held* is in the present tense, passive voice.

Step 84. Matt ought to have been there.

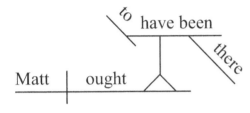

To have been is a complementary infinitive. It is in the present-perfect tense.

Step 85. We are going to go to the game and scream.

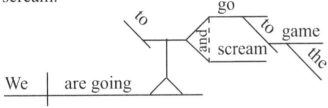

To go to the game and scream is a compound complementary infinitive phrase.

Step 86. Ed is about to speak.

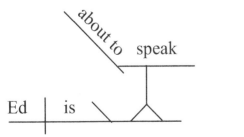

In my opinion, *about to* is a phrasal particle. Harman calls this *about*, which she admits has "very little prepositional force," a preposition, whose object is the infinitive *to speak*. She would diagram the sentence as follows:

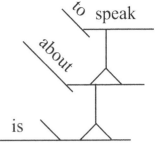

Step 87. A small dinosaur appears to have been partially digested by the large dinosaur.

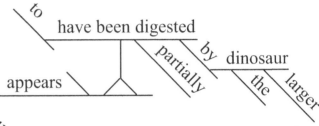

The infinitive phrase introduced by the present-perfect passive infinitive *to have been digested* functions as a predicate adjective after the linking verb *appears*.

Step 88. It is said to be a good idea to rise early.

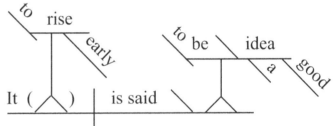

The passive verb *is said* functions as a linking verb. The infinitive phrase *to rise early* is in apposition with the subject, *it*.

Step 89. To be sure, the second computer is for the children to use.

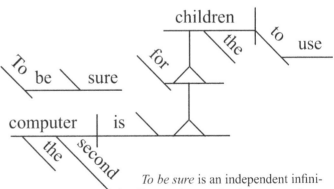

To be sure is an independent infinitive phrase; therefore, its diagram is completely separate from the rest of the diagram. *For the children to use* is a prepositional phrase that functions as a predicate adjective. *Children* is the subject of the infinitive *to use*.

Exercise 12: Infinitives (2)

122. The students are to go immediately to their desks.

123. Charlotte had to sit there and listen.

124. He seems to have wanted to see them suffer.

125. To have to be told three times to behave is a sign of immaturity.

126. For them to become angry is not helpful to our cause.

127. Bob said for the children to be ready to leave in ten minutes.

128. Students, remain silent and wait for the others to finish the test!

129. The president was about to speak.

130. They are thought to have been kidnapped by insurgents.

131. To speak frankly, everyone is tired of your lies.

Writing Correctly 12

You may have heard of a dangling participle (to be discussed later), but have you heard of a dangling infinitive? In general, this error is not so egregious that it impedes understanding. An infinitive (or an infinitive phrase) dangles when, functioning as a modifier of the verb, it has no subject (agent), either expressed or unambiguously implied. Here are several sentences with dangling infinitives:

> (A) *To even consider a Caribbean cruise, a travel agent recommended austere measures*

> (B) *To appease disgruntled fishermen, thousands of small bass and crappies are now swimming in the lake.*

> (C) *To ascertain the general level of interest in the project, all members must attend.*

In Sentence A, the infinitive phrase *to even consider a Caribbean cruise* (did you notice that the infinitive is split?) modifies the verb *recommended* whose subject is *travel agent*. But it is not the travel agent who might consider a Caribbean cruise. Here are some possible revisions:

> *To even consider a Caribbean cruise, the couple ought to adopt austere measures.*

> *Even to consider a Caribbean cruise requires the adoption of austere measures.* (In this sentence, the infinitive phrase functions as a noun, not a modifier of the verb; consequently, it does not need a subject.)

> *The mere consideration of a Caribbean cruise mandates the adoption of austere measures.* (The infinitive phrase is replaced by a noun.)

Because of the dangling infinitive phrase, Sentence B is unintentionally funny (well, I must confess I tried to make it "unintentionally" funny). The thousands of fish couldn't appease anyone. The sentence must be rephrased. Here are three possibilities:

> *To appease disgruntled fishermen, the board of directors has added thousands of small bass and crappies to the lake.*

> *The addition of thousands of small bass and crappies to the lake was an attempt to appease disgruntled fishermen.* (The infinitive phrase in this revision is an adjectival modifier; it modifies the noun *attempt*.)

> *The appeasement of disgruntled fisherman underlay the addition of thousands of small bass and crappies to the lake.* (The infinitive phrase is replaced by a noun.)

In Sentence C, the members are not ascertaining the general level of interest; someone else is. The infinitive phrase dangles: it modifies the verb and it has no logical subject. And it doesn't help if *in order to* is used instead of *to*; since *in order to* is a phrasal expression of *to*, the infinitive phrase still modifies the verb. Here are two possible revisions:

> *To ascertain the general level of interest in the project, the committee will ask all members to attend.*

> *All members must attend so that the committee can ascertain the general level of interest in the project.*

In the passive voice, the subject of the sentence is not the doer of the action (the agent). What do you think of this sentence? *To encourage students to earn their own money, they are being offered summer jobs.* The logical subject of the infinitive phrase is the unexpressed agent, not the subject of the sentence, *they* (whose referent is *students*). A more successful sentence would be *To encourage students to earn their own money, the city is offering them summer jobs.*

* * * * *

Even though *in order to* is the phrasal equivalent of *to*, there are times when one has to use *in order to* instead of *to* in order to achieve clarity. Consider these two sentences:

> *The principal disclosed her desire to encourage honesty among the faculty.*

> *The principal disclosed her desire in order to encourage honesty among the faculty.*

The first infinitive phrase is adjectival, the second adverbial.

* * * * *

For sentence variety, use infinitives and infinitive phrases as nouns (subjects, direct objects, objective complements, predicate nominatives, appositives), as adjectives (attributive and predicate), as adverbs (modifiers of verbs, adjectives, and adverbs), and as complementary infinitives. You have seen examples of each of these uses in Lessons 11 and 12. You may want to challenge yourself to write a single sentence using infinitives in as many different ways as possible. Or your teacher may wish to offer you this challenge. In any case, I hope you will try. It could be fun, even addictive.

* * * * *

Use *try to* instead of *try and* in formal communication. The illogic of *try and* becomes clear when one tries to use it in the past tense: *I tried and saw if I could reach her.* The two verbs are not parallel.

Lesson 13: Gerunds

A gerund is a verbal noun; that is, it is both a noun and a verb. As a noun, it can function as other nouns function, i.e., as the subject of a sentence, as a direct object, as a predicate nominative, etc. As a verb, it can, if it is a linking verb, be followed by a predicate nominative or a predicate adjective; it can, if it is transitive, take a direct object; and it can, if it is a verb of saying, giving, or showing, take an indirect object. As a noun, it can be modified by adjectives and by words functioning as adjectives (nouns, prepositional phrases, etc.) . As a verb, it can be modified by adverbs and by words functioning as adverbs (adverbial objectives, prepositional phrases, etc.). Like infinitives, gerunds have tense, and (in the case of transitive gerunds) voice, but not person and number. If a verb is intransitive (a verb that does not transfer action to an object), it has only two gerund forms. For example, the verb *be* has only the present and present-perfect gerunds *being* and *having been*. These two gerunds could be used in a sentence like *Being in love is better than having been in love*. Transitive verbs have two active forms and two corresponding passive forms. The verb *to see*, a transitive verb, has a present active gerund (*seeing*) and a present passive gerund (*being seen*) as well as a present-perfect active gerund (*having seen*) and a present-perfect passive gerund (*having been seen*). A gerund with its complements, objects, and modifiers constitutes a gerund phrase. Gerund phrases can, like simple gerunds, function as subjects, predicate nominatives, appositives, direct objects, objects of prepositions, objective complements, and adverbial objectives.

Gerunds and gerund phrases as subjects . . .

> *Waiting is not fun.*
> *Walking for at least thirty minutes daily is healthy.*
> *Eating out can get boring.*

Gerunds and gerund phrases as predicate nominatives . . .

> *Her hobby is running.*
> *Giving free food to friends is regarded by the manager as stealing.*
> *Learning to walk is putting one foot in front of the other.*

Gerunds and gerund phrases as appositives . . .

> *These are a few of my grandchildren's favorite things: coloring, listening to stories, and watching videos.*
> *It was a pleasure getting to know you.*
> *This is the life for me, just lying on the sand and soaking up the sun.*

Gerunds and gerund phrases as direct objects . . .

> *She doesn't like hitting.*
> *Do you enjoy their ranting and raving?*
> *Have you tried starting at the beginning?*

Gerunds and gerund phrases as objects of prepositions . . .

> *In the wintertime you can lower your heating bill by freezing.*
> *Sunday afternoons are reserved for doing fun things with their children.*
> *Since his heart surgery, he has given much thought to eating and drinking healthfully.*

Gerunds and gerund phrases as objective complements . . .

> *Do you call that dancing?*
> *The judge condemned their door-to-door sales as taking advantage of the elderly.*
> *Anyone in his right mind would consider that strategy manipulating the books.*

Gerunds and gerund phrases as adverbial objectives (pretty much limited to modifiers of *worth*). . .

> *Anything worth doing is worth doing right.*

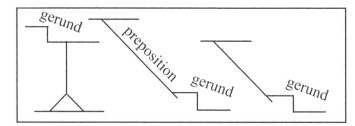

Step 90. Diagramming is a symbolic way of showing grammatical relationships between the words of a sentence.

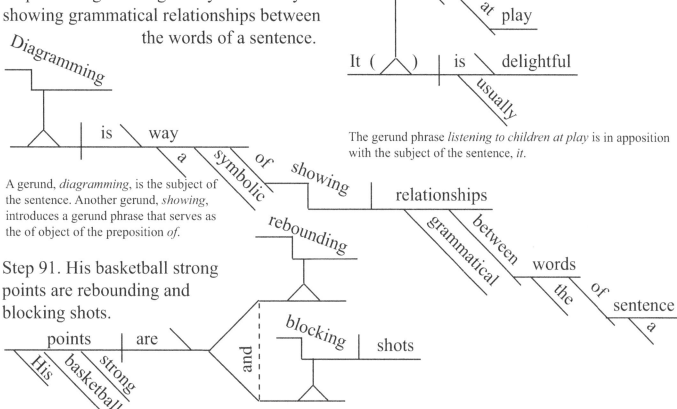

Step 93. It is usually delightful listening to children at play.

The gerund phrase *listening to children at play* is in apposition with the subject of the sentence, *it*.

A gerund, *diagramming*, is the subject of the sentence. Another gerund, *showing*, introduces a gerund phrase that serves as the of object of the preposition *of*.

Step 91. His basketball strong points are rebounding and blocking shots.

The compound predicate nominative comprises a gerund and a gerund phrase. Because gerunds are not only nouns but also verbs, some of them take direct objects.

Step 92. Everyone in the family teases him about his snoring during favorite TV programs.

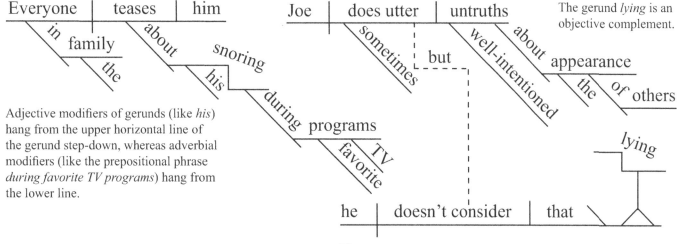

Step 94. Joe does sometimes utter well-intentioned untruths about the appearance of others, but he doesn't consider that lying.

The gerund *lying* is an objective complement.

Adjective modifiers of gerunds (like *his*) hang from the upper horizontal line of the gerund step-down, whereas adverbial modifiers (like the prepositional phrase *during favorite TV programs*) hang from the lower line.

Exercise 13: Gerunds

132. Sleeping is her favorite "activity."

133. His summer job was cutting grass.

134. By listening attentively in class you can improve your grade.

135. The landlord increased his profit by raising the rent and reducing the amenities.

136. Tiny appreciated your having come to his rescue.

137. Ms. Shelby, a teacher at our school, calls her friendship with Mr. Moss, a teacher at a rival school, "fraternizing with the enemy."

138. Something worth quoting is worth quoting accurately.

139. It was a pleasure talking with Rodney.

140. The men are playing golf, and the women are going shopping.

141. The joylessness in Mudville is the result of Casey's not having hit a home run.

Writing Correctly 13

Gerunds sometimes need an expressed agent. Now I'll bet that's something you haven't worried about in the wee hours of the morning, but it's true nevertheless; and it's important. This agent is often called the subject of the gerund, even when it is expressed by the possessive case (by possessive nouns or possessive pronouns). Here are two sentences in which agency is neither expressed nor needed and one sentence in which the subject of the sentence is the agent (subject) of the gerund.

> *Seeing is believing.*
> *Working with flowers is relaxing.*
> *They succeeded by staying together.*

And here are three sentences in which agency is expressed by a possessive noun or pronoun:

> *Without our knowing it, the weather changed.*
> *Amelie likes his helping her.*
> *Because of Stacy's speaking out, Mr. Jones resigned.*

The subject (agent) of a gerund must be expressed if its omission would result in ambiguity, unintentional humor, factual error, or nonsense. *Without knowing it, the weather changed* gives weather a mind, which is nonsensical. The sentence *Amelie likes his helping her* and the sentence *Amelie likes helping her* are both grammatically correct; however, they mean entirely different things. (Whether or not one can say *Amelie likes him helping her* will be discussed in Lesson 14.)

Because of speaking out, Mr. Jones resigned implies that Mr. Jones was the one who spoke out. When an introductory prepositional phrase in which a gerund is used as the object of the preposition modifies the verb, an unexpressed subject of the gerund is usually assumed to be the person or thing represented by the subject of the sentence. When this assumption is misleading, either the agency must be expressed or the subject of the sentence must be changed. Failure to do this can result in the kind of sentence I heard recently in a TV news broadcast: "People can buy guns in Virginia without checking into the buyer's background." Because the listener assumes that the subject of *checking* and the subject of the sentence represent the same person, the sentence is nonsensical. The following sentences are, happily, not taken from a printed or broadcast source:

> *By volunteering at the Humane Society as often as possible, the animals benefited.* It sounds like the animals were the volunteers. The intended meaning can be obtained by inserting a possessive noun or pronoun before the gerund: *By our volunteering at the hospital as often as possible, the patients benefited.*

> *In learning to drive a nail, the thumb is always at risk of injury.* The subject of the sentence, *thumb*, is not learning anything. The error can be corrected by changing the subject: *In learning to drive a nail, you always risk injuring your thumb.*

Except for laughing too much, she likes him. Who laughs too much? A possessive pronoun saves this sentence: *Except for his laughing too much, she likes him.*

Because of winning three of the last four races, the Preakness odds were expected to be low. The gerund needs an agent: *Because of Barbaro's winning three of the last four races, the Preakness odds were expected to be low.*

Without going into detail, the project is on track for completion at the end of October. The sentence needs a subject that the gerund phrase can modify: *Without going into detail, I can tell you that the project is on track for completion at the end of October*

Before buying a used car, Johanna advises customers to request the car's history. Johanna is advising, not buying. A correct expression of this would be *Johanna advises customers to request a used car's history before buying it.*

Despite winning the lottery, thoughts of retirement were out of the question. We are not sure who won the lottery or who didn't consider retirement. We are sure, however, if we rephrase as follows: *Despite his wife's winning the lottery, thoughts of retirement were far from his mind* or *Despite winning the lottery, she did not even consider retirement.*

Instead of riding the roller coaster, walking around the park was fun. *Walking* is not an agent. The sentence can be improved by introducing a personal subject: *Instead of riding the roller coaster, they enjoyed walking around the park.*

Not all prepositional phrases with a gerund as the object of the preposition look to the subject of the sentence for the agent of the gerund when agency is unexpressed by a possessive noun or pronoun. Check out these sentences:

> *The Internet assists buyers in finding that perfect house.*
> *Few qualities are more important for running a business than foresight.*
> *The new book covers everything from planning a garden to harvesting the crops.*

In finding that perfect house modifies the verb; however, no confusion results from the omission of expressed agency. *For running a business* modifies the adjective *important*, not the verb. *From planning a garden to harvesting the crops* modifies the pronoun *everything*, not the verb.

Lesson 14: Participles

A participle is a verbal adjective; that is, it is both a verb and an adjective. Like infinitives and gerunds, participles have tense and voice but no person and number. There are five participial forms of most transitive verbs: present active (*carrying*), present passive (*being carried*), present-perfect active (*having carried*), present-perfect passive (*having been carried*), and past (*carried*). Participles can function both as attributive adjectives and as predicate adjectives. They can also serve as objective complements. They have an essential role in nominative absolutes, and they have an independent use. Let's examine these uses of participles.

Participles **as attributive adjectives**: Participles and participial phrases can modify subjects, predicate nominatives, direct objects, indirect objects, objects of prepositions, appositives, objective complements, and adverbial objectives. Here are several examples:

> *Lost, the puppy wandered from house to house in search of food.* A past participle modifies a subject.
> *Having run all the way from Marathon to Athens, the messenger died.* A participial phrase introduced by a present-perfect participle modifies a subject.
> *Having been shot, he was rushed to a nearly hospital.* A present-perfect passive participle modifies a subject.
> *The first thing they saw was a uniformed man riding a white horse.* A participial phrase introduced by a present active participle modifies a predicate nominative.
> *Do you know the person being arrested?* A present passive participle modifies a direct object.
> *They gave the girl sleeping in the corner an award for honesty.* A participial phrase introduced by a present participle modifies an indirect object.
> *The children found all the eggs except the one hidden in an old flower pot.* A participial phrase introduced by a past participle modifies an objcet of a preposition.
> *Sandy's life was saved by her sister, the woman standing next to her.* A participial phrase introduced by a present participle modifies an appositive.
> *Thomas Heywood considered Mistress Frankford a woman killed with kindness and so titled his play.* A participial phrase introduced by a past participle modifies an objective complement.
> *The finished product did not seem to be worth the time and effort invested in it.* A participial phrase introduced by a past participle modifies a compound adverbial objective.

Participles **as predicate adjectives**:

> *The children came running.* The intransitive verb *came* functions as a linking verb in this sentence.
> *You were seen lying on a park bench across from the train station.* The passive verb *were seen* acts as a linking verb.

Participles **as objective complements**:

> *They feel themselves being drawn through a tunnel.*
> *Each morning the neighbors heard him whistling the same tune.*

Participles in **nominative absolutes**: A nominative absolute is a grammatically independent expression consisting of a noun or a pronoun modified by a participle. Here are two examples (the underlined expressions are nominative absolutes):

> *Emergency funds exhausted, they knew one of them had to find a job fast.*
> *Victory having been accomplished at a terrible price, the homecoming was bittersweet at best.*

While careful speakers of English avoid a dangling participle like the plague, they typically allow themselves to dangle the present participle *speaking*. Here is an example of this participle **used independently**:

> *Speaking of food, it's time to head home and light the grill.* The participle *speaking* has nothing to modify; one can argue that it functions here as a preposition. The use of participles as prepositions is discussed on pages 73 and 108.

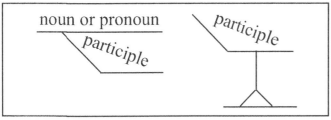

Step 95. Letting the guests wait, she kept talking on the phone.

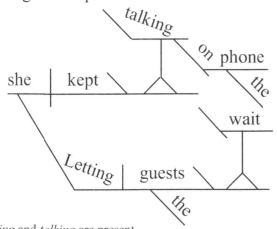

Letting and *talking* are present participles. The former serves as an attributive adjective, the latter as a predicate adjective after the verb *kept*, which in this sentence is a linking verb. The "*to*-less" infinitive *wait* is an objective complement.

Step 96. Speaking of superfluity, you will find at least forty boxes stacked in the closet.

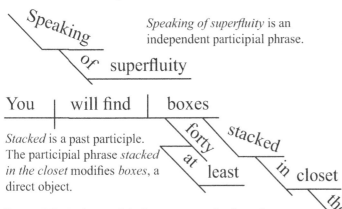

Speaking of superfluity is an independent participial phrase.

Stacked is a past participle. The participial phrase *stacked in the closet* modifies *boxes*, a direct object.

Step 97. John told the person being interviewed the reason for his unusual questions.

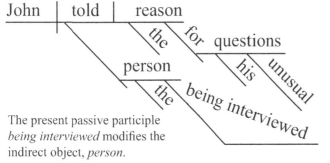

The present passive participle *being interviewed* modifies the indirect object, *person*.

Step 98. Her eyes turned toward two people sitting in the corner.

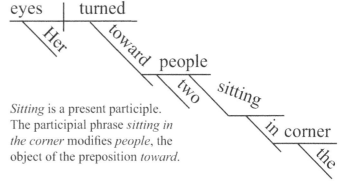

Sitting is a present participle. The participial phrase *sitting in the corner* modifies *people*, the object of the preposition *toward*.

Step 99. Upon awakening, Gretchen saw the witch attempting to light the oven.

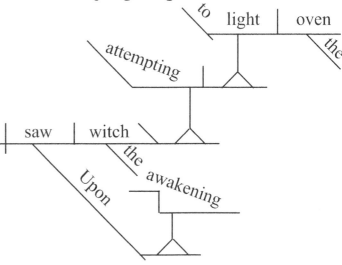

Awakening, the object of the preposition *upon*, is a gerund, not a participle. The participial phrase *attempting to light the oven* is an objective complement. Within this phrase, the infinitive phrase *to light the oven* functions as the direct object of the present active participle *attempting*.

Step 100. His chores finished, Kenny went outside to play.

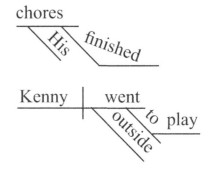

Finished is a past participle. It is used here in a nominative absolute.

~ 70 ~

Exercise 14: Participles

142. Still running smoothly after twenty-five miles, Annie left the park and headed for the finish line.

143. Chewing, spitting, and occasionally talking, the three old-timers watched the people and the trains go by.

144. Take this book to the woman standing by the window.

145. They saw prisoners being abused by guards.

146. The escapees were last seen running into a large forest

147. Having reached the end of her twelve-hour shift, the exhausted nurse heaved a sigh of relief.

148. The bridge having collapsed, some interstate commuters were forced to drive much farther each day.

149. The witch kept Hansel locked in a pen.

150. A chickadee came flying through an open window.

151. Speaking of rascals, Oscar just knocked at the door.

Writing Correctly 14

Even if you wouldn't know dangling participles from potato peelers, you have probably heard of them. Here's one:

> *Nathan had a good view of Lake Powell flying from Denver to Los Angeles.*

"In which direction was the lake flying?" one could ask. Do you know how to correct this sentence without changing a single word? I'm inclined to think you do, but I'll show you just to be sure:

> *Flying from Denver to Los Angeles, Nathan had a good view of Lake Powell.*

The secret is to place the participle in a position that forces the reader to associate it with the noun or pronoun that it needs to modify. This position is usually next to the that noun or pronoun. Here are several more sentences containing dangling participles:

> *Hoping not to intrude, you must go about your normal activities during my visit.* Since the intended meaning of the sentence does not allow the participle *hoping* to modify the subject *you*, the participle dangles. The sentence could be changed as follows: *Hoping not to intrude, I ask you to go about your normal activities during my visit.*

> *Having vowed never to procrastinate again, her next novel was finished in seven months.* It is at best a questionable practice to make a participle modify a possessive pronoun, even when the latter is the first word of the main clause. The sentence should be changed, perhaps like this: *Having vowed never to procrastinate again, she finished her next novel in seven months.* Now the introductory participle modifies the subject of the sentence, and all is once again right with the world.

> *Anticipating an imminent rise in gasoline prices, an unscheduled stop at the gas station seemed prudent.* There is nothing for the participle *anticipating* to modify; an unscheduled stop cannot anticipate anything. One way of making this an acceptable sentence is to change the participial phrase into an adverb clause, as follows: *Because he anticipated an imminent rise in gasoline prices, an unscheduled stop at the gas station seemed prudent.*

Not only participles (verbal adjectives) can dangle, but regular adjectives can as well. Check out this sentence:

> *Unable to walk, they had to carry her into the house.*

One wonders how they succeeded in carrying her into the house if they were unable to walk, but that's what the sentence says they did. Like introductory participles, introductory adjectives modify the subject of the sentence. To bring grammar and intended meaning into harmony, we could go with *Unable to walk, she had to be carried into the house.*

* * * * *

A word of caution: Some participles have taken on prepositional status and do not modify anything. Three such words are *concerning, regarding*, and *excepting.*

> *Concerning the issue of global warming, the accelerated melting of polar ice will cause the oceans to rise significantly. Concerning the issue of global warming* is not an introductory participial phrase; therefore, it does not need to modify the subject of the sentence, the gerund *melting.*

A list of other participles seen as marginal prepositions, or as subordinating conjunctions, includes *speaking* (in the expressing *speaking of), given, granted, assuming, barring* (when used to mean "except for"), *judging, failing* (in the sense of "in the absence of"), and *owing* (when followed by *to*). These participles are discussed at some length in Lesson 21.

* * * * *

Nominative absolutes: Be careful not to repeat, in the main part of the sentence, the noun or pronoun used in the absolute expression. Here is an example of what not to do:

> *The kitten having been lost, it was found the next day.* Change to *Having been lost, the kitten was was found the next day.*

> *The kitten having been lost, we found it the next day.* Change to *The next day we found the kitten that had been lost.*

How would you use the absolute expression *the kitten having been lost* in a sentence? Here's one way (of many): *The kitten having been lost, Josie was heartbroken and cried for hours. Kitten* does not (and should not) appear in the main clause, either as a noun or a pronoun.

* * * * *

The participial phrases *being that* (*Being that we're all here, let's party*) and *being as how* (*Being as how I don't have enough time now, I'll cut the grass tomorrow*) are considered substandard.

Lesson 15: Adverb Clauses

A clause is a group of words that has a subject and a predicate (the verb, its objects, and the modifiers of the verb and of its objects). An independent, or main, clause is a clause that can stand alone as a complete sentence. Every sentence must have at least one main clause. A dependent, or subordinate, clause cannot stand alone as a complete sentence but is dependent upon another clause. Up till now, we have been considering (and diagramming) only independent clauses. There are three types of dependent clauses: adverb clauses, adjective clauses, and noun clauses. In this lesson, you will be introduced to adverb clauses. A sentence that has at least one dependent clause is called a **complex sentence**.

* * * * *

Some adverb clauses are introduced by **subordinating conjunctions** (*because, since, although, if,* etc.). Here are several sentences that contain subordinating conjunctions:

> *Tom stayed home on Derby day because it was raining.*
> *Since none of us has a basketball, we can't play basketball.* For *since* to be a subordinating conjunction, it must be causal (i.e., it must mean "because").
> *Although she had just bought a new dress, she decided to wear an old one.*
> *I would have left earlier if I hadn't had to clean my room. If* is a subordinating conjunction only when it is conditional.

* * * * *

Other adverb clauses are introduced by **relative adverbs** (*when, where, after, before, while, since, as,* etc.). Relative adverbs are adverbs because they modify the kinds of words that adverbs modify. They are called *relative* adverbs because, in part, they function as prepositions with relative-pronoun objects. This will become clear as you examine the following sentences and read the explanations:

> *We can do our homework when we return.* The relative adverb *when* can be expressed as *at the time at which.* This expression comprises two prepositional phrases: *at the time* and *at which,* the former modifying the verb *do* and the latter modifying the verb *return. Which* in *at which* is a relative pronoun. You will learn about relative pronouns and relative clauses in Lesson 17.

> *Dave wanted to go where his friends were going.* The relative adverb *where* is the equivalent of *to the place to which.*

> *When we retire, we can go hiking whenever the weather is accommodating.* Both *when* and *whenever* are relative adverbs. The latter is the equivalent of *at any time at which.*" (*When* and *where* can also be interrogative adverbs and, as such, introduce direct and indirect questions (the latter being noun clauses, the topic of Lesson 18).

> *Make hay while the sun shines. While,* a relative adverb, can be restated as *during the time at which.*

> *After she had worked in the garden for an hour, she sat down and fell asleep.* The relative adverb *after* can be restated as *after the time at which.* Notice that *after* in the expression *after the time at which* is not a relative adverb but a preposition.

> *He hasn't stopped talking since he got here.* The relative adverb *since* is temporal, not causal. It is the equivalent of *since the time at which.* The latter *since* is a preposition.

* * * * *

The relative adverbs *as* and *than* are used in equal and unequal comparisons, respectively. You will learn about them, and be introduced to *the* as a relative adverb, in the next lesson.

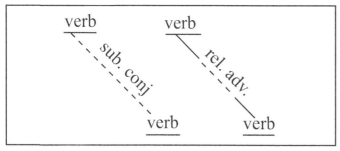

Step 101. Marty wanted to climb Mt. Everest because it is the world's highest mountain.

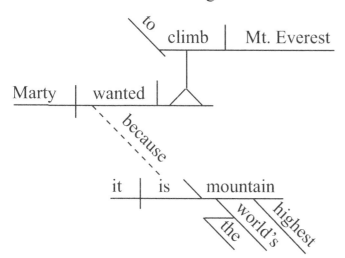

The subordinating conjunction *because* introduces a dependent clause (which, in this sentence, is everything from *because* on). The infinitive phrase *to climb Mt Everest* is a direct object. *Mountain* is a predicate nominative. *The* modifies *world's* and not *mountain*. You can test this by asking which word *my* modifies in the phrase *my teacher's grade book*. If *my* modifies *teacher's* (and it must), does it not follow that *the* modifies *world's* in the phrase *the world's highest mountain*?

Step 102. Although school had been dismissed early, we got home late.

We got late / Although / home / school / had been dismissed / early

In sentence diagrams, dependent clauses are placed below independent clauses regardless of word order. *Home* is diagrammed as an adverbial objective here. It can also be construed and diagrammed as a simple adverb.

Step 103. He finished planting the tree just when the rain began.

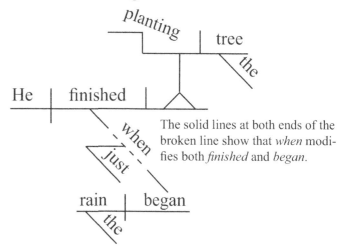

The solid lines at both ends of the broken line show that *when* modifies both *finished* and *began*.

The relative adverb *when* is modified by the adverb *just*. The gerund phrase *planting a tree* functions as a direct object.

Step 104. Vonny volunteers whenever and wherever her help is needed.

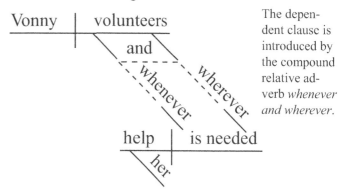

The dependent clause is introduced by the compound relative adverb *whenever and wherever*.

Step 105. Although the store is closed on weekends, we will arrange to deliver on Saturdays if the customer agrees to pay to a delivery charge.

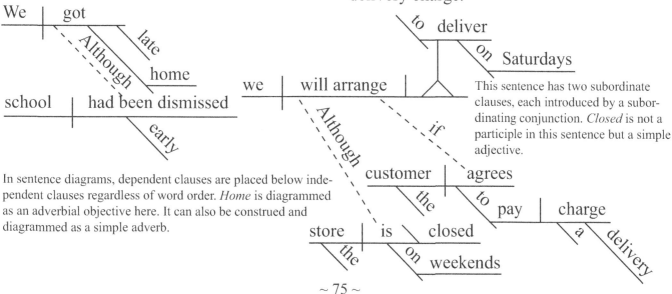

This sentence has two subordinate clauses, each introduced by a subordinating conjunction. *Closed* is not a participle in this sentence but a simple adjective.

Exercise 15: Adverb Clauses

152. Although snow was expected later in the day, most schools were open.

153. Ellen knows a lot about the world because she travels a lot.

154. If I were you, I would try to be more optimistic.

155. When they entered the theater, they went to their seats immediately.

156. Wes squinted as he left the cathedral.

157. Claire promised to shovel the snow after she checked her email.

158. Did Bruce live here when he was a child?

159. Marty arrived after the party had begun but before the food had been served.

160. Whenever she crossed the old bridge, she thought of a night many years ago.

161. Dorothy arrived just as the others were leaving.

162. Because they did not trust the vendor, they did not pay for the product until it arrived.

163. Scott acted as if nothing had happened.

Writing Correctly 15

Which is correct: *if I was* or *if I were?*
Which is correct: *if he was* or *if he were?*
Which is correct: *if it was* or *if it were?*

All six are correct at one time or another; it depends on the meaning of *if* ("on condition that" or "whether") and on context. If you answered correctly, you can skip this section and go to the head of the class.

In Lesson 2, you learned that there are two kinds of conditional clauses: real and unreal (or contrary-to-fact). Real conditional sentences require the indicative mood, unreal the subjunctive. Here is an example of each:

> *If you have a dollar* [it's possible that you do], *he wants it.*
> *If you had a dollar* [but you don't], *he would want it.*

The difference between real and unreal conditional sentences is often subtle. The following sentences illustrate this:

> *If you tell Jack you love him* [it's possible you will tell him], *he will be the happiest person in the world.*
> *If you told Jack you loved him* [it's possible you will tell him], *he would be the happiest person in the world.*

So what gives? Do both sentences mean exactly the same thing? Yes, but the first sentence is expressed more optimistically than the second. Regardless, the first sentence is called a real conditional sentence, and the second is called an unreal conditional sentence. I'll throw you one more curve ball (imagine two kids arguing):

> *If I'm a baboon* [I'll go along with you just to make a point], *you're a stupid baboon.*
> *If I were a baboon* [I'm not], *you would be a stupid baboon.*

The indicative is a more forceful mood than the subjunctive; it is effective here even though the condition is unreal.

The unreal conditional sentence *If she hurried, she would be on time* can be expressed in five other ways:

> *If she were to hurry, she would be on time.*
> *Were she to hurry, she would be on time.*
> *She would be on time if she hurried.*
> *She would be on time if she were to hurry.*
> *She would be on time were she to hurry.*

Unreal conditional sentences do not have a distinct future tense; the present tense is used for both present and future time.

The unreal conditional sentence *If she had hurried, she would have been on time* can be expressed in three other ways:

> *Had she hurried, she would have been on time.*
> *She would have been on time if she had hurried.*
> *She would have been on time had she hurried.*

Conditional sentences, both real and unreal, can have mixed tense: one tense in the subordinate clause and a different tense in the main clause. Here are examples:

> *If Joe wins the jackpot, I will expect half of it.* (real condition, present tense indicative; main clause, future tense indicative)
> *If Joe won the jackpot* [he may have], *I have a right to half of it.* (real condition, past tense indicative; main clause, present tense indicative)
> *If Joe won the jackpot* [he may have], *I will quit my job.* (real condition, past tense indicative; main clause, future tense indicative)
> *If Joe had won the jackpot* [he didn't], *I would go back to school.* (unreal condition, past tense sunjunctive; main clause, present conditional)

Speakers and writers get in trouble when they mix tenses or moods problematically, as in the following sentence:

> *If she saw the movie, she would have been able to talk about it.*

This sentence uses either the past indicative or the present subjunctive in the *if*-clause and the past conditional in the main clause. Neither combination is logical. Here are ways of keeping *If she saw the movie* while changing the main clause:

> *If she saw the movie, she would be able to talk about it.*
> *If she saw the movie, she is able to talk about it.*
> *If she saw the movie, she was able to talk about it.*

One can also keep the main clause intact and change the subordinate clause, as follows:

> *If she had seen the movie, she would have been able to talk about it.*
> *Had she seen the movie, she would have been able to talk about it.*

* * * * *

When speaking or writing formally, take care not to use *would* in the conditional clause (the *if*-clause); *would* should be used only in the conclusion. Thus, *If you asked me, I would tell you* is better than *If you would ask me, I would tell you*, and *If you had asked me, I would have told you* is better than *If you would have asked me, I would have told you.*

Exercise 16: Adverb Clauses (2)

There are **two types of comparisons**: equal and unequal. Both are expressed by using relative adverbs and (often elliptical) subordinate clauses. Equal comparisons require the positive (or basic) form of an adjective or adverb preceded by *as* or *so* (ordinary adverbs) and followed by *as* (a relative adverb). Unequal comparisons require the comparative form of an adjective or adverb followed by the relative adverb *than*.

Adjectives and adverbs have three gradations: positive, comparative, and superlative. Here are several examples: (adjectives) *tall, taller, tallest; good, better, best; beautiful, more beautiful, most beautiful*; (adverbs) *soon, sooner, soonest; well, better, best; awkwardly, more awkwardly, most awkwardly.*

* * * * *

The sentence *You are as tall as she* expresses an **equal comparison**; that is, the two people being compared are equal in height. Every comparison contains a subordinate clause, which is usually expressed elliptically. *You are as tall as she*, in its expanded form, is *You are as tall as she is tall.* The first *as* of the correlatives *as . . . as* is a regular adverb; it modifies the adjective *tall* (the first one). The second *as* is a relative adverb and modifies the second (or unexpressed) *tall*. To see why the second *as* is not an ordinary adverb but a relative adverb, consider this equivalent restatement: *You are tall in the degree in which she is tall.* The first *as* is rendered by *in the degree*, the second by *in which*. Since this *which* is a relative pronoun, the second *as* is called a relative adverb. Here are three more equal comparisons:

> *Janel can run as fast as her brother.* Expanded sentence: *Janel can run as fast as her brother can run fast.* Equivalent sentence: *Janel can run fast in the degree in which her brother can run fast. Fast* is an adverb in this sentence.
> *The Smiths are not so wealthy as the Joneses.* Expanded sentence: *The Smiths are not so wealthy as the Joneses are wealthy.* Equivalent sentence: *The Smiths are not wealthy in the degree in which the Joneses are wealthy.*
> *They are as honest as they are kind.* This sentence is not elliptical. Equivalent sentence: *They are honest in the degree in which they are kind.*

* * * * *

The sentence *You are taller than she* expresses an **unequal comparison**; that is, the two people being compared are unequal in height. The expanded form of this elliptical sentence is *You are taller than she is tall.* This is equivalent to *You are tall beyond the degree in which she is tall.* In this restatement, *taller* is rendered as *tall beyond the degree*, and *than* is expressed as *in which*, a prepositional phrase containing a relative pronoun; thus, *than* is called a relative adverb. Here are several unequal comparisons:

> *Her work is more difficult than his.* Expanded sentence: *Her work is more difficult than his is difficult.* Equivalent sentence: *Her work is difficult beyond the degree in which his is difficult.*
> *Jack was hurt worse than Jill.* Expanded sentence: *Jack was hurt worse than Jill was hurt badly.* Equivalent sentence: *Jack was hurt badly beyond the degree in which Jill was hurt badly.*
> *I would rather write a report than read one.* Expanded sentence: *I would rather write a report than I would gladly read one.* Equivalent sentence: *I would write a report gladly beyond the degree in which I would gladly read one.*

* * * * *

You have been introduced to the **correlatives** *as . . . as* and *so . . . as* and have noted that they are used with the positive degree of adjectives and adverbs (in so-called equal comparisons). Another correlative expression, ***the . . . the***, is used with the comparative degree. In the sentence *The bigger they are, the harder they fall*, which can be rephrased as *They fall harder in the degree in which they are bigger*, *the* in *the bigger* is a relative adverb, while *the* in *the harder* is a regular adverb.

* * * * *

In the sentence *We were so tired that we fell asleep right away*, ***so . . . that*** (always with an intervening word or words) is a correlative expression expressing result. It is not to be confused with *so that* (written together), which expresses purpose (e.g., *Debbie turned off the TV so that she could study better*); *so that* is a phrasal subordinating conjunction. In the case of *so . . . that*, *so* is a regular adverb and *that* is a relative adverb. The sentence *We were so tired that we fell asleep right away* can be restated as *We were tired to the degree at which we fell asleep right away.*

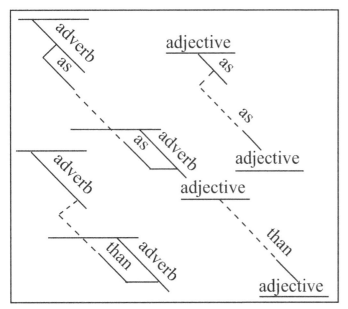

Step 106. This store is as large as that one.

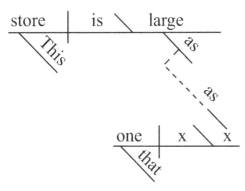

The sentence expresses an equal comparison. Like most comparative sentences, it is elliptical. The expanded sentence is *This store is as large as that one is large.* The *x*'s in the diagram represent the words *is* and *large.* The sentence can be restated as *This store is large in the degree in which that store is large.* The first adverb is a regular adverb; it modifies the first *large.* The second *as* is a relative adverb. In the rephrased sentence, it is expressed by *in which,* a prepositional phrase containing a relative pronoun.

Step 107. My dog is friendlier than my cat.

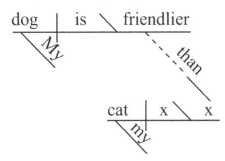

This sentence, which expresses an unequal comparison, is elliptical. The expanded sentence is *My dog is friendlier than my cat is friendly*; hence, the *x*'s in the diagram represent the words *is* and *friendly.* An equivalent sentence is *My dog is friendly beyond the degree in which my cat is friendly.* *Than* is a relative adverb.

Step 108. The tan chair is softer and more comfortable than the green one.

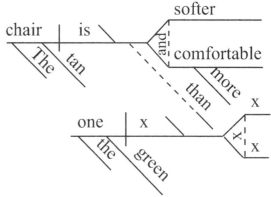

An equivalent sentence would be *The tan chair is soft and comfortable beyond the degree in which the green one is soft and comfortable.* *Than* is a relative adverb.

Step 109. The more time we have, the more time we seem to waste.

This sentence can be rephrased as *We seem to waste more time in the degree in which we have more time.*

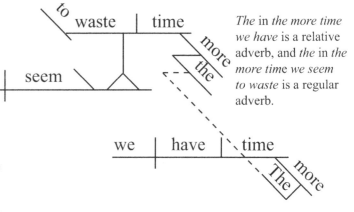

The in *the more time we have* is a relative adverb, and *the* in *the more time we seem to waste* is a regular adverb.

Step 110. I was so hungry that I ate ten pancakes.

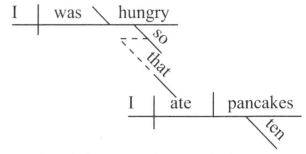

This sentence is equivalent to *I was hungry to the degree at which I ate ten pancakes.* *So* is a regular adverb, and *that* is a relative adverb.

Exercise 16: Adverb Clauses (2)

164. Be as quiet as a mouse!

165. She is as pretty as can be.

166. We worked as hard as possible.

167. I can write faster than you.

168. He is kinder and more generous than his sister.

169. Most kids would rather play than eat.

170. The more it rains, the faster the grass grows.

171. The more, the merrier.

172. It was so late that no more trick-or-treaters were expected.

173. After the guests arrive but before the food is brought out, let's remind them of the reason for the party.

174. When our family does a jigsaw puzzle, the children always put in more pieces than the parents.

Writing Correctly 16

More often than we care to remember, all of us have heard something like this: "Papa's Pride Potato Chips are fresher and crunchier." That's an incomplete comparison, and it says next to nothing. The good folks at Papa's Pride [a fictitious name, I hope] want us to complete the comparison with "...than any other potato chips." Of course, they can't just come right out and say this because they either know it isn't true or they have no proof that it is. What the listener ought to ask (but most of us don't) is "Fresher than what? Fresher than Papa's Pride used to be when they were deep fried in recycled lard? Crunchier than what? Crunchier than the average shoe lace?" The incomplete comparison may be a staple of modern advertising, but it's not acceptable for people who want to say something meaningful.

* * * * *

There is another kind of incomplete comparison, and we have probably all been guilty of using it at one time or another. It can be called the incomplete alternative comparison. Here is an example:

This cereal is as good or better than any other cereal.

Do you see the error? No one would say *This cereal is as good than any other cereal*, and yet this is exactly what the sentence in question is saying. To correct it, you have to insert the word *as* after *good*, as follows:

This cereal is as good as, or better than, any other cereal.

Another error--let's call it an error of illogical inequality--happens when a speaker or writer forgets that something cannot be compared unequally with itself. The result is a sentence like *The cheetah is faster than any animal in the world*. Of course, it isn't faster than itself.

* * * * *

Using the incorrect case of personal pronouns after *than* can result in unintended humor or even in miscommunication:

You like cars more than me. Imagine the confusion this sentence could cause if the person meant *You like cars more than I [do]*.

* * * * *

In general, one should use the comparative, not the superlative, when only two people or things are being compared. An exception is made for certain traditional expressions like *Put your best foot forward*.

* * * * *

Ill-chosen ellipses have a way of producing illogic in comparisons, for example:

Whirlpool's earnings for the month of March were greater than General Electric.

This sentence compares earnings with General Electric, which doesn't make sense; the ellipsis doesn't work. Either the words *those of* must be inserted (*Whirlpool's earnings for the month of March were greater than those of General Electric*) or one has to make General Electric a possessive (*Whirlpool's earnings for the month of March were greater than General Electric's*).

Check out this sentence:

The letter was longer than according to her.

The noun *letter* is being compared with *according to her*, a prepositional phrase, which is nonsensical. The error is corrected by rewording: *The letter was longer than she said it was.*

* * * * *

To form the comparative and superlative degrees of monosyllabic adjectives (except *good, bad,* and *much*); of most two-syllable adjectives ending in -*y*, -*er*, -*le*, and -*ow*; and of a few negative three-syllable adjectives (*unholy*), use -*er* and -*est*; otherwise, use *more* and *most* with the positive degree of the adjective (*more pleasant, most fortunate*). When you are uncertain, consult a dictionary.

* * * * *

Speaking of negatives (but no longer of comparatives and superlatives), the proscription of double negatives is not universally applicable. For example, it is not unidiomatic (note the double negative) to say that to say that someone's efforts on behalf of world peace have not gone unrewarded (another double negative).

* * * * *

The adverb *hardly* should not be used with negatives like *no, not, never,* and verbs ending in -*n't*, as it is in the first sentence in both of the following pairs of sentences:

I have hardly no time. Change to *I have hardly any time.*

She can't hardly see the board. Change to *She can hardly see the board.*

Avoid *without hardly.* Instead of *They arrived without hardly any furniture*, write *They arrived with hardly any furniture.*

Lesson 17: Adjective Clauses

An adjective clause is a clause that modifies a noun or any word or words that substitute for a noun. There are two kinds of adjective clauses: those introduced by a relative pronoun and those introduced by a relative adverb. Adjective clauses introduced by relative pronouns (*who, whom, whose, which,* and *that,* among other words) are called relative clauses. Every relative pronoun has an antecedent, i.e., a preceding word or words to which the relative pronoun refers. A relative pronoun agrees with its antecedent in number, and gender* but not in case. It takes its case from its use in its own clause. A good understanding of this allows one to choose confidently between *who* and *whom.* Here are some sentences with relative clauses:

> *That is the man whom* (or *that*) *we saw at the game.* The relative pronoun *whom* (or *that*) is the direct object in its clause. *Man,* the antecedent, is a predicate nominative. Careful speakers and writers do not use *who* in the objective case in formal speech and writing.
> *Do you know the person who* (or *that*) *wrote this book?* The relative pronoun *who* (or *that*) is the subject of its clause. Its antecedent, *person,* is a direct object. One never uses *whom* in the nominative case.
> *They are the neighbors whose cat was stolen. Neighbors,* a predicate nominative, is the antecedent of *whose,* a relative pronoun in the possessive case.
> *Distracted, Joe nearly pulled out in front of a fast-moving truck, which made him look twice at the next intersection.* The antecedent of the relative pronoun *which* is not *truck* but the entire clause *he nearly pulled out in front of a fast-moving truck.* Not the truck but his having nearly pulled out in front of it made him look twice at the next intersection. *Which* is the subject of the relative clause.

Often, when the relative pronoun *whom* or *that* is a direct object or the object of a preposition, we omit it. Of the previous examples, only the first can be expressed without an expressed relative pronoun: *That is the man we saw at the game.* Another example would be *Those are the tools I work with every day* (the relative pronoun *that,* the object of the preposition *with,* is unexpressed).

* * * * *

The indefinite relative pronouns *whoever, whomever, whosever, whichever,* and *whatever* (along with those with an inserted *so,* such as *whosoever*) ordinarily do not have expressed antecedents. Examples:

> *"I'll give a bonus point to whoever can tell me what page we're on,"* said the frustrated French teacher. Many people, even many educated people, would say *whomever* here, thinking (incorrectly) that the indefinite relative pronoun is the object of the preposition *to.* It isn't. The unexpressed antecedent *anyone* is the object of the preposition; *whoever* is the subject of the relative clause.
> *They plan to give the money to whomever they find in the shelter.* This time *whomever* is correct because it is the direct object in its own clause. The object of the preposition *to* is the unexpressed antecedent *anyone.*

The word *what* can mean *that which.* When it does, it is considered a relative pronoun. Example: *They did what the lieutenant ordered.* In this sentence, an unexpressed *that,* the direct object of the verb *did,* is the antecedent of *what,* a relative pronoun. *What* is the direct object of the verb *ordered.*

* * * * *

Some adjective clauses are introduced not by relative pronouns but by relative adverbs. Here are three examples:

> *That is the reason why I was late.* Since *why* is equivalent here to the prepositional phrase *for which,* it is called a relative adverb. Notice that this sentence can be expressed without an expressed *why: That is the reason I was late.*
> *From here you can see the hospital where our children were born. Where,* a relative adverb, is equivalent to *in which.*
> *Clayton remembers a time when candy bars cost five cents.* The relative adverb *when* is equivalent to *at which.*

* Relative pronouns also agree with their antecedents in person. Notice the subject-verb agreement in this sentence: *You, who <u>are</u> my child, love me, and I, who <u>am</u> your father, love you.*

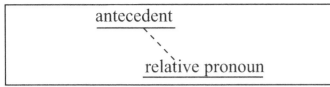

In diagramming, one draws a broken line between a relative pronoun and its antecedent. Like all other dependent clauses, a relative clause is diagrammed below its main clause.

Step 111. I have to see the shipment that came in today.

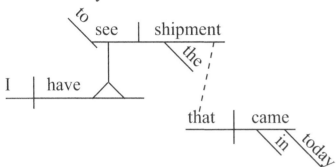

The relative pronoun *that* is the subject of its clause. Its antecedent, *shipment*, is a direct object. *To see the shipment that come in today* is a complementary infinitive phrase.

Step 112. I know the person whose ring was stolen.

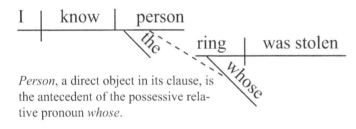

Person, a direct object in its clause, is the antecedent of the possessive relative pronoun *whose*.

Step 113. That's the book that I've been waiting for.

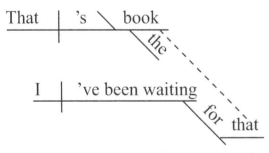

That, the object of the preposition *for*, is a relative pronoun. Its antecedent is *book*, a predicate nominative. The second *that* could be omitted: *That's the book I've been waiting for.* In diagramming this sentence, one would represent the missing relative pronoun with a *x*.

Step 114. Are you still the man I used to know?

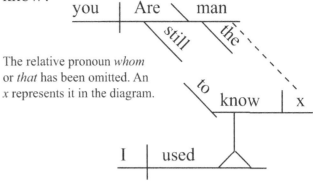

The relative pronoun *whom* or *that* has been omitted. An *x* represents it in the diagram.

Step 115. Tell whoever asks.

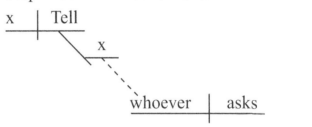

The first *x* stands for the unexpressed subject, *you*. The second x stands for *anyone*, the unexpressed antecedent of the indefinite relative pronoun *whoever*.

Step 116. They read into the text whatever they want to find.

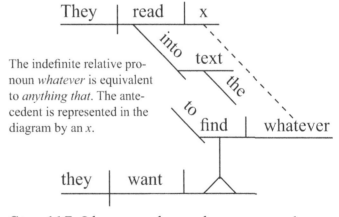

The indefinite relative pronoun *whatever* is equivalent to *anything that*. The antecedent is represented in the diagram by an *x*.

Step 117. I know a place where we can have the reunion.

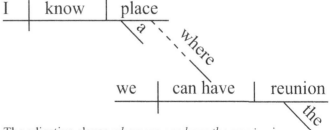

The adjective clause *where we can have the reunion* is introduced by the relative adverb *where* (the equivalent of *at which*).

Exercise 17: Adjective Clauses

175. Do you know the woman who called?

176. I forgot the title of the book that we have to read.

177. Choose carefully the person in whom you place your full trust.

178. The guy whose car is parked illegally may soon be looking for a ride.

179. This is the day I've been waiting for.

180. Did anyone find the pen you lost?

181. The accident happened on the day they arrived in Miami.

182. Whoever leaves last must turn off the lights.

183. The other prizes will be given to whoever answers correctly.

184. She will go with whomever she likes best.

185. Do you remember the time when you hid stinky cheese in my sock drawer?

186. I have already told you the reason I can't be there.

Writing Correctly 17

The relative pronouns *who, whom, whoever,* and *whomever* (the latter two are called indefinite relative pronouns) give most of us problems. What do you think of these sentences?

> *That's the person who I was talking about.*
> *That's the contractor who we want to hire?*
> *Whoever I find will have to help with dishes.*
> *He doesn't need to do what whoever he is with does.*

If there were a rigid logic to grammar, each *who* and each *whoever* in the previous sentences would have to be changed to *whom* and *whomever,* respectively. After all, *who* and *whoever* are in the nominative case, used for subjects and predicate nominatives, whereas *whom* and *whomever* are in the objective case, used for objects (direct objects and objects of prepositions). But, honestly, how many educated people do you know who would express themselves informally as follows?

> *That's the person whom I was talking about.*
> *That's the contractor whom we want to hire.*
> *Whomever I find will have to help with dishes.*
> *He doesn't need to do what whomever he is with does.*

If one can speak of a consensus of grammarians on this matter --and I'm not sure one can--the first set of sentences above are acceptable (perhaps even preferable) informally, but problematic formally. For formal occasions, I recommend the second set of sentences.

There are times, to be sure, when *who* is just plain wrong, as it would be in *That's the person about who I was talking.*

Sometimes one can find a way (or ways) around *who/whom*:

> (1) One can use *that* as the relative pronoun, as follows:
>
> *That's the person that I was talking about.*
> *That's the contractor that we want to hire.*
>
> (2) One can omit the relative pronoun:
>
> *That's the person I was talking about.*
> *That's the contractor we want to hire.*

When you choose either of these options, you don't have to worry about *who* and *whom.* And, presto, everyone is happy.

It's always a little sad when someone uses *whom* where *who* is required. You know the person is trying; people who don't care just *who who* their way through everything. What do you think of the following sentences?

> *His friend was the poet whom, as you know, was honored with an invitation to the White House.*
> *The hostess saved several pieces of cake for whom-*

ever arrived late.
> *Dewey was the candidate whom most people thought would win the election.*

Each *whom* should be changed to *who,* as follows:

> *His friend was the poet who, as you know, was honored with an invitation to the White House.* The relative pronoun is not the object of *know* but the subject of *was honored.*
> *The hostess saved several pieces of cake for whoever arrived late.* The indefinite relative pronoun is not the object of *for* but the subject of *arrived.*
> *Dewey was the candidate who most people thought would win the election.* The relative pronoun is not the object of *thought* but the subject of *would win.*

* * * * *

The relative pronouns *who* and *whom* are used mostly with personal antecedents; occasionally, their antecedents are animals. In contrast, antecedents of the possessive relative pronoun *whose* run the gamut from personal to inanimate; moreover, *whose* can introduce both restrictive and nonrestrictive relative clauses. Here are a few examples:

> *Will the person whose car is parked in the fire lane please move it.* (personal antecedent, restrictive relative clause)
> *The Donahues, whose son is in Kelly's class, have offered us a ride to the meeting.* (personal antecedent, nonrestrictive relative clause)
> *They agreed to bid only on dressers whose mirrors, knobs, and handles were all intact.* (inanimate antecedent, restrictive relative clause)
> *She began to dislike the new car, whose most attractive feature was its color.* (inanimate antecedent, nonrestrictive relative clause)

Sometimes, *of which* can be used instead of *whose,* as follows:

> *She began to dislike the new car, the most attractive feature of which was its color.*

* * * * *

The relative pronoun *that* can replace *who, whom,* or *which* in restrictive relative clauses.

> *I know the man that won the race.* (*that* replaces *who*)
> *She wondered how well she knew the person that she had married.* (*that* replaces *whom*)
> *Is this the house that your father built?* (*that* replaces *which*)

That cannot introduce nonrestrictive relative clauses.

Lesson 18: Noun Clauses

A noun clause is a clause that functions as a noun. Noun clauses are used as subjects, predicate nominatives, direct objects, objects of prepositions, adverbial objectives, and appositives. They may be introduced by the expletives *that, whether,* and *if* (in the sense of *whether*); by the interrogative pronouns *who, whom, whose, which,* and *what*; by the interrogative adjectives *which* and *what*; and by the interrogative adverbs *how, when, where,* and *why*. Some noun clauses have no special introductory word or words.

* * * * *

Let's look first at noun clauses introduced by the expletive *that* (whether expressed or unexpressed). Examples:

Jim knew that he had forgotten something. The noun clause *that he had forgotten something* functions as a direct object. The same sentence can be expressed without *that: Jim knew he had forgotten something.*

That they scored so few points is a source of great embarrassment to the team, which prides itself on its potent offense. The noun clause *that they scored so few points* is the subject of the sentence.

Why doesn't it bother the teacher that most of her students are talking? The noun clause *that most of her students are talking* serves as an appositive. It is in apposition with the subject of the sentence, *it*.

The answer is that she encourages group work at certain times of the day. The noun clause *that she encourages group work at certain times of the day* is a predicate nominative.

I'm sorry that we can't wait that long. The noun clause *that we can't wait that long* functions as an adverbial objective. It modifies the predicate adjective *sorry*. The same sentence can be expressed with an understood *that: I'm sorry we can't wait that long.*

* * * * *

Many noun clauses are introduced by the expletives *whether* and *if*. Here are several examples:

Whether we succeed or not often depends on how much effort we are willing to expend. *Whether we succeed or not* is the subject of the sentence. *Whether or not* is a phrasal expletive.

Can you tell me if the Kramers live on this street? *If the Kramers live on this street* is a direct object. *If* as an introductory expletive can sometimes be used instead of *whether*.

The big question was whether it was going to rain. The noun clause *whether it was going to rain* functions as a predicate nominative. *Whether* is an expletive.

The two brothers disagree about whether the Pope is infallible. *Whether the Pope is infallible*, a noun clause, is used here as the object of the preposition *about*.

* * * * *

Noun clauses can be introduced by interrogative pronouns, interrogative adjectives, and interrogative adverbs. Examples:

Who was required to attend the meeting had never been clarified. The noun clause *who was required to attend the meeting* acts as the subject of the sentence. *Who* is an interrogative pronoun.

They asked what they could do to help and what tools were available. The noun clauses form a compound direct object. The first *what* is an interrogative pronoun, the second an interrogative adjective.

We are puzzled about why we have to stay. The noun clause *why we have to stay* is the object of the preposition *about*. *Why* is an interrogative adverb.

It is amazing how long Beth can remain under water. The noun clause *how long Beth can remain under water* is an appositive. It is in apposition with the subject of the sentence, *it*. *How* is an interrogative adverb.

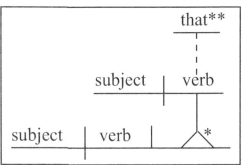

*This particular noun clause is a direct object; however, noun clauses can also function as subjects, predicate nominatives, objects or prepositions, appositives, and adverbial objectives.

**If the expletive *that* is unexpressed, an *x* represents it in a diagram. Other words that can introduce noun clauses are the expletives *whether* and *if* as well as interrogative pronouns, interrogative adjectives, and interrogative adverbs.

Step 118. The trouble is that she doesn't do her homework.

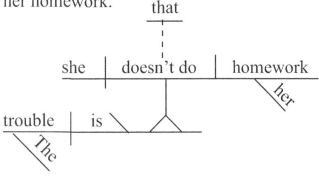

The noun clause *that she doesn't do her homework* functions as a predicate nominative. *That* is an expletive.

Step 119. She wondered whether he was sorry he had hurt her.

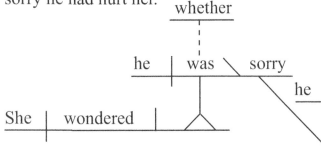

This sentence features a noun clause within a noun clause. The larger noun clause, *whether he was sorry he had hurt her*, functions as a direct object. The smaller noun clause, *he had hurt her*, is an adverbial objective. The expletive *that* is unexpressed. It is represented in the diagram by an *x*.

Step 120. Jeff is always uncertain about which pages he should study.

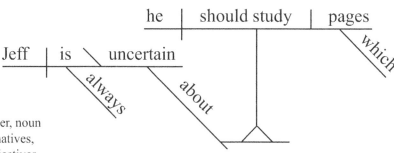

The noun clause *which pages he should study* is the object of the preposition *about*. *Which* is an interrogative adjective.

Step 121. It has never been disclosed why they did what they did.

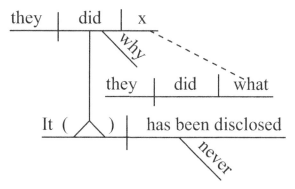

The noun clause *why they did what they did* is in apposition with the subject of the sentence, *it*. The relative pronoun *what* is the equivalent of *that which*.

Step 122. You are not as big as you think.

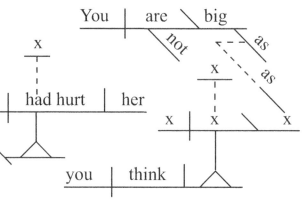

This elliptical sentence ends with the unexpressed noun clause *that you are big*. These four words are represented by *x*'s in the diagram. The sentence contains a so-called equal comparison. The second *as* is a relative adverb; it introduces an adverb clause, of which the unexpressed noun clause is a part.

Exercise 18: Noun Clauses

187. She noticed that his coat was hanging between two others.

188. An unintended result of the experiment was that many birds died.

189. It is a widespread belief that poinsettias are poisonous.

190. I don't know when the game starts.

191. We were told how long we were going to stay.

192. Do you know if we have school tomorrow?

193. Tell me whether or not you agree.

194. The professor attempted to find out who damaged his car.

195. The station manager claimed to be uncertain as to why the station had lost so many listeners.

196. I am confident you will find a solution.

197. How many angels could fit on the head of a pin was a question that some medieval theologians are said to have found intriguing.

Writing Correctly 18

Direct statements after verbs of saying and direct questions after verbs of asking are noun clauses enclosed by quotation marks. In the United States, periods and commas are placed inside closing quotation marks, like this:

> *She said, "I would like to see that movie sometime."*
> *"I would like to see it, too," he replied.*

Question marks are placed inside closing quotation marks if the quotation is a question. If the sentence is a question but the quotation is not, the question mark follows the closing quotation marks. Examples:

> *He asked, "Do you want to see the movie with me?"*
> *Did she really say, "I'll have to think about it"?*
> *Did he ask, "How much time will you need?"*

Other important uses of quotation marks are these:

- for the titles of articles in books, newspapers, and magazines
- for the titles of essays and short stories
- for chapter titles
- for the titles of short poems
- for the titles of radio and TV episodes
- for the titles of songs
- for words used ironically: *The first graders finished their "dissertations" and ran out to play.*
- for slang words that are not an ordinary part of the writer's vocabulary: *He sprinted across the meadow, avoiding as many "cow pies" as he could.*

Unless they appear as offset blocks, quotations of multiple paragraphs or stanzas from a single source require quotation marks at the beginning of each paragraph or stanza as well as quotation marks at the end of the final paragraph or stanza.

* * * * *

What's wrong with the following sentence: *Disease is when the body malfunctions*? *When*-clauses can be noun clauses, as they are in *Prentis asked when the boys were leaving* and in *When terrorists will strike next is unknown*; however, a *when*-clause is unsatisfactory as the definition of a noun. A better (although assailable) definition would be *Disease is a malfunctioning of the body.*

Because-clauses are also used occasionally as noun clauses, as in *Because they had been sick was their answer to the question why they had arrived late*; however, a *because*-clause is never an acceptable predicate in a sentence that begins *The reason is (was)*. As an example consider the sentence *The reason for their tardiness was because they had stopped along the way for breakfast. Because* means "for the reason that." The above sentence therefore means *The reason for their tardiness was for the reason that. . .* , which makes no sense.

* * * * *

Like their relative pronoun counterparts, the interrogative pronoun *who* is used for subjects and predicate nominatives, while the interrogative pronoun *whom* is used for objects (direct objects and objects of prepositions). Let's look at some sentences in which *who* and *whom* are used in noun clauses:

> *I wonder who they are going to the play with.*
> *Why didn't you tell them who you saw there?*
> *May I ask whom you want to be?*
> *Skip was well informed about whom had been reassigned.*

According to a strict application of the rules of grammar, each *who* in the above sentences needs to be changed to *whom*; unequivocally, each *whom* should be *who*. So changed, the sentences read as follows:

> *I wonder whom they are going to the play with.* The interrogative pronoun *whom* is the object of the preposition with.

> *Why didn't you tell them whom you saw there?* The interrogative pronoun *whom* is the direct object of the verb saw.

> *May I ask who you want to be?* The interrogative pronoun *who* is not the direct object of *ask* but a predicate nominative in the noun clause *who you want to be*).

> *Skip was well informed about who had been reassigned.* The interrogative pronoun *who* is not the object of the preposition *about* but the subject of the noun clause *who had been reassigned.*

* * * * *

Let's look at the question of number when the subject of a sentence is the unexpressed antecedent of the indefinite relative pronoun *what*. Which sentences of the following pairs do you consider correct?

> *What has been added are end-zone bleachers.*
> *What has been added is end-zone bleachers*

> *What is needed are hundreds of used books.*
> *What is needed is hundreds of used books.*

The second sentence in each pair of sentences is preferable because the main verb agrees in number with the unexpressed *that*; however, it seems one can also say *What have been added are end-zone bleachers* and *What are needed are hundreds of used books.*

Lesson 19: Compound-Complex Sentences

A compound-complex sentence is a sentence that has more than one independent clause and at least one dependent clause. Let's examine a few of the many possible combinations:

- Two independent clauses and an adverbial clause that is dependent on one of the independent clauses: *The mouse was walking nonchalantly towards the cat, but it scampered away when it caught sight of its archenemy.*

- Two independent clauses and two dependent clauses (an adjective clause modifying a word in the first independent clause and an adverb clause subordinate to the second independent clause): *The mouse was walking nonchalantly towards the spot where the cat lay, but it scampered away when it caught sight of its archenemy.*

- Two independent clauses and a noun clause that is used as a direct object in the second independent clause: *Cathy left immediately, and Scott opined that all of us ought to consider heading for home.*

- Two independent clauses, a noun clause used as a direct object in the second independent clause, and an adverb clause dependent on both main clauses: *When the clock struck twelve, Cathy left immediately, and Scott opined that all of us ought to consider heading for home.*

- Two independent clauses with a noun clause used as an adverbial objective in each: *Witherspoon is afraid that he will strike out, and Armstrong is sure that he will hit every pitch.*

- Two independent clauses, the first with a noun clause and an adverb clause, the second with a noun clause and an adjective clause: *Witherspoon is afraid that he will strike out if the pitcher throws a fast ball, and Armstrong is sure that he will hit every pitch that comes within a foot of the strike zone.*

- Two independent clauses, each with an adjective clause and a noun clause, and an adverb clause dependent on both main clauses: *Because it had snowed hard during the night, the adults who were headed for work were conscious of the fact that they must drive with heightened caution, but the children who were headed for school were aware only that they could be the target of well-directed snowballs.*

- Two independent clauses, each with an adjective clause, a noun clause, and an adverb clause; and an adverb clause dependent on both main verbs: *Because it had snowed hard during the night, the adults who were headed for work were conscious of the fact that they must drive with heightened caution if they and others were to arrive safely, but the children who were headed for school were aware only that they could be hit by well-directed snowballs if they did not remain alert.*

- Three independent clauses, each with an adjective clause: *The guy who had a ticket to Indianapolis traveled to Nashville instead, and the guy who had a ticket to Nashville traveled to Indy instead, but the guy who had a ticket to Louisville actually went to Louisville.*

- Three independent clauses, each with an adjective clause and an adverb clause: *The guy who had a ticket to Indianapolis traveled to Nashville instead because he wanted to visit the Grand Ole Opry, and the guy who had a ticket to Nashville traveled to Indy instead because he wanted to see the Colts play, but the guy who had a ticket to Louisville actually went to Louisville because he wanted to see the Mohammed Ali Museum, the Louisville Slugger Museum, and the Kentucky Derby Museum.*

- Three independent clauses and an adverb clause that depends on all three main verbs: *Because the weather has become quite cold, leaves have begun to fall from the trees, birds have begun to fly south, and people have begun to shop for Christmas.*

- Three independent clauses, each with an adjective clause, and an adverb clause that depends on all three main verbs: *Because the weather has become quite cold, leaves, which only a few weeks ago were still green, have begun to fall from the trees; birds, which only a few weeks ago were chirping merrily, have begun to fly south; and people, who only a few weeks ago were buying patio furniture at Walmart, have begun to shop for Christmas.*

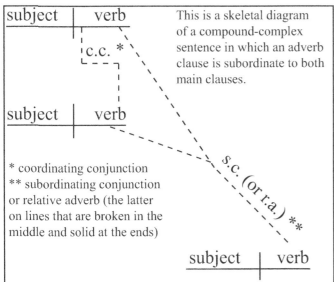

This is a skeletal diagram of a compound-complex sentence in which an adverb clause is subordinate to both main clauses.

* coordinating conjunction
** subordinating conjunction or relative adverb (the latter on lines that are broken in the middle and solid at the ends)

Step 123. Because the students are not in school today, Mrs. Brown, the sixth-grade English teacher, has agreed to meet with Mrs. Smith, whose son is struggling in English, and later the two women are going to have lunch together in a local restaurant.

Step 124. The first pig built his house of straw, and the second pig, who was little wiser than the first, built his house of sticks; however, the third pig, thinking that his brothers' houses were too weak, used bricks.

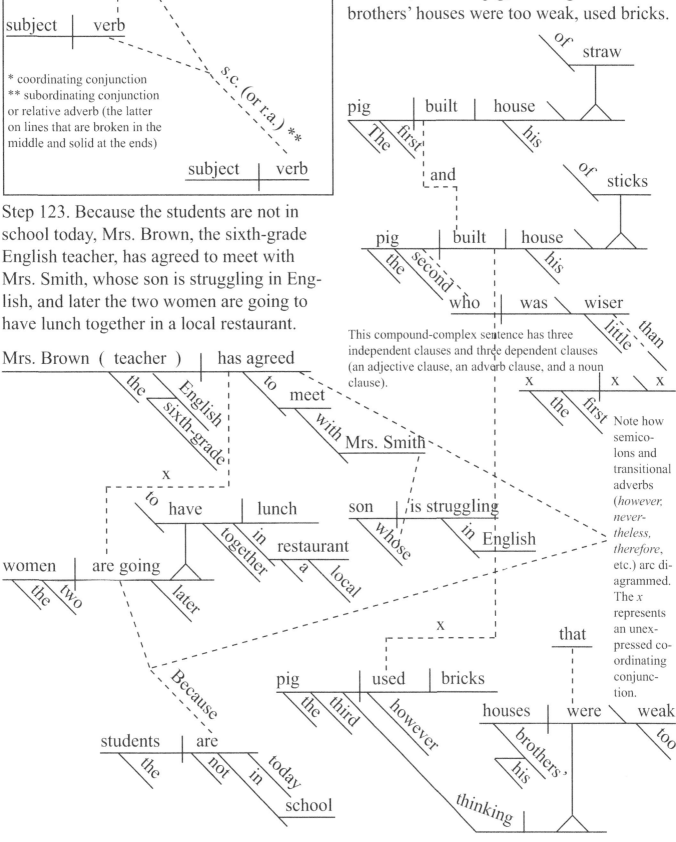

This compound-complex sentence has three independent clauses and three dependent clauses (an adjective clause, an adverb clause, and a noun clause).

Note how semicolons and transitional adverbs (*however, nevertheless, therefore,* etc.) are diagrammed. The *x* represents an unexpressed coordinating conjunction.

Exercise 19: Compound-Complex Sentences

198. When the rental truck broke down, father went to find help, and the rest of us waited by the side of the road.

199. Before the game, Jim wandered all around the stadium, but after the game began, he stayed in his seat and watched the game intently.

200. The lottery winner said that he would keep almost all the money; nevertheless, he was swamped with calls from friends, family, and strangers, most of whom claimed to be desperate.

201. The rains came and filled the lakes and rivers, and the few people and animals that remained alive could again drink to their heart's content.

202. I am not about to buy you a new suit, and that means either you wear your old one or you stay home.

203. When we reached the campsite to which we had been assigned, Mom and Dad unloaded the car, which we had crammed so full that we had been unable to move, and Sis and I put up the old tent, whose many holes had often evoked from Mom the suggestion that it be retired as a monument to mosquitoes.

Be sure to position the correlative conjunctions *not only . . . but also* logically with respect to each other. Here's a sentence in which that doesn't happen: *Mickey plays not only on the tennis team, but she also has time for her school work*. The reader expects to hear what other team or teams Mickey plays on. The sentence could be corrected as follows: *Mickey not only plays on the tennis team but also has time for school work*.

I hope you don't care for this sentence: *Joe not only plays bridge, but his wife plays as well*. The reader expects to hear what else Joe does. Corrections: *Not only Joe plays bridge, but his wife plays as well*, or *Not only does Joe play bridge, but his wife plays as well*. (The second option is somewhat problematic because it must be properly intoned; specifically, *Joe*, not *bridge*, must be accented.)

* * * * *

The semicolon is a useful punctuation mark; many people who know how to use it correctly love it. I am one of them. Semicolons are placed as follows:

- between separate clauses in a compound sentence when the clauses themselves include commas: *A good friend of mine, Bruce Barnstable, lives in the house on the corner; his dentist, Dr. Gutmann, lives next to him; and a mutual friend, Ellen Lane, lives just around the corner.*
- between two independent clauses of a compound sentence when the clauses are not connected by a conjunction: *Detective Brown arrived early; to his amazement, the tall blonde was waiting for him.*
- before transitional adverbs like *however, therefore, moreover, besides, then, thus*, and *indeed* when these words are used between independent clauses: *I don't know the answer; moreover, I don't care.* When similarly positioned, *yet* and *so* are preceded by a comma.

* * * * *

Commas are used as follows:

- (except in very short sentences) before coordinating conjunctions when they separate independent clauses: *Hard Spun led for more than a mile, but Street Sense passed him in the stretch.*
- after an introductory adverbial clause: *Because cancer research is expensive and necessary, it behooves those of us who can to give generously.*
- between items of a series of three or more items (unless one or more of the items contains commas): *Breakfast included cereal, eggs, bacon, toast, orange juice, coffee.*
- before a conjunction joining the last two elements of a series: *They spent most of their money on gasoline, lodging, and food* (see page 18 for a discussion of the Oxford comma).
- after introductory participial phrases: *Expecting rain, the picnickers brought raincoats and umbrellas.*
- to set off interjections, transitional adverbs, parenthetical

elements, and nouns of direct address: *Hey, that hurts! Jacob, however, wore a tux. Our team lost, to tell the truth, to a better team. I wonder, Doug, if you have time to help me.*
- to set off *that is, namely, i.e., for example*, and *e.g.* when these expressions introduce words or phrases: *In his opinion, this country would be better off without one divisive attitude, namely, stubborn certitude.*
- to set off nonrestrictive relative clauses: *Albert Einstein, who accomplished so much in his younger years, searched in vain in his later years for a theory that would unite relativity and quantum mechanics.*
- to set off nonrestrictive appositives: *Her best friend, Jennifer Collins, could not attend.*
- between coordinate attributive adjectives: *The train moved slowly through a long, dark tunnel.*
- to set off *et cetera, etc., and so on*, and *and so forth*: *They were burning grass, leaves, sticks, paper, etc., without a permit.*
- to set off certain antithetical phrases and clauses: *The more they work, the less they complain. He needed a pat on the shoulder, not a kick in the rear.*
- to separate two or more phrases that find completion in the same word or phrase: *Defense lawyers can, and sometimes do, help guilty clients avoid punishment. She prefers to hint at, rather than hit her readers over the head with, matters she considers important.*
- to set off individual elements of place names and of addresses (but not between the state and the zip code): *Ed sent the letter to 750 Bennighof Avenue, Evansville, IN 42214, without knowing if that was the correct address.*
- to set off quotations used as direct objects and as nonrestrictive appositives (but not quotations used as subjects, predicate nominatives, objects of prepositions, or restrictive appositives): *Ed yelled, "Charlotte, bring me a pencil." "I can't," she replied.* (*His exact words were "Charlotte, bring me a pencil."*) If a quotation ends in a question mark or an exclamation mark, no comma is used after it: *"Why do you need a pencil?" she asked.*
- to facilitate reading or to prevent a misreading: *For those who enjoy baking, ham and fish are good choices. For those who enjoy baking ham and fish, this magazine has just the right recipes.*

* * * * *

Italics are used as follows:

- for words used as words: The subject of the sentence is *car*.
- for the titles of books: *To Kill a Mockingbird, The Random House Dictionary of the English Language*
- for the names of newspapers and magazines: *The New York Times, The Washington Post, Newsweek, National Geographic*
- for the titles of operas: *Le Nozze di Figaro, Die Fledermaus*
- for the titles of paintings: *Mona Lisa, Whistler's Mother*

Lesson 20: Prepositional Phrases (2)

To determine whether a particular prepositional phrase is adjectival, ask if it describes, limits, or modifies a noun or pronoun. Also, it is sometimes helpful to try moving a problematic prepositional phrase around in the sentence; if it resists being moved from its position next to a noun or pronoun, it is probably adjectival. For example, in the sentence *If you look carefully, you can read the title of the book*, the prepositional phrase *of the book* limits *title* to a particular title. What's more, you simply cannot move *of the book* successfully (*of the book you can read the title* and *you can read of the book the title* just don't work); therefore, it is adjectival. In the sentence *Pat bought five new fish for the aquarium in the den,* the prepositional phrase *in the den* cannot be moved successfully (try it!), but *for the aquarium in the den* can. *In the den* is adjectival and *for the aquarium in the den* is adverbial. *In the den* restricts *aquarium* to a particular one.

Let's take a look at the familiar sentence *She has rings on her fingers and bells on her toes.* Once in a while, one meets prepositional phrases that seem to work well as adverbial modifiers and as adjectival modifiers. Here is a reconstruction of the sentence that argues for adverbial modification: *On her fingers she has rings, and on her toes she has bells.* But the following rewording seems to point to adjectival modification: *She wears finger rings and toe bells.* If you favor adverbial modification in this case (and I think I do), then you have to do something unorthodox with the diagram to show (1) that *on her fingers* modifies *has* with respect to the direct object *rings* and (2) that *on her toes* modifies the same verb with respect to the direct object *bells.* The diagram of a similar sentence is shown on the next page.

There are additional criteria for distinguishing prepositional phrases used as predicate adjectives from those that are adverbial. In the sentence *We are still at the beginning of robot evolution,* the prepositional phrase *at the beginning of robot evolution* is adjectival. To be a predicate adjective, a prepositional phrase has to indicate a quality or characteristic (an attribute) of the subject and not a physical place where the subject happens to be. *At the beginning of robot evolution* meets this requirement. Also, a prepositional phrase that functions as a predicate adjective can usually be replaced by a simple adjective; for example, in the sentence *She is in a good mood, in a good mood* can be replaced by *happy. At the beginning* can by replaced by *neophytic.*

* * * * *

The phrase *nothing to do* is easy to diagram. Just show that the infinitive *to do* modifies *nothing.* But how does one diagram *nothing to work with* (after all, one can't diagram an objectless preposition)? This noun phrase is an elliptical form of *nothing with which to work*; however, this phrase is also elliptical. It cannot be diagrammed because *which* is a relative pronoun and must appear in a relative clause. Instead it makes sense to expand *nothing to work with* to *nothing with which one is able to work.* Now we have a relative clause (*with which one is able to work*), with *nothing* as the antecedent of the relative pronoun *which,* and this of course can be diagrammed. A simpler (and defensible) solution is to construe *with* as an adverb in an infinitive phrase.

* * * * *

Like: In the sentence *He slept like a log*, one can construe *like a log* as an adverbial prepositional phrase modifying the verb *slept.* Susan Emolyn Harman would argue that this *like* can also been seen as an adverb because *like* is able to be compared (*more like, most like*); in this case, *log* would be an adverbial objective. Because it is unnecessarily complicated and moreover involves a questionable use of the word *like,* one should not consider *like a log* an elliptical subordinate clause (the full clause being *like a log sleeps*).

In the sentence *He looked like a person who had been run over by a truck, like a person* is a prepositional phrase functioning as a predicate adjective. Harman would prefer to call *like* a predicate adjective, with *person* as an adverbial objective.

Near: In a sentence like *They hope they are near the end of their struggles, near* can be understood as a preposition or as a predicate adjective. In the former case, *end* would be the object of a preposition, in the latter case an adverbial objective. In *They slept near the edge of the canyon, near* can be construed as an adverb or a preposition.

* * * * *

Where can be a pronoun as it is in the following sentence, in which it is used as the object of a preposition: *Where was the smoke coming from?*

Step 125. Along with grapefruit, Mary Jo wants toast with jelly.

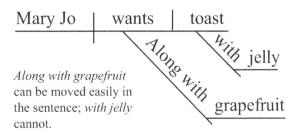

Along with grapefruit can be moved easily in the sentence; *with jelly* cannot.

Step 126. Many people in the race looked out of shape.

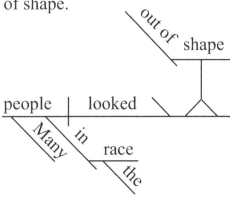

The prepositional phrase *in the race* limits *people* to a particular group. *Out of shape*, a prepositional phrase in the predicate, describes (expresses a quality or characteristic) of many people in the race. *Out of* is a phrasal preposition. Phrasal prepositions consist of more than one word, e.g., *because of, out of, instead of, along with,* and *as for.*

Step 127. Little Johnny is in his room, where he has no one to play with.

In his room, a prepositional phrase following a linking verb, does not function as a predicate adjective for it does not express a quality or characteristic of little Johnny but where he happens to be at that moment. *Where* is a relative adverb; it is equivalent to *in which*. *To play with* can be construed as an elliptical relative clause. The unexpressed words are *he is able* and *whom* (on the right). It is, however, easier to explain the infinitive phrase as a modifier of the pronoun *no one*; in that case, *with* is an adverb (above).

Step 128. I've got my mind on my honey and my honey on my mind.

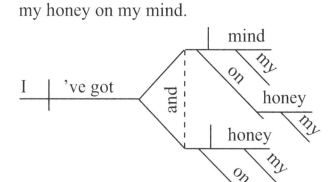

Notice that the vertical direct-object line is not placed immediately after the verb, which is its usual position (even in the diagram of a clause or phrase containing a compound direct object), but instead one such line appears on the top branch before *mind* and the other on the bottom branch before *honey*. In this way, each prepositional phrase is able to be shown to modify the verb with respect to a different direct object.

Step 129. It looks like the tornado touched down near my hometown.

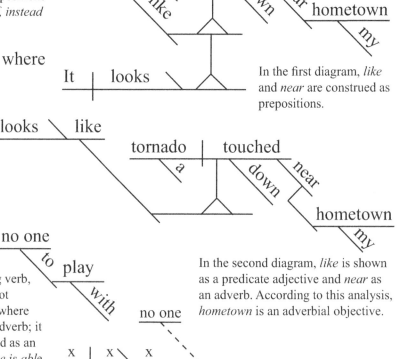

In the first diagram, *like* and *near* are construed as prepositions.

In the second diagram, *like* is shown as a predicate adjective and *near* as an adverb. According to this analysis, *hometown* is an adverbial objective.

Exercise 20: Prepositional Phrases (2)

204. I finally have an answer to your question about my summer plans.

205. We met an old man on a street corner in Lexington; he was from the hills of Kentucky.

206. Gloria was carrying groceries with one hand and books with the other, and I could tell she was in a hurry.

207. Some guests have nothing to sit on.

208. We have nothing like that in our store.

209. The whole vacation was like showing up for a concert with no ticket.

210. He sneaked like a mouse into the room that the unaccustomed sounds were coming from.

211. They built their house near a woods that is near a small river.

H. W. Fowler (II, 410) points out that the preposition *without* with a compound object yields one meaning, while the same preposition, repeated (each time with a single object), may yield another. Here is an example:

> *A fortunate few accomplish great things in life*
> *without education or financial resources.*
> *A fortunate few accomplish great things in life*
> *without education or without financial resources.*

In the first sentence, *without education or financial resources* means "without education and without financial resources." Of those who rise to great heights, a fortunate few have neither education nor financial resources. This is not the case in the second sentence, whose meaning is that a fortunate few succeed despite the fact that they lack either education or financial resources--one or the other.

Fowler warns his readers to be aware of the possibility of the omission of a necessary *of* or of the inclusion of a nonsensical *of*. He calls such abuses of *of* "crimes against grammar"; here are several examples (mine, not Fowler's):

> *The cessation of hostility between the warring*
> *factions, which had gone on unabated for decades*
> *with great loss of life and destruction of property,*
> *and of the formation of a government seemed impos-*
> *sible.* The writer is misled by his own use of *of* to insert a nonsensical *of* before *the formation*.

> *Lynn recalled the thrill of standing at the podium and*
> *of seeing all eyes directed at her.* The second *of* is a distraction; it tends to separate the *standing* and the *seeing*, which belong together.

> *The couple hoped that the addition of a swimming*
> *pool and a three-car garage would make the house*
> *more attractive to potential buyers.* Did they add the three-car garage? If so, an *of* is needed after *and*. If not, the sentence needs to be reconstructed.

Even though it is often heard, do not use *these kind of* in formal writing. If you want to use the demonstrative adjective *this/these* with *kind of* and *kinds of*, your choices are *this kind of* and *these kinds of*.

Likewise to be avoided is *of a* in expressions like *that big of a deal* or that *nice of a girl*. Corrections: *that big a deal, that nice a girl*.

Use *off*, not *off of*. *Robbie got off the bus* is quite sufficient.

For the most part, *all* can replace *all of*. Exceptions:

> - before a personal pronoun: *all of them, all of you*
> - in fixed expressions like *all of a sudden*

Between requires a compound object. It is never correct to say *between you and between me*.

* * * * *

When *but* is used as a preposition (as another way of saying *except*), its pronoun object is in the objective case. When *but* is used as a conjunction introducing an elliptical clause, the pronoun takes the case it would take if the clause were complete. Simple in theory, these rules are difficult to apply. Authorities often cannot decide if a given use of *but* is prepositional or conjunctive. A compromise rule that has been offered is this: If the pronoun in question comes at the end of a sentence, use the objective case. If it comes elsewhere, make the pronoun agree with the noun or pronoun with which it is connected by *but*. Examples:

> *Todd wanted no one but her.*
> *No one but she wanted him.*
> *Everyone but he stood.*
> *Everyone stood but him.*

It is rather easy to misplace a prepositional phrase in which *unlike* is the preposition. Consider the following sentence:

> *The recruit feared that he would never develop--*
> *unlike his drill sergeant--nerves of steel.*

What the sentence is supposed to say is *The recruit feared that he would never develop--like his drill sergeant--nerves of steel.* To retain the original preposition, the prepositional phrase must be relocated:

> *The recruit feared that he--unlike his drill sergeant--*
> *would never develop nerves of steel.*

* * * * *

Many verbs and adjectives are tied to certain prepositions. Sometimes even native speakers don't know which preposition to use after a particular verb or adjective. Here are some of the troublesome expressions:

> - *compare with*: Use *with* when you are examining two or more things for the purpose of discovering their similarities and dissimilarities.
> - *compare to*: Use *to* when you are representing something as like something else: *She compared his voice to a foghorn.*
> - *enamored of*
> - *different from*: Use *from* unless the prepositional object is a clause.
> - *different than*: Use *than* when the prepositional object is a clause.
> - *dissimilar to*

Lesson 21: Participles (2)

In the sentence *While driving through the park, Matt saw two deer,* the words *while driving through the park* constitute an elliptical clause. They are short for *while he was driving through the park,* in which the present participle *driving* is the participial component of a present progressive finite verb. The analysis of expressions like *before closing the door* or *after leaving the party* is more difficult; it will be undertaken in Lesson 23.

* * * * *

Not every past participle is passive. A few intransitive verbs have past participles, and since intransitive verbs have no voice, their past participles are, strictly speaking, neither active nor passive. They resemble passive participles in form and active participles in meaning: *gone, grown, fallen, risen,* and *slept.* We can say that someone is *gone* for the day or *slept* out. A middle-aged couple may have several *grown* children. Christians speak of *fallen* angels and a *risen* Lord.

* * * * *

In particular cases, it can be difficult to differentiate between participles and mere adjectives. One of the criteria is the consensus of dictionaries. If most dictionaries show *hurt,* for example, as an adjective, then it is an adjective in a sentence like *He is hurt.* Of course, it is a participle when used as part of the passive voice, e.g., *Ten firemen were hurt when the roof collapsed.* Another criterion is replaceability: If *tired* in a sentence like *We are tired* can be replaced by another adjective of the same meaning, then it is an adjective; it can, in fact, be replaced by *weary,* a pure adjective. *Tired* in *We are tired* is an adjective.

All true passive-voice forms have a functioning past participle as a component. A static (or false) passive, on the other hand, includes a past participle that functions as a simple adjective. Notice the use of the word *closed* in the following sentences: 1) *At the beginning of the period, the classroom door is closed by the teacher;* 2) *The door is closed until the end of the period.* The first *closed* is a true participle, part of the present passive *is closed.* The second *closed* is a predicate adjective after the linking verb *is.* It is important to keep in mind that in the passive voice something is happening. Nothing is happening in the sentence *The door is closed until the end of the period.*

* * * * *

Participles used as nouns: *The injured and the dying were placed on stretchers and rushed to field hospitals. Injured* is a past participle and *dying* is a present participle. Both are used here as nouns.

* * * * *

There being no time for discussion is a nominative absolute using the present participle *being* and introduced by the expletive *there.* It is diagrammed on the next page.

* * * * *

In expressions like *fishing pole* and *batting helmet, fishing* and *batting* are not participles; if they were, the poles would be fishing and the helmets would be batting. It is best to think of these words, which are actually gerunds used as adjectives, as simple adjectives. Similarly, *hunting* and *drinking* are gerunds used as adjectives in the expressions *hunting license* and *drinking fountain.*

* * * * *

Some words that look like participles are actually regular adjectives. For example, while *loved, mitigated, rewarding,* and *fulfilling* are participles, *unloved, unmitigated, unrewarding,* and *unfulfilling* are not. Some words ending in *-ed* are formed from nouns and not verbs (e.g., *diseased, talented, cultured*); such words often look like participles, but they are simply adjectives.

* * * * *

Concerning and *regarding,* which can be used as participles (e.g., *Regarding his job as untouchable and all others as expendable, the CEO announced today that another 1000 jobs would be eliminated*), are often used as prepositions (e.g., *The CEO refused to disclose details regarding the massive job cuts*).

Step 130. While taking a shower, Jeff sang.

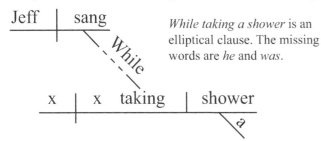

While taking a shower is an elliptical clause. The missing words are *he* and *was*.

Step 131. Mary Magdeline said that she had seen the risen Lord.

Risen is a past participle of an intransitive verb.

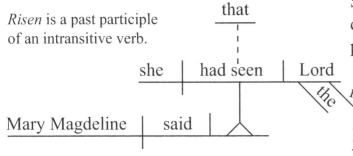

Step 132. Not all people are interested in sports.

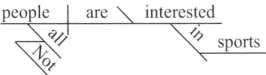

Yes, *interested* is the past participle of the verb *interest*; however, it is also a mere adjective. Check any dictionary. In this sentence, it is used as a mere adjective.

Step 133. Everyone could see that the vase, which had been broken by thieves, was still broken.

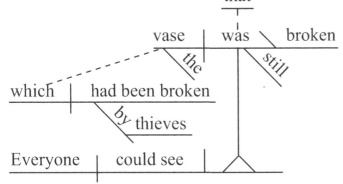

The first *broken* is the participial component of a finite verb (past-perfect tense, passive voice); the *second* broken is a simple adjective.

Step 134. Both the bullies and the bullied lose.

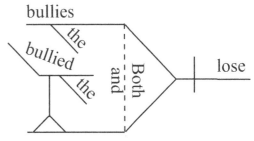

Bullied is a past participle used as a noun.

Step 135. Regarding the debate team's request for funds, I will do everything in my power to help.

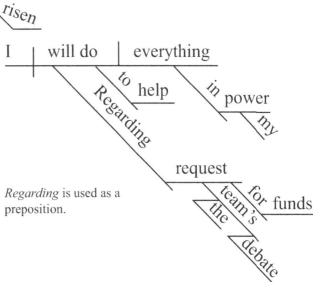

Regarding is used as a preposition.

Step 136. There being no time for discussion, the meeting was adjourned.

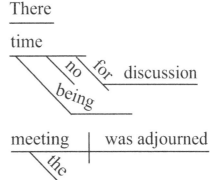

The expletive *there* introduces a nominative absolute containing the present participle *being*.

Exercise 21: Participles (2)

212. I know a teacher who says she is able to correct papers while watching television.

213. The fallen soldiers, many of whom were not yet grown men, are gone from this world forever.

214. We decided to cut down the diseased tree behind our house.

215. The windshield, undamaged in 150,000 miles of driving, was cracked by an errant golf ball while the car was sitting in our driveway.

216. Supplies were distributed to the living and the dying without regard for age or race.

217. Concerning the living conditions of the homeless, there is much more to be said.

218. There being much to do and little time for doing it, let's get started.

219. A talking duck talks, and a rolling stone rolls, but a swimming pool does not swim, which means that the modifier of *pool* is not a present participle.

Writing Correctly 21

According to *Fowler II,* certain participles may be used as prepositions or as adverbs (*adverbs* has been changed, correctly in my opinion, to *subordinating conjunctions* in *Fowler III*). Among these participles are *speaking* (in the expression *speaking of*), *given, granted, assuming, barring* (when used to mean "except for"), *considering, judging, failing* (in the sense of "in the absence of"), *excepting, and owing* (when followed by *to*). Take a look at the following sentences and see if you find them acceptable:

> *Barring a thunderstorm, the race will begin on time.*
> *Failing her expertise, we cannot proceed.*
> *Speaking of prepositions, how many are there?*
> *Considering Anne's love of warm temperatures and low humidity, Arizona may be the right place for her.*
> *Given these facts, the choice is simple.*
> *Assuming that all goes well on Monday, the presidency will be hers on Tuesday.*
> *Judging from his strength in the primaries, he will be hard to stop.*
> *Granted that standards have changed, such actions are still beyond the pale of respectability.*

I agree that the participles in these sentences do not have to modify the subject of the sentence; however, I do not go along with R. W. Burchfield, the editor of *Fowler III,* when he exempts the participle *knowing* as well. Burchfield finds the sentence *Knowing my mother, this is her way of punishing us* acceptable. I do not. I prefer a sentence like this: *Knowing my mother, I can assure you that this is her way of punishing us,* in which the participle *knowing* modifies the subject *I.* Our language is constantly changing. The best we can do is try to assess the current status of particular points of grammar. How are the majority of scholars, editors, and other erudite individuals speaking and writing? It is these people, not grammarians alone, who determine correct grammar. For that matter, it is these same people, not lexicographers alone, who determine the meanings and acceptability of words.

* * * * *

Although they must be used judiciously, foreign words and expressions can be a shortcut, a welcome variation, and a mind opener. Here are some that I like:

cui bono? (L.) - for whose benefit?

pièce de résistance (Fr.) - the most noteworthy item (event, etc.) of a series of items (events, etc.)

la dolce vita (It.) - the sweet life, life devoted to pleasure

sic (L.) - thus (used in brackets to show that a quotation containing an error has been copied exactly)

fait accompli (Fr.) - something completed, a "done deed"

id est (L.) - that is

exempli gratia (L.) - for example

lapsus linguae (L.) - slip of the tongue

au courant (Fr.) - up-to-date

mot juste (Fr.) - the appropriate word

Schadenfreude (Ger.) - joy at another's misfortune

In print, these words must be in italics. Many other foreign words and expressions (such as d*éjà vu, double entendre, ex officio, tour de force, ex post facto, faux pas, hoi polloi, ingénue, nom de plume, non sequitur, qua, sine qua non, ad hoc, a fortiori, corpus delicti, nouveau riches,* and *obiter dictum*) have been fully incorporated into English and no longer need to be italicized (except when used qua words, as in this sentence).

* * * * *

Very by itself doesn't make sense with past participles. Since we don't say *I loved him very,* we also shouldn't say *He was very loved.* It does make sense to say *He was much loved* or *He was very much loved.* Since we don't say *I appreciated it very,* we also shouldn't say *It was very appreciated.* We can say *It was much appreciated* or *It was very much appreciated. Very* is an acceptable modifier of a word that has lost its participial force and become a simple adjective, such as *interested. They were very interested* is correct; *they were much interested* is not. A gray area does exist here.

* * * * *

Use nominative absolutes in various places in sentences, not always first. Check out these sentences:

> (nominative absolute first) *His unopened schoolbooks piled neatly on the table in the corner, the usually industrious Marty spent the entire evening munching on snack food and playing video games.*
> (nominative absolute after the subject) *The usually industrious Marty, his unopened schoolbooks piled neatly on the table in the corner, spent the entire evening munching on snack food and playing video games.*
> (nominative absolute last) *The usually industrious Marty spent the entire evening munching on snack food and playing video games, his unopened schoolbooks piled neatly on the table in the corner.*

Lesson 22: Adverbs (2) and Adverbial Objectives (2)

When is *only* an adverb, and when is it an adjective? It seems that every dictionary on the planet calls *only* in the sense of "without others," "without anything further," or "and no(thing) more" an adverb. I can find only one source (the second edition of *Descriptive English Grammar,* by Susan Emolyn Harman—an excellent diagramming reference, by the way) that implicitly calls it, when so used, an adjective. In her diagram of *Only the men smoked,* Harman presents *only* as a modifier of *men*. She offers no explanation and makes no apology. According to the dictionaries I consulted, *only* is an adjective only when it means "sole," as in *We were the only customers there.* But what about *only* in a sentence like *It takes Vonny only seconds to solve the Rubik's Cube?* To make a case for this *only* being an adverb, one could reword as follows: *It takes Vonny, to the exclusion of larger units of time, seconds to solve the Rubik's Cube.* In this rephrased (albeit somewhat awkward) sentence, the prepositional phrase *to the exclusion of larger units of time* is adverbial. So is *only* an adverb here? Does it modify *takes?* Maybe, but let's look at one more sentence: *They collect only ashtrays.* This means that they collect one thing: ashtrays. But the relationship between *thing* and *ashtrays* is appositional, therefore (in the case of two nouns) adjectival. If the function of *only* is adverbial in this sentence, then the diagram of *They collect only ashtrays* would be exactly the same as the diagram of *They only collect ashtrays* (that is, they don't use them for smoking, they don't break them to keep others from using them, and they don't recycle them; they only collect them). Still, diagramming is not a perfect instrument. After a good deal of thought and vacillation, I have concluded, with dictionaries, that *only* is an adjective only when it means "sole"--only when it comes after an article (*an* or *the*): *an only child, the only survivor.* Harman's sentence *Only the men smoked* can be rephrased (not elegantly but accurately) as *The men, to the exclusion of boys, girls, and women, smoked.* Surely the infinitive phrase modifies the verb. The same argument, *mutatis mutandis,* can be made for *just*. Only when an adjective like "upright," "impartial," or "accurate" can be substituted for *just,* is it an adjective; otherwise, it's an adverb. In *Wait just a minute* and *Just the thought of you makes me smile, just* is an adverb. Of course, *just* and *only* can modify adjectives. If a bookstore owner says, *Bob had only five customers* today *and sold just one book, only* and *just* are adverbs modifying numbers used as attributive adjectives.

* * * * *

In the sentence *They are not always friendly,* not only Reed and Kellogg but also Susan Emolyn Harman would call both *not* and *always* modifiers of the verb *are*. It's a close call. A response to the question *Are they friendly?* might be *Not always.* This response, albeit elliptical, seems to argue that *not* is a modifier of *always*. In any case, our manner of diagramming verb contractions involving *n't* (the *-n't* always stays with the verb) is consistent with R & K's analysis. Would it make any difference if the sentence were changed to *Not always are they friendly?* I think it would. In my opinion, *not* modifies *always* in this sentence.

* * * * *

Like adverbs, adverbial objectives can modify prepositions, prepositional phrases, and relative adverbs. Here is an example of each:

> *John left town an hour before sunrise.* The adverbial objective *hour* modifies the preposition *before*.
> *The coffee was a trifle on the weak side.* The adverbial objective *trifle* modifies the prepositional phrase *on the weak side*.
> *We finished cleaning the house five minutes before they arrived.* The adverbial objective *minutes* modifies the relative adverb *before*.

* * * * *

What is the function of *there* in *Tiny asked for a ride there?* If it is an adverb, it must modify the verb *asked*, the preposition *for*, or the prepositional phrase *for a ride*, and it clearly modifies none of these. So what's going on? *There* can be a noun when it means "that point"; however, our *there* doesn't mean that. One solution is to construe *there* as an elliptical expression, short for an infinitive phrase like *to take them there*; however, there is a better analysis available. If nouns can function as adjectives and as adverbs, and if adjectives can function as nouns, why should adverbs not be able to function as adjectives? That would seem to be the simplest solution to the problem. A little thought and research uncovers a rather long list of adverbs that sometimes function as adjectives. Here are some of them used in noun phrases (adverbs functioning as an adjective are underlined):

the long way <u>around</u>	an <u>off</u> day	the hike <u>down</u>
on the way <u>over</u>	this <u>very</u> lesson	the way <u>out</u>
on the trip <u>back</u>	the <u>up</u> escalator	the <u>above</u> words

The underlined words do not function as adverbs for, as adverbs, they would have nothing to modify. Clearly they are used as adjectives. Similarly, *there* in the sentence *Tiny asked for a ride there* is an adverb that functions as an adjective; it modifies the noun *ride*.

Step 137. Is that the only reason you can think of?

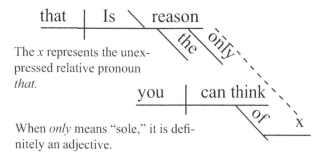

The *x* represents the unexpressed relative pronoun *that*.

When *only* means "sole," it is definitely an adjective.

Step 138. Prentis drinks only tea.

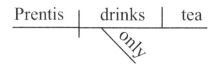

This *only* is an adverb. It means *to the exclusion of all other drinks*, which is an adverbial expression modifying the verb.

Step 139. She would not often drink green tea, even if it were the only tea available.

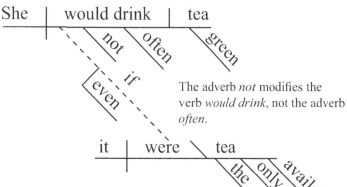

The adverb *not* modifies the verb *would drink*, not the adverb *often*.

In diagramming a phrase like *wouldn't often drink*, R & K, Harman, and many others do not separate the *-n't* from the verb *would*. Surely they wouild separate it if they thought it modified *often*. Still, I can't help wondering how they would diagram *Not often does she drink green tea*.

Step 140. A month before they were to depart, the company canceled the trip.

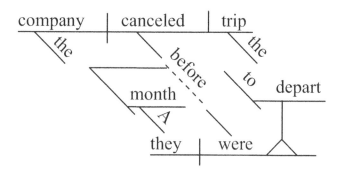

The adverbial objective *month* modifies the relative adverb *before*. *To depart* is a complementary infinitive.

Step 141. I have here a picture of some lakes there in northern Minnesota.

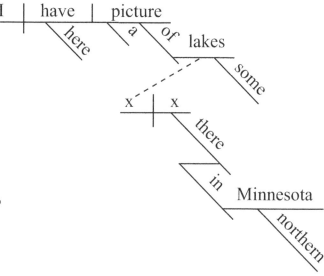

The adverb *there* cannot modify *have* (it would make no sense); instead it can be construed as part of an elliptical relative clause, *that are there in northern Minnesota*. There is, however, an easier solution: there can be construed as an adverb used as an adjective. Diagrammed according to this analysis, the sentence looks like this:

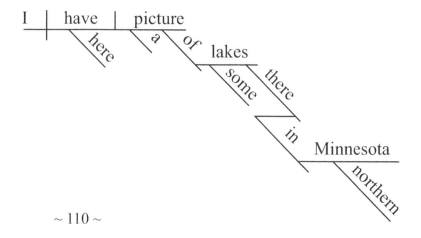

Exercise 22: Adverbs (2), Adverbial Objectives (2)

220. You may play outside only if you do your homework first.

221. We got lost on the way back.

222. "It's only money," she said as she spent her last dollar frivolously.

223. This is the only wine we have, and we serve it only when we have company.

224. Grocery stores sell not only groceries but almost everything.

225. The job took just a few minutes.

226. Even on our off days, we do a better job of selling real estate than our competitors.

227. A year and a half after they moved to Cincinnati, they moved back to California.

228. There are many houses in my hometown that look like the houses here.

229. They are not always ready to work, for they don't always have their pens.

Writing Correctly 22

The ability to use the *mot juste* will make you a better speaker and writer. Here are some words that I find useful:

acronym - a word formed from the first letters of words in a fixed phrase, e.g., NATO, OPEC, UNESCO

acumen - keen insight

adamant - unyielding in attitude or opinion despite opposition

ambivalence - uncertainty resulting from simultaneous conflicting feelings or desires

antithesis - opposition or contrast; the exact opposite

augur - to predict, foretell

bourgeois - characteristic of the middle class in beliefs, attitudes, and practices

circumlocution - a roundabout or indirect way of expressing something

conundrum - a riddle whose answer involves a pun; anything puzzling

demagogue - someone who gains power or popularity by appealing to the passions and prejudices of the people

demur - to hesitate because of doubts

didactic - intended for instruction

dilatory - tending to delay; tardy

disingenuous - lacking in frankness; insincere

elicit - to draw out, bring out, evoke

epithet - a word or phrase, often disparaging, intended to characterize someone or something

evince - to show that one has a certain quality or feeling

exigency - a situation demanding immediate attention; *pl.* urgent needs

impregnable - that cannot be broken through or entered by force

incongruous - lacking harmony of parts; inconsistent

incredulous - unwilling to believe; doubting

inculcate - to impress upon the mind by repeated statement or admonition

intransigent - refusing to come to an agreement or a compromise; inflexible

irascible - easily provoked to anger; irritable

malapropism - confusion of two words similar in sound but different in meaning

militate - to be directed (against), to work (against)

mitigate - to make less severe or intense

mnemonic - assisting, or meant to assist, the memory

nihilism - the denial of an objective basis for knowledge

obdurate - stubborn; obstinate

officious - meddlesome; too ready to give advice

ostensible - apparent (sometimes implying a concealment of the truth); professed

pejorative - a derogatory or disparaging word or phrase, especially one whose basic meaning has changed for the worse

peremptory - precluding debate; final, decisive; dogmatic

precipitous - steep like a precipice; headlong

prescience - an apparent knowledge of things before they take place

proscribe - to prohibit; to interdict

prolific - producing new individuals abundantly; 2) highly productive

protégé - a person who is cared for and guided by another, especially in a career

recondite - profound, abstruse, hard to understand

reticent - reluctant to speak

sardonic - bitterly ironic, sarcastic, or derisive

self-aggrandizement - the act of aggressively increasing one's own wealth, power, or prestige

specious - seemingly sound or logical, but not actually so

tautology - unnecessary repetition of an idea in different words; redundancy

tortuous - twisting, winding; circuitous; devious

truculent - fierce, cruel

turbid - murky, clouded

turgid - swollen; overblown, pompous

vacuous - (said of a person) having no ideas or intelligence; (said of a thing) showing a lack of ideas or intelligence

Lesson 23: Gerunds (2)

If the word *playing* in the expression *while playing the National Anthem* is the present-participial component of a partially unexpressed progressive verb (*while playing the National Anthem* could, for example, be expanded to *while they were playing the National Anthem*), is *playing* to be analyzed similarly if *before* or *after* replaces *while*? In other words, what is the function of the word *playing* in the expressions *before playing the National Anthem* and *after playing the National Anthem*? In the sentence *Before the playing of the National Anthem, the band marched onto the field*, there is no doubt that *playing* is a gerund, because it is modified by the article *the*. But is the same word a gerund in the sentence *Before playing the National Anthem, the band marched onto the field*? Or is it a participle? *Playing* used this way feels like a participle. But if it is, one should be able to express the unexpressed words of its elliptical clause. Is *before playing the National Anthem* short for *before it was playing the National Anthem*? Who would ever say that? Wouldn't everyone say *before it played . . . ?* Consider the sentence *After glancing just once at his watch, Kenny got up and left the room*. If we are to call *glancing* a participle, we should be able to reword the first part of the sentence this way: *After he had been glancing just once at his watch*. We can't use *had been glancing*, a progressive form to express an action that cannot be extended over time. Well, if we don't have an elliptical clause here, we don't have a participle. So, what is going on? It turns out that a gerund, when used without a modifier, sometimes needs a subject. Consider these four sentences:

> *Before the playing of the National Anthem, the crowd stood up.* The gerund *playing* is modified by *the* and does not need a subject.
> *Before playing the National Anthem, the crowd stood up.* The unmodified gerund *playing* finds its subject in *crowd*, resulting in nonsense.
> *After our playing of the National Anthem, the crowd sat down.* The gerund *playing* is modified by *our*, which acts as its subject.
> *After playing the National Anthem, the crowd sat down.* The unmodified gerund *playing* searches for a subject and finds one in *crowd*, rendering the sentence nonsensical.

The second and fourth sentences make us laugh because they have dangling gerunds, i.e., unmodified gerunds with improper subjects. An example of a sentence using an unmodified gerund with a proper subject is *Before playing the National Anthem, the band marched onto the field*. It's not that every unmodified gerund needs an expressed subject. *Seeing is believing* is, of course, a perfectly acceptable sentence because no expressed subjects of the gerunds *seeing* and *believing* are needed.

* * * * *

Speaking of subjects of gerunds, there is a reluctance these days to use the possessive case. What do you understand when you read *The strict parents don't like the boy talking with their daughter*? Strictly speaking, this sentence, which uses a participle instead of a gerund, means that the parents don't like the boy who is talking with their daughter. All too many people, however, understand it to mean that the parents disapprove of conversation between the boy and their daughter. To express the latter thought, one can give the gerund a subject in the possessive case as follows: *The strict parents don't like the boy's talking with their daughter.*

* * * * *

Gerunds of transitive verbs can be passive as well as active. Active gerunds were introduced in Lesson 13. Here are two sentences with passive gerunds:

> *Not being allowed to stay out after midnight is not the worst thing in the world. Being allowed* is a present passive gerund.
> *Her insecurity resulted from her not having been praised as a child. Having been praised* is a present-perfect passive gerund.

* * * * *

Not all nouns ending in *-ing* are gerunds. Many are ordinary nouns. For instance, in the sentence *Rodney was caught in traffic and missed the beginning of the game, beginning* is an ordinary noun; however, *beginning* is a gerund in the sentence *You can't read most novels successfully by beginning in the middle.* Gerunds come from verbs; therefore, *-ing* nouns that do not come from verbs are not gerunds, e.g., *ceiling, inkling, weakling*. If you don't know whether a particular *-ing* word can be used as an ordinary noun, check an unabridged dictionary.

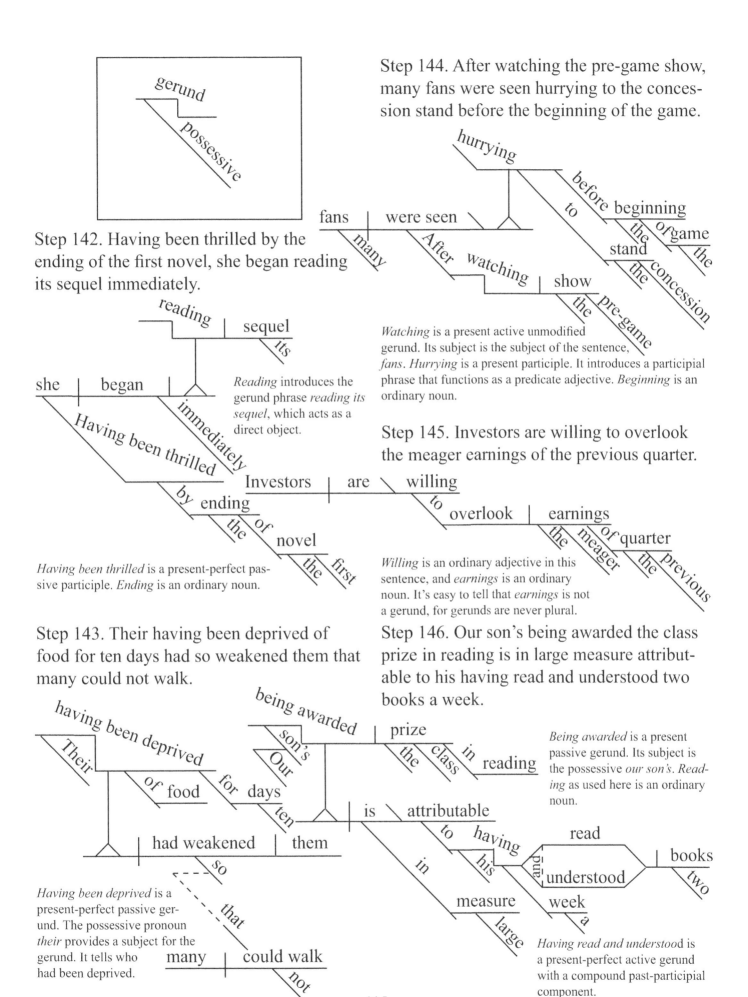

Step 142. Having been thrilled by the ending of the first novel, she began reading its sequel immediately.

Reading introduces the gerund phrase *reading its sequel*, which acts as a direct object.

Having been thrilled is a present-perfect passive participle. *Ending* is an ordinary noun.

Step 143. Their having been deprived of food for ten days had so weakened them that many could not walk.

Having been deprived is a present-perfect passive gerund. The possessive pronoun *their* provides a subject for the gerund. It tells who had been deprived.

Step 144. After watching the pre-game show, many fans were seen hurrying to the concession stand before the beginning of the game.

Watching is a present active unmodified gerund. Its subject is the subject of the sentence, *fans*. *Hurrying* is a present participle. It introduces a participial phrase that functions as a predicate adjective. *Beginning* is an ordinary noun.

Step 145. Investors are willing to overlook the meager earnings of the previous quarter.

Willing is an ordinary adjective in this sentence, and *earnings* is an ordinary noun. It's easy to tell that *earnings* is not a gerund, for gerunds are never plural.

Step 146. Our son's being awarded the class prize in reading is in large measure attributable to his having read and understood two books a week.

Being awarded is a present passive gerund. Its subject is the possessive *our son's*. *Reading* as used here is an ordinary noun.

Having read and understood is a present-perfect active gerund with a compound past-participial component.

~ 115 ~

Exercise 23: Gerunds (2)

230. After running 26 miles, she knew that she could run the final 385 yards.

231. Before buying a car, Norm spent hours on the Internet trying to find the best deal.

232. Jim Nabors' singing of "Back Home Again in Indiana" will be followed by Mari Hulman George's announcement, "Gentlemen, start your engines."

233. Having lost confidence in their father's driving, his now grown children persuaded him to let them drive.

234. Being punished for something one hasn't done can be extremely frustrating.

235. Many of her problems as an adult stem from her having been habitually criticized and scolded as a child.

236. There was only one prop for the opening scene: a long, black wall with a door-sized opening in the middle.

237. Knowing that gerunds must come from verbs keeps one from calling words like *ceiling* gerunds.

According to traditional grammar, the agent (subject) of a gerund is often in the possessive case. Thus we teach our children to write *We were troubled by their jumping to conclusions, Bob was concerned about his son's playing in the street*, and *The teacher noted the student's chewing gum in class* (not *We were troubled by them jumping to conclusions, Bob was concerned about his son playing in the street*, and *The teacher noted the student chewing gum in class*). Even if we sometimes stray from this model in conversation, we recognize that the possessive case is used to express the subject of a gerund. Or do we? Are you sure?

Envisioning or experiencing a prolonged rain, someone might say, "I am worried about the possibility of water seeping into the basement." Who would say, "I am worried about the possibility of water's seeping into the basement"?

How about this? *Recalling a juvenile misdemeanor, the defendant spoke to his lawyer about the possibility of this being held against him in court.* This does not even have a possessive form.

And one more for good measure: *What are the odds of something falling from the sky and hitting you on the head?* It's simply unidiomatic to say *What are the odds of something's falling from the sky and hitting you on the head?*

To given a name to this well-established phenomenon, some grammarians have settled on the expression "fused participle" (a noun and a participle taken together as a single noun). It's an expression that I do not care for. In my opinion, what we have is a gerund with its subject in the objective case instead of a gerund with its subject in the possessive case. I see no participle at all, only a gerund, which happens to be modified by an objective-case subject instead of a possessive-case subject. If I were to diagram such an expression, let's say *something falling* in the example above, I would simply hang *something* down from the gerund *falling* on a diagonal line, like any other adjectival modifier of a gerund, as follows:

Please don't misunderstand. I am not advocating that we stop using the "fused participle"; however, I would welcome a different name. The phenomenon won't go away; it's too much a part of the language. And, honestly, we probably would not want it to disappear because, used cautiously, it provides a welcome diversity in our language. How would you ever use a possessive to express the subject of the gerund in this sentence: *A person from the lower class having a chance to become a millionaire is a matter of pride for many Americans*? Try putting *'s* on *person* and see how the sentence sounds. Of course,

's on *class* would be illogical. Try, if you like, putting *of* before *person*. Nothing works. To be sure, you could replace *a person from the lower class having a chance* with the noun clause *that a person from the lower class has a chance*, but there goes a certain amount of diversity.

Here are two general recommendations for using the "fused participle" judiciously:

1 - Use the objective case when the subject of the gerund is not a person or, if a person, is indefinite.

> *There must be a law against cell phone rates going up two hundred percent in one month.*
> *There was little chance of someone finding out what they had done.*

2 - Use the objective case when a word or phrase comes between the gerund and its subject.

> *I look forward to a friend of mine coming to visit.*

Use the possessive case when the subject of the gerund is a proper name, a noun representing a person, or a personal pronoun.

> *John's being hit in the abdomen by a classroom bully prompted his parents to request a conference with the boys' teacher.*
> *Until she experienced her brother's begging to use the car, Mary Jo had never known groveling could sink to such depths.*
> *His friends grew tired of his pretending to be someone he wasn't.*

Sometimes, even with the best of intentions, a gerund and its subject don't quite get the job done.

> *Gloria hated his growing tobacco.* Does this sentence mean that Gloria hated the fact that he was growing tobacco or that she hated the tobacco that was growing?

> *Gloria hated him growing tobacco.* Does this sentence mean that she hated him because he was growing tobacco or that she hated the fact that he was growing tobacco?

We all misspeak, some of us often. Here's a sentence heard on a national radio talk show: *By them doing that, it's a great distraction.* A possessive subject of the gerund *doing* would be preferable. Given time, the speaker might have said either *Their doing that is a great distraction* or *By doing that, they create a great distraction*. In the latter sentence, the subject of the sentence is the subject of the gerund.

Lesson 24: Miscellaneous

In this chapter, we will pick up bits and pieces that have slipped through the cracks of the previous chapters, and we will examine some of the problems and limitations of traditional grammar.

A few transitive verbs, such as *lack* (*They lacked expertise*), *fit* (*The sweater fits me*), *fail* (*The system failed her*), *become* (*That outfit becomes you*), *resemble* (*She resembles her mother*), *suit* (*Nothing suits him*), and even *have* (*He has a cold*) are unable to be used passively. Try it. *Expertise was lacked by them, I am fit by the sweater, She was failed by the system*, etc. This isn't English as we know it. We have to say either that these verbs are not transitive (and it seems obvious that they are) or that the language really could accommodate them in the passive voice but just doesn't. I could get used to *Expertise was lacked by them, She was failed by the system*, and one or two more. But *You are become by that outfit* and *Her mother is resembled by her*? No way! I think we just have to accept that not all transitive verbs can be used in the passive voice. What seems at first to be an ironclad rule has exceptions. Some grammarians--the few who bother at all--call these exceptional verbs "midverbs" or "middle verbs."

* * * * *

The passive expression *to be supposed to* does not have a corresponding active form. Since *You are supposed to work hard* is approximately equivalent to *You should work hard*, *to work* would seem to be best construed as a complementary infinitive.

* * * * *

Occasionally, a verb and a preposition share an object, as in the sentence *She grew up with, and later married, the future king*.

* * * * *

As is a relative pronoun after the adjective *same*. Example: *That play is the same as they used earlier to score a touchdown*.

Whoever, whichever, whatever, etc, as well as however, whenever, and *wherever,* can introduce elliptical concessive clauses whose expanded forms are introduced by the subordinating conjunction *although*. Example: *However bright you are, you still need a dictionary*, which is more or less equivalent to *Although you are as bright as you may be, you still need a dictionary*.

* * * * *

The verb *look* is usually intransitive. If someone says *Look who's coming*, neither *What should I look?* nor *Whom should I look?* is an appropriate response because the noun clause *who's coming* is not the direct object of *look*. But what is it? It seems best to construe *Look who's coming* as elliptical, short for *Look and see who's coming*. Now *who's coming* is the direct object of *see*, which is acceptable. Here is a sentence that uses *look* transitively: *He looked his opponent into a corner. Opponent* is the direct object of *looked*.

* * * * *

In the expression *many a time,* how is *many a* to be construed? Can *many* (a plural adjective) modify *time* (a singular noun)? The best answer would seem to be that it cannot, that *many a* is a phrasal modifier. But what if *a* precedes *many* as in *a great many* or *a good many?* In that case, it seems best to think of *a* as a modifier of the pronoun *many*, just as *a* modifies *few* in the expression *a few*. In numbers like *a hundred* and *a thousand, a* simply means "one" and modifies the nouns *hundred* and *thousand*. Like *many a*, the expressions *what a* and *quite a* also seem to be phrasal modifiers. In *how great an undertaking, how* modifies *great*, and both *great* and *an* modify *undertaking*.

* * * * *

What do we call the objectless particles that remain when the objects of prepositions in active sentences become subjects in corresponding passive sentences? Here is an example: The active sentence *What were they looking at?*, in which *what* is the object of the preposition *at*, becomes the passive sentence *What was being looked at?*, in which *what* is the subject of the sentence and *at* is left to hang at the end. Here are three more examples of similar passive sentences:

> *That's nothing to be sneezed at.*
> *The problem was being dealt with.*
> *The house was not being lived in.*

The best solution would seem to be to construe *look at, sneeze at, deal with, live in*, etc. as phrasal verbs when they are used in the passive voice.

~ 119 ~

Step 147. One can diagram the unidiomatic expression *She is fit by the dress.*

In another context, *fit* can be used in the passive voice, e.g., *He was fitted with braces.*

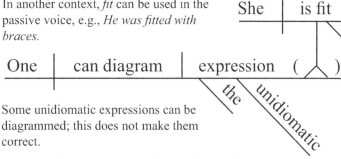

Some unidiomatic expressions can be diagrammed; this does not make them correct.

Step 148. In the 60s the U.S. had men on the moon, a proud accomplishment.

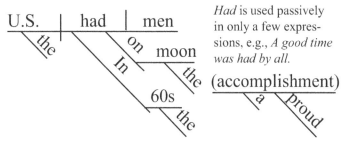

Had is used passively in only a few expressions, e.g., *A good time was had by all.*

Accomplishment is in apposition with the entire preceding clause; thus, in the diagram, it is not associated with a particular word. *Had* is a transitive verb despite the fact that one cannot say *Men were had on the moon by the U.S.*

Step 149. You are supposed to stay here.

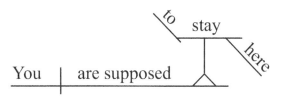

The passive verb *are supposed to stay* is equivalent to *should stay*. This equivalence identifies *to stay* as a complementary infinitive.

Step 150. She both knows and corresponds with the queen.

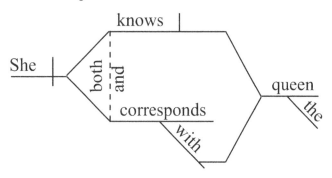

Queen is the direct object of *knows* and the object of the preposition *with*.

Step 151. He will be the same person tomorrow as he is today.

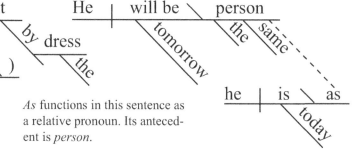

As functions in this sentence as a relative pronoun. Its antecedent is *person*.

Step 152. However boring the trial is, jurors must remain alert.

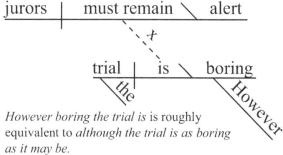

However boring the trial is is roughly equivalent to *although the trial is as boring as it may be.*

Step 153. Many a time he fished all day without catching anything.

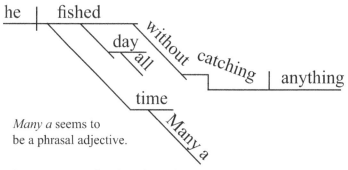

Many a seems to be a phrasal adjective.

Step 154. The leader chose a few good men.

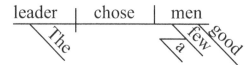

There's no getting around it: the singular article *a* modifies the plural noun *few*, which is used here as an adjective.

Step 155. Civilians were shot at by snipers.

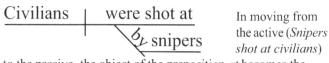

In moving from the active (*Snipers shot at civilians*) to the passive, the object of the preposition *at* becomes the subject of the sentence. Since all prepositions must have objects, and since *at* is not an adverb, we must construe *were shot at* as a phrasal verb.

Exercise 24: Miscellaneous

238. This dress will fit my friend Janel's little sister.

239. It is believed that he resembles his mother, which he denies.

240. He was supposed to cut the grass, but he fell asleep instead.

241. We are planning and looking forward to our vacation but wondering how we will pay for it.

242. She has the same beautiful voice as her mother had.

243. However often he says to stop talking, it does no good because the students are not listening.

244. Whoever he is, I don't like him.

245. You didn't pay attention, and now look what happened.

246. Quite a few people congratulated him, which made me angry.

247. Could you see who was being talked to?

Writing Correctly 24

In my opinion, the expression *one of those who* should always be used with a plural verb. *Fowler III* allows for the use of a singular verb in the exceptional case in which *one* and not *those* is emphasized. I don't like it, do you? If it is important to use a singular verb, why not go with an expression such as *someone who* or *a person who* instead of *one of those who*?

> *I am one of those who prefer logic to illogic.*
> *I am someone who prefers logic to illogic.*

* * * * *

It is considered bad form to use a compound expression consisting of the preposition *to* and its object as one element and a *to*-infinitive as another. Example:

> *On the same day, Marty was invited to a party at Carolyn's house and to go bowling with Barbara.* Correction: *On the same day, Marty was invited to attend a party at Carolyn's house and to go bowling with Barbara.*

* * * * *

The expression *the fact that* can come in handy in subjects and objects; however, it is usually best to avoid using the expression *because of the fact that*. *John's parents kept him home because of the fact that he was sick* is a less successful sentence than *John's parents kept him home because he was sick.*

* * * * *

Avoid using reflexive pronouns as ordinary personal pronouns. *He issued a warning to my friend and myself* seems to be a way of getting around deciding which first-person singular personal pronoun to use in a compound expression following the preposition *to*. The right way to do this is, of course, *He issued a warning to my friend and me*, and that's what we ought to say and write.

* * * * *

That was one of, if not the best movie, I have ever seen is an incorrect sentence because it uses an unacceptable ellipsis. And it wouldn't help to add *the* or even *the best* after *of*. The sentence would still be faulty; it would still contain an unacceptable ellipsis. The easiest way to correct the mistake is simply to eliminate the ellipsis: *That was one of the best movies, if not the best movie, I have ever seen.*

* * * * *

What's wrong with this sentence: *They serve free soup with every meal, which I like that*? It's grammatically redundant. Don't use a demonstrative pronoun when a relative pronoun has already done the job.

Relative clauses beginning with *who is (are), which is (are),* and *that is (are),* can be and often ought to be reduced to adjectival modifiers such as participles, appositives, and prepositional phrases. This is accomplished simply by dropping the relative pronoun and the *be*-verb. Here are three examples:

> *The fellow who is standing at the head of the line has waited all night.* Change the relative clause to a participial phrase: *The fellow standing at the head of the line has waited all night.*

> *You can't miss our house, which is the last one on the left.* Change the relative clause to an appositive: *You can't miss our house, the last one on the left.*

> *Everything that's on the floor must be picked up immediately.* Change the relative clause to a prepositional phrase: *Everything on the floor must be picked up immediately.*

* * * * *

A tautological *is* has crept into the speech patterns of many Americans. I have not yet seen it in print but I have heard it on TV. This insidious *is*, which somehow eludes the logical radar of those who use it, needs to be nipped in the bud. Here are two examples:

> *My feeling is, is that they were unwilling to ask for help.* Correction: *My feeling is that they were unwilling to ask for help.*

> *The fact of the matter is, is that he has more tools than he will ever use.* Correction: *The fact of the matter is that he has more tools than he will ever use.*

* * * * *

Don't use chains of nouns as attributive adjectives--except to make a point, as I do here: *They hoped to found a world population reduction strategy center*. This is, of course, terrible. One way of rewording it for real people is *They hoped to found a center where people could come up with ways of reducing the world's population.*

* * * * *

The sentence *Which one of us would invite a stranger into our home?* contains an agreement error. Do you see it? *Which one of us would invite a stranger into his home?* solves the agreement problem but introduces a gender problem. To solve the gender problem, one could say *Which one of us would invite a stranger into his or her home?* But *his or her* is cumbersome, and many of us don't care for it. How about this: *Which one of us would invite a stranger into the home?* Otherwise a radical revision may be in order.

~ 123 ~

People in the Park: Story 1

Go! Go to the park! Children are playing there. Parents are watching the children. They are proud. Do you see them? Do you also see the teenagers over there? Some older girls are throwing a Frisbee, and a boy is flying a kite. Have you ever flown a kite? A man and a woman are jogging around the lake. A very old man is fishing. A woman is sitting on a blanket with a book in her hand. There are many people in the park. I am a storyteller. I will tell you stories about them.

Here are the individual sentences of Story 1. Grammar information about the underlined words is found on the right.

1. Go!

2. Go to the park!

3. Children are playing there.

4. Parents are watching the children.

5. They are proud.

6. Do you see them?

7. Do you see the teenagers over there?

8. Some older girls are throwing a Frisbee, and a boy is flying a kite.

9. Have you ever flown a kite?

10. A man and a woman are jogging around the lake.

11. A very old man is fishing.

12. A woman is sitting on a blanket with a book in her hand.

13. There are many people in the park.

14. I am a storyteller.

15. I will tell you stories about them.

1. imperative

2. adverbial prepositional phrase

3. present progressive / adverb modifying a verb
4. direct object

5. linking verb / predicate adjective

6. question

7. adverb modifying an adverb

8. attributive adjectives / coordinating conjunction (compound sentence)
9. present-perfect tense

10. coordinating conjunction (compound subject)
11. adverb modifying an adjective

12. adjectival prepositional phrase / (*her*) possessive pronoun
13. expletive

14. predicate nominative

15. indirect object

Diagram the sentences of Story 1.

1. Go!

2. Go to the park!

3. Children are playing there.

4. Parents are watching the children.

5. They are proud.

6. Do you see them?

7. Do you see the teenagers over there?

8. Some older girls are throwing a Frisbee, and a boy is flying a kite.

9. Have you ever flown a kite?

10. A man and a woman are jogging around the lake.

11. A very old man is fishing.

12. A woman is sitting on a blanket with a book in her hand.

13. There are many people in the park.

14. I am a storyteller.

15. I will tell you stories about them.

People in the Park: Story 2

Yesterday morning Tommy Tucker was playing in the park with his older brother. His brother's name is Timmy. Their mother, a stay-at-home mom, had brought the boys to the park. The morning paper was in her purse, but she did not read it. Instead she sat and thought about her son Tommy's remarkable progress. A premature baby, Tommy had weighed only two pounds at birth. Tommy's physical progress had been slow and difficult. He could not run fast, he could not jump high, and he could not throw far. As his mother watched, Tommy practiced on the monkey bars. Over and over he struggled to get all the way across. For weeks he had been trying to do this. The task seemed impossible. What did Tommy do? He took a deep breath, summoned all his courage, and reached the other end. Then he rushed to his mother, who gave him a big hug.

Here are the sentences of Story 2. Grammar information about the underlined words is found on the right.

16. Yesterday <u>morning</u> Tommy Tucker was playing in the park with his older brother.

16. adverbial objective

17. His <u>brother's</u> name is Timmy.

17. possessive noun

18. Their mother, a stay-at-home <u>mom</u>, had brought the boys to the park.

18. appositive

19. The morning paper was in her purse, <u>but</u> she did not read it.

19. coordinating conjunction (compound sentence)

20. Instead she sat <u>and</u> thought about her son Tommy's remarkable progress.

20. coordinating conjunction (compound predicate)

21. A premature <u>baby</u>, Tommy had weighed only two <u>pounds</u> at birth.

21. preceding appositive / adverbial objective

22. Tommy's physical progress had been slow <u>and</u> difficult.

22. coordinating conjunction (compound predicate adjective

23. He <u>could</u> not run fast, he <u>could</u> not jump high, and he <u>could</u> not throw far.

23. modal auxiliary verb

24. <u>As</u> his mother watched, Tommy practiced on the monkey bars.

24. relative adverb (subordinate clause)

25. <u>Over and over</u> he struggled <u>to get</u> all the <u>way</u> across.

25. compound adverb / infinitive phrase (modifies verb) / adverbial objective

26. For weeks he had been trying <u>to do this</u>.

26. infinitive phrase as direct object

27. The task <u>seemed</u> impossible.

27. linking verb

28. <u>What</u> did Tommy do?

28. interrogative pronoun as direct object

29. He took a deep breath, summoned all his courage, <u>and</u> reached the other end.

29. coordinating conjunction (triple compound predicate)

30. Then he rushed to his mother, <u>who</u> gave him a big hug.

30. relative pronoun (subject of relative clause)

Diagram the sentences of Story 2.

16. Yesterday morning Tommy Tucker was playing in the park with his older brother.

17. His brother's name is Timmy.

18. Their mother, a stay-at-home mom, had brought the boys to the park.

19. The morning paper was in her purse, but she did not read it.

20. Instead she sat and thought about her son Tommy's remarkable progress.

21. A premature baby, Tommy had weighed only two pounds at birth.

22. Tommy's physical progress had been slow and difficult.

23. He could not run fast, he could not jump high, and he could not throw far.

24. As his mother watched, Tommy practiced on the monkey bars.

25. Over and over he struggled to get all the way across.

26. For weeks he had been trying to do this.

27. The task seemed impossible.

28. What did Tommy do?

29. He took a deep breath, summoned all his courage, and reached the other end.

30. Then he rushed to his mother, who gave him a big hug.

People in the Park: Story 3

Astrid Krueger, an exchange student from Germany, is in the park today. Astrid is a shy girl, for whom adjustment to life in a foreign country has not been easy. During her first days in the States, her American "sister," whose name is Katie, attempted many times to include Astrid in her plans. Astrid, ashamed of her imperfect English, would say that she had something to do. Katie would say, "Astrid, don't worry," but Astrid always stayed home. Astrid sat with Katie and Katie's friends in the school cafeteria, but she spoke little. Yes, the strong survive, but she was not ready to be strong. She became sad and wondered why she had left her own country.

Today Cindy, a girl whom Astrid did not know well, called and asked, "Hey, would you like to play Frisbee?" Astrid knew that she had to change her life. She knew the time to be strong had come. There are times in life when one either sinks or swims. Astrid chose to swim, which was not easy to do. Now she feels at home in her host country. I'm sure you can pick her out because she's the girl with the biggest smile on her face.

Here are the sentences of Story 3. Grammar information about the underlined words is found on the right.

31. Astrid Krueger, an <u>exchange</u> student from Germany, is in the park today.

31. noun used as adjective

32. Astrid is a shy girl, for <u>whom</u> adjustment to life in a foreign country has not been easy.

32. relative pronoun as object of a preposition

33. During her first days in the States, her American "sister," <u>whose</u> name is Katie, attempted many times to include Astrid in her plans.

33. relative pronoun (possessive case)

34. Astrid, ashamed of her imperfect English, would say <u>that</u> she had something <u>to do</u>.

34. expletive *that* introducing a noun clause / adjectival infinitive

35. Katie would say, "<u>Astrid, don't</u> worry," but Astrid always stayed home.

35. vocative (noun of direct address) / contraction with *not*

36. Astrid sat with Katie <u>and</u> Katie's friends in the school cafeteria, but she spoke little.

36. compound object of a preposition

37. <u>Yes</u>, the <u>strong</u> survive, but she was not ready to be strong.

37. independent word / adjective used as noun

38. She became sad and wondered <u>why</u> she had left her own country.

38. interrogative adverb introducing an indirect question

39. Today Cindy, a girl <u>whom</u> Astrid did not know well, called and asked, "<u>Hey</u>, would you like to play Frisbee?"

39. relative pronoun used as a direct object / interjection

40. Astrid knew that she had <u>to change</u> her life.

40. complementary infinitive

41. She knew the time to be strong had come.

41. (omission of expletive *that*)

42. There are times in life <u>when</u> one <u>either</u> sinks <u>or</u> swims.

42. relative adverb introducing an adjective clause / correlative conjunctions

43. Astrid chose to swim, <u>which</u> was not easy to do.

43. relative pronoun whose antecedent is an entire clause

44. Now she <u>feels at home</u> in her host country.

44. *feel* as linking verb / prepositional phrase as a predicate adjective

45. <u>I'm</u> sure you can pick her out because <u>she's</u> the girl with the biggest smile on her face.

45. subject-verb contractions

Diagram the sentences of Story 3.

31. Astrid Krueger, an exchange student from Germany, is in the park today.

32. Astrid is a shy girl, for whom adjustment to life in a foreign country has not been easy.

33. During her first days in the States, her American "sister," whose name is Katie, attempted many times to include Astrid in her plans.

34. Astrid, ashamed of her imperfect English, would say that she had something to do.

35. Katie would say, "Astrid, don't worry," but Astrid always stayed home.

36. Astrid sat with Katie and Katie's friends in the school cafeteria, but she spoke little.

37. Yes, the strong survive, but she was not ready to be strong.

38. She became sad and wondered why she had left her own country.

39. Today Cindy, a girl whom Astrid did not know well, called and asked, "Hey, would you like to play Frisbee?"

40. Astrid knew that she had to change her life.

41. She knew the time to be strong had come.

42. There are times in life when one either sinks or swims.

43. Astrid chose to swim, which was not easy to do.

44. Now she feels at home in her host country.

45. I'm sure you can pick her out because she's the girl with the biggest smile on her face.

People in the Park: Story 4

Rodney and Jenny Long, who are jogging together around the lake, call the park their second home. Running relaxes them and helps them think clearly. About three months ago, their lives changed when the agency Rodney had been working for abruptly went out of business. He had just been appointed department head, but that was of little use now. Jenny had no choice but to take the first job she found even though she hated the job and would have preferred to continue staying home with the couple's two small children. Rodney has been searching diligently for another job in his field; however, so far his efforts have brought him nothing but headaches. He has taken over the job of caring for the children. It has been hard to get interviews because good job openings are scarce. His letters have mostly gone unanswered, his calls unreturned. Some time back, he got a call requesting him to come for an interview. Sadly, the interview fizzled as did two or three others, and lately he has been offered no interviews at all.

   Setting out for the park this morning, both Jenny and Rodney were in a strange mood. It looked as if Rodney would have to broaden his job search to include other cities and even other states. As they jog around the lake, they agree on a new course for their lives: they will move to Oregon, a state they have both loved from a distance. The decision made, a pleasant excitement gently moves aside the anxious discontent of recent weeks.

Here are the sentences of Story 4. Grammar information about the underlined words is found on the right.

46. Rodney and Jenny Long, who are jogging together around the lake, call the park their second <u>home</u>.

46. objective complement

47. <u>Running</u> relaxes them and helps them <u>think</u> clearly.

47. gerund as subject / "*to*-less" infinitive as objective complement

48. About three months ago, their lives changed when the agency Rodney had been working for abruptly <u>went</u> <u>out of</u> business.

48. *go* as linking verb / phrasal preposition

49. He had just been appointed department <u>head</u>, but that was of little use now.

49. predicate nominative after passive voice of factitive verb

50. Jenny had no choice <u>but</u> to take the first job she found <u>even</u> though she hated the job and would have preferred to continue <u>staying home with the couple's two small children</u>.

50. *but* as preposition / adverb modifying a conjunction / gerund phrase as direct object

51. Rodney has been searching diligently for another job in his field<u>;</u> <u>however</u>, so far his efforts have brought him nothing <u>but</u> headaches.

51. semicolon / transitional adverb / *but* as preposition

52. He has taken over the job of <u>caring for the children</u>.

52. gerund phrase as object of a preposition

53. It has been hard <u>to get interviews</u> because good job <u>openings</u> are scarce.

53. infinitive phrase as appositive / not a gerund

54. His letters have mostly gone <u>unanswered</u>, his calls <u>unreturned</u>.

54. not participles / ellipsis

55. Some time <u>back</u>, he got a call <u>requesting</u> him to come for an interview.

55. adverb used as an adjective / present active participle

56. <u>Sadly</u>, the interview fizzled as did two or three others, and lately he has been offered no <u>interviews</u> <u>at all</u>.

56. adverb as sentence modifier / retained object / phrasal adverb

57. <u>Setting out</u> for the park this morning, <u>both</u> Jenny <u>and</u> Rodney were in a strange mood.

57. present active participle of a phrasal verb / correlative conjunctions

58. It looked <u>as if</u> Rodney would have to broaden his job search to include other cities and <u>even</u> other states.

58. phrasal subordinating conjunction / adverb modifying a verb with respect to only one of two direct objects

59. As they jog around the lake, they agree on a new course for their lives: <u>they will move to Oregon, a state they have both loved from a distance</u>.

59. noun clause as appositive / appositive within an appositive / (unexpressed relative pronoun)

60. <u>The decision made</u>, a pleasant excitement gently moves aside the anxious discontent of recent weeks.

60. nominative absolute

Diagram the sentences of Story 4.

46. Rodney and Jenny Long, who are jogging together around the lake, call the park their second home.

47. Running relaxes them and helps them think clearly.

48. About three months ago, their lives changed when the agency Rodney had been working for abruptly went out of business.

49. He had just been appointed department head, but that was of little use now.

50. Jenny had no choice but to take the first job she found even though she hated the job and would have preferred to continue staying home with the couple's two small children.

51. Rodney has been searching diligently for another job in his field; however, so far his efforts have brought him nothing but headaches.

52. He has taken over the job of caring for the children.

53. It has been hard to get interviews because good job openings are scarce.

54. His letters have mostly gone unanswered, his calls unreturned.

55. Some time back, he got a call requesting him to come for an interview.

56. Sadly, the interview fizzled as did two or three others, and lately he has been offered no interviews at all.

57. Setting out for the park this morning, both Jenny and Rodney were in a strange mood.

58. It looked as if Rodney would have to broaden his job search to include other cities and even other states.

59. As they jog around the lake, they agree on a new course for their lives: they will move to Oregon, a state they have both loved from a distance.

60. The decision made, a pleasant excitement gently moves aside the anxious discontent of recent weeks.

People in the Park: Story 5

LaToya Jackson has brought her kindergarten students to the park, where they have fun while learning about nature. Born and raised on the south side of Chicago, LaToya never knew her father and lost her mother early in life. After being shuffled from one relative to another, the eight-year-old girl landed on the farm of an aunt and uncle in rural Mississippi. Her foster parents, although poor and saddled with four children of their own, nourished and loved the youngster. For her part, LaToya did whatever she could to help around the house, such as sweeping the floors, dusting the furniture, and drying dishes. She worked hard in school and studied at least an hour every evening. Whenever she could, she read to the younger children in the family so that they themselves might find reading exciting.

In time it became necessary for LaToya to take on additional responsibilities. She made herself use every minute productively. Still, however busy she was, she always found the time to help others. She became convinced that helping others is a key to happiness. The older she became, the more she valued education. Because she was at or near the top of her high-school class, it surprised no one that she received a full scholarship to the University of Mississippi. In college, she majored in, and thoroughly enjoyed, early childhood education. Today LaToya's smile is, if possible, bigger than usual, for today is her birthday, and she is doing what she always wanted to do: helping others.

Here are the sentences of Story 5. Grammar information about the underlined words is found on the right.

61. LaToya Jackson has brought her kindergarten students to the park, where they have fun <u>while learning</u> about nature.

61. elliptical clause

62. <u>Born</u> and <u>raised</u> on the south side of Chicago, LaToya never knew her father and lost her mother early in life.

62. past participles

63. <u>After being shuffled</u> from one relative to another, the eight-year-old girl landed on the farm of an aunt and uncle in rural Mississippi.

63. passive gerund w/ *after*

64. Her foster parents, although poor and saddled with four children of their own, <u>nourished and loved the youngster</u>.

64. two verbs with the same direct object

65. For her part, LaToya did <u>whatever</u> she could to help around the house, <u>such as</u> sweeping the floors, dusting the furniture, and drying dishes.

65. indefinite relative pronoun / expletive introducing an appositive

66. She worked hard in school and studied at least an <u>hour</u> every <u>evening</u>.

66. two adverbial objectives

67. <u>Whenever</u> she could, she read to the younger children in the family so that they <u>themselves</u> might find reading <u>exciting</u>.

67. indefinite relative adverb / intensive pronoun / not a participle

68. In time it became necessary <u>for LaToya to take on additional responsibilities</u>.

68. appositive: infinitive phrase (with a subject) as object of the particle *for*

69. She made <u>herself</u> <u>use every minute productively</u>.

69. reflexive pronoun / "to-less" infinitive phrase as objective complement

70. Still, <u>however busy she was</u>, she always found the time to help others.

70. special concessive clause (unexpressed *although*)

71. She became convinced <u>that helping others is a key to happiness</u>.

71. noun clause used as adverbial objective

72. <u>The</u> older she became, <u>the</u> more she valued education.

72. correlative adverbs

73. Because she was <u>at or near the top of her high-school class</u>, it surprised no one <u>that she received a full scholarship to the University of Mississippi.</u>

73. prepositional phrase as predicate adjective / compound preposition / *near* as preposition / noun clause as appositive

74. In college, she majored <u>in</u>, and thoroughly <u>enjoyed</u>, early childhood education.

74. preposition and verb have the same object

75. <u>Today</u> LaToya's smile is, if possible, <u>bigger than</u> usual, for <u>today</u> is her birthday, and she is doing <u>what</u> she always wanted to do: helping others.

75. *today* as an adverb and as a noun / unequal comparison / indefinite relative pronoun

Diagram the sentences of Story 5.

61. LaToya Jackson has brought her kindergarten students to the park, where they have fun while learning about nature.

62. Born and raised on the south side of Chicago, LaToya never knew her father and lost her mother early in life.

63. After being shuffled from one relative to another, the eight-year-old girl landed on the farm of an aunt and uncle in rural Mississippi.

64. Her foster parents, although poor and saddled with four children of their own, nourished and loved the youngster.

65. For her part, LaToya did whatever she could to help around the house, such as sweeping the floors, dusting the furniture, and drying dishes.

66. She worked hard in school and studied at least an hour every evening.

67. Whenever she could, she read to the younger children in the family so that they themselves might find reading exciting.

68. In time it became necessary for LaToya to take on additional responsibilities.

69. She made herself use every minute productively.

70. Still, however busy she was, she always found the time to help others.

71. She became convinced that helping others is a key to happiness.

72. The older she became, the more she valued education.

73. Because she was at or near the top of her high-school class, it surprised no one that she received a full scholarship to the University of Mississippi.

74. In college, she majored in, and thoroughly enjoyed, early childhood education.

75. Today LaToya's smile is, if possible, bigger than usual, for today is her birthday, and she is doing what she always wanted to do: helping others.

People in the Park: Story 6

Almost every day the octogenarian Jesse Able can be found sitting at the park lake's edge with a fishing pole in his hand. To most park regulars he is known simply as old Jesse. Old Jesse, whose wife died a little over a year ago, does not enjoy fishing as much as he used to. He knows that he uses it as a crutch in order to assuage the pain of his great loss. For him to heal, it would be necessary to open his heart and mind to someone else's problems. If Jesse is to go this route, he had best not consider an activity that requires great strength because he is not as strong as he once was. Still, he is a lot stronger than his appearance would lead you to believe. It would be nice to be able to teach, but he knows that his assuming the role of a classroom teacher would be like a parrot's offering language lessons to a newspaper editor. On the other hand, only someone who doesn't know him well would deny that he knows a great deal about natural phenomena. Leaning back, Jesse mentally juxtaposes two images: pulling in a huge bass and teaching others about nature. He feels his spirits soar as he realizes that he likes the latter image better than the former. One thing is certain: such a job would require that he stay in shape both mentally and physically.

"Well, Jesse," he says to himself, "perhaps you need to let it be known that you are interested in sharing your knowledge, and we'll see if you get any bites." Chuckling at his own pun, the old man considers that he doesn't even know whether or not such a position is available. But it would be worth checking into.

Here are the sentences of Story 6. Grammar information about the underlined words is found on the right.

76. Almost every day the octogenarian Jesse Able can be found sitting at the park lake's edge with a fishing pole in his hand.

76. linking verb / participle as predicate adjective / false participle

77. To most park regulars he is known simply as old Jesse.

77. linking verb / expletive

78. Old Jesse, whose wife died a little over a year ago, does not enjoy fishing as much as he used to.

78. equal comparison / complementary infinitive (ellipsis)

79. He knows that he uses it as a crutch in order to assuage the pain of his great loss.

79. expletive / objective complement / phrasal preposition

80. For him to heal, it would be necessary to open his heart and mind to someone else's problems.

80. infinitive (w/ subj.) as object of *for* / infinitive phrase as appositive / adjective with apostrophe

81. If Jesse is to go this route, he had best not consider an activity that requires great strength because he is not so strong as he once was.

81. adverb / complementary "*to*-less" infinitive

82. Still, he is a lot stronger than his appearance would lead you to believe.

82. adverbial objective / unequal comparison

83. It would be nice to be able to teach, but he knows that his assuming the role of a classroom teacher would be like a parrot's offering language lessons to a newspaper editor.

83. "subjects" of gerunds

84. On the other hand, only someone who doesn't know him well would deny that he knows a great deal about natural phenomena.

84. adverb or adjective?

85. Leaning back, Jesse mentally juxtaposes two images: pulling in a huge bass and teaching others about nature.

85. compound gerund phrase as appositive

86. He feels his spirits soar as he realizes that he likes the latter image better than the former.

86. "*to*-less" infinitive as objective complement / comparative of *well*

87. One thing is certain: such a job would require that he stay in shape both mentally and physically.

87. linking verb / correlative conjunctions joining compound adverb

88. "Well, Jesse," he says to himself, "perhaps you need to let it be known that you are interested in sharing your knowledge, and we'll see if you get any bites."

88. exclamatory expression / vocative / objective complement

89. Chuckling at his own pun, the old man considers that he doesn't even know whether or not such a position is available.

89. phrasal expletive

90. But it would be worth checking into.

90. coordinating conjunction introducing a sentence / adverbial objective

Diagram the sentences of Story 7.

76. Almost every day the octogenarian Jesse Able can be found sitting at the park lake's edge with a fishing pole in his hand.

77. To most park regulars he is known simply as old Jesse.

78. Old Jesse, whose wife died a little over a year ago, does not enjoy fishing as much as he used to.

79. He knows that he uses it as a crutch in order to assuage the pain of his great loss.

80. For him to heal, it would be necessary to open his heart and mind to someone else's problems.

81. If Jesse is to go this route, he had best not consider an activity that requires great strength because he is not so strong as he once was.

82. Still, he is a lot stronger than his appearance would lead you to believe.

83. It would be nice to be able to teach, but he knows that his assuming the role of a classroom teacher would be like a parrot's offering language lessons to a newspaper editor.

84. On the other hand, only someone who doesn't know him well would deny that he knows a great deal about natural phenomena.

85. Leaning back, Jesse mentally juxtaposes two images: pulling in a huge bass and teaching others about nature.

86. He feels his spirits soar as he realizes that he likes the latter image better than the former.

87. One thing is certain: such a job would require that he stay in shape both mentally and physically.

88. "Well, Jesse," he says to himself, "perhaps you need to let it be known that you are interested in sharing your knowledge, and we'll see if you get any bites."

89. Chuckling at his own pun, the old man considers that he doesn't even know whether or not such a position is available.

90. But it would be worth checking into.

People in the Park: Story 7

Justin Healy, or Skip as he prefers to be called, is the boy flying the kite. Skip--now, that's one determined fourteen-year-old. One Friday afternoon, having decided to build a kite, the youngster got on his bike and pedaled two miles to a hobby shop. What he didn't know is that the shop doors are locked each day at five o'clock sharp. Undiscouraged and undeterred, he returned on Monday after school. He knew, of course, what supplies he needed, and so he bought wood, fabric, and string and began pedaling home cautiously. Caution notwithstanding, he fell as he rounded a corner where sand had been spilled on the pavement. When he had picked up himself and the supplies, he found the latter to be in shreds. Please don't despair, dear reader, for the ending of Skip's kite adventure is happier than the beginning. A third trip to the store having produced its intended result, the long and arduous task of assembling a flightworthy kite began. Not only a box kite but also a rectangular kite failed to fly, even when Skip's sister Amy held the kite so that Skip could let out lots of string before running. It goes without saying that the fault was not hers but lay in the design of the kite. Next Skip tried building kites with three sides and with five sides, but to no avail. Being forced to become conventional, he finally built the diamond-shaped kite that you see flying gloriously overhead. Let's give him--and Amy, too--a big hand.

Here are the sentences of Story 7. Grammar information about the underlined words is found on the right.

91. Justin Healy, <u>or</u> Skip <u>as</u> he prefers to be called, is the boy flying the kite.

91. expletive / relative pronoun

92. Skip--<u>now,</u> <u>that</u>'s one determined fourteen-year-old.

92. interjection / pleonastic

93. One Friday afternoon, <u>having decided</u> to build a kite, the youngster <u>got on</u> his bike and pedaled two <u>miles</u> to a hobby shop.

93. present-perfect participle modifying the subject / phrasal verb / not a direct object

94. <u>What</u> he didn't know is that the shop doors are locked each day at five o'clock <u>sharp</u>.

94. unexpressed *that* as subject of sentence / adverb modifying a prepositional phrase

95. <u>Undiscouraged</u> and <u>undeterred</u>, he returned on Monday after school.

95. not participles

96. He knew, of course, <u>what</u> supplies he needed, and so he bought <u>wood, fabric, and string</u> and began pedaling home cautiously.

96. interrogative adjective / triple compound direct object within compound predicate

97. Caution <u>notwithstanding</u>, he fell as he rounded a corner where sand had been spilled on the pavement.

97. preposition that follows its object

98. When he had picked up <u>himself</u> and the supplies, he found the latter <u>to be in shreds</u>.

98. reflexive pronoun / infinitive phrase as objective complement, with prepositional phrase as predicate adjective

99. <u>Please</u> don't despair, dear reader, for the <u>ending</u> of Skip's kite adventure is happier than the <u>beginning</u>.

99. adverb / false gerunds

100. <u>A third trip to the store having produced its intended result</u>, the long <u>and</u> arduous task of assembling a flightworthy kite began.

100. nominative absolute / coordinating conjunction joining attributive adjectives

101. <u>Not only</u> a box kite <u>but also</u> a rectangular kite failed to fly, <u>even</u> when Skip's sister Amy held the kite so that Skip could let out lots of string <u>before running</u>.

101. correlatives / adverb modifying a relative adverb / preposition with gerund

102. It goes without saying that the fault was not <u>hers</u> but lay in the design of the kite.

102. absolute possessive

103. Next Skip tried building kites <u>with three sides and with five sides</u>, but <u>to no avail.</u>

103. compound prepositional phrase / elliptical clause

104. <u>Being forced</u> to become conventional, he finally built the diamond-shaped kite that you see flying gloriously overhead.

104. present passive participle

105. <u>Let's</u> <u>give</u> <u>him--and Amy</u>, too--a big hand.

105. contraction of verb and direct object. / "*to*-less" infin. as objective complement / compound indirect object

Diagram the sentences of Story 7.

91. Justin Healy, or Skip as he prefers to be called, is the boy flying the kite.

92. Skip--now, that's one determined fourteen-year-old.

93. One Friday afternoon, having decided to build a kite, the youngster got on his bike and pedaled two miles to a hobby shop.

94. What he didn't know is that the shop doors are locked each day at five o'clock sharp.

95. Undiscouraged and undeterred, he returned on Monday after school.

96. He knew, of course, what supplies he needed, and so he bought wood, fabric, and string and began pedaling home cautiously.

97. Caution notwithstanding, he fell as he rounded a corner where sand had been spilled on the pavement.

98. When he had picked up himself and the supplies, he found the latter to be in shreds.

99. Please don't despair, dear reader, for the ending of Skip's kite adventure is happier than the beginning.

100. A third trip to the store having produced its intended result, the long and arduous task of assembling a flightworthy kite began.

101. Not only a box kite but also a rectangular kite failed to fly, even when Skip's sister Amy held the kite so that Skip could let out lots of string before running.

102. It goes without saying that the fault was not hers but lay in the design of the kite.

103. Next Skip tried building kites with three sides and with five sides, but to no avail.

104. Being forced to become conventional, he finally built the diamond-shaped kite that you see flying gloriously overhead.

105. Let's give him--and Amy, too--a big hand.

People in the Park: Story 8

Joan Monroe enjoys sitting in the park and letting her mind wander. Usually she thinks happy thoughts about friends and food and faraway places; today, however, she has allowed her mind to fill itself with doubts about her fiancé. How can she be sure that he really loves her, that his love is more than a merely physical attraction? Will he console her when she's distraught, care for her when she's sick, stay by her side when physical beauty begins to fade? What will she do if he forgets to give her cards and presents, if their marriage is no longer as important to him as it is to her, if he becomes interested in other women? How can she know what the future holds for them?

   Just then Jerry Traylor comes running down the hill towards the bench on which Joan is sitting, takes her in his arms, and kisses her lovingly. Then he takes her hand in his, and they walk slowly together around the lake, lost in the moment. They talk, but there's no real need for words. Joan's doubts of a few minutes before are like vague memories from the distant past and of no consequence. He is here now, with her; moreover, he loves her, and she loves him. In the present, where life is lived, things couldn't be better.

Here are the sentences of Story 8. Grammar information about the underlined words is found on the right.

106. Joan Monroe enjoys <u>sitting in the park and letting her mind wander</u>.

106. compound gerund phrase used as direct object

107. Usually she thinks happy thoughts about friends and food and faraway places; today, however, she has allowed <u>her mind to fill itself with doubts about her fiancé</u>.

107. direct object with objective complement

108. How can she be sure <u>that he really loves her</u>, that his love is more than a merely physical attraction?

108. noun clause as adverbial objective

109. Will he <u>console her when she's distraught, care for her when she's sick, stay by her side when physical beauty begins to fade</u>?

109. compound predicate, each section with an adverb clause.

110. What will she do <u>if he forgets to give her cards and presents, if their marriage is no longer as important to him as it is to her, if he becomes interested in other women</u>?

110. Can you find all four adverb clauses?

111. How can she know <u>what the future holds for them</u>?

111. noun clause (indirect question) used as a direct object

112. Just then Jerry Traylor comes <u>running</u> down the hill towards the bench on <u>which</u> Joan is sitting, takes her in his arms, and kisses her lovingly.

112. present active participle as predicate adjective / relative pronoun as object of preposition

113. Then he takes her hand in <u>his</u>, and they walk slowly together around the lake, <u>lost</u> in the moment.

113. absolute possessive / past participle

114. They talk, but <u>there's</u> no real need for words.

114. expletive-verb contraction

115. Joan's doubts of a few minutes before are <u>like vague memories from the distant past and of no consequence</u>.

115. prepositional phrases as compound predicate adjective

116. He is here now, with her; <u>moreover</u>, he loves her, and she loves him.

116. transitional adverb

117. In the present, <u>where</u> life is lived, things couldn't be better.

117. relative adverb introducing an adjective clause

Diagram the sentences of Story 8.

106. Joan Monroe enjoys sitting in the park and letting her mind wander.

107. Usually she thinks happy thoughts about friends and food and faraway places; today, however, she has allowed her mind to fill itself with doubts about her fiancé.

108. How can she be sure that he really loves her, that his love is more than a merely physical attraction?

109. Will he console her when she's distraught, care for her when she's sick, stay by her side when physical beauty begins to fade?

110. What will she do if he forgets to give her cards and presents, if their marriage is no longer as important to him as it is to her, if he becomes interested in other women?

111. How can she know what the future holds for them?

112. Just then Jerry Traylor comes running down the hill towards the bench on which Joan is sitting, takes her in his arms, and kisses her lovingly.

113. Then he takes her hand in his, and they walk slowly together around the lake, lost in the moment.

114. They talk, but there's no real need for words.

115. Joan's doubts of a few minutes before are like vague memories from the distant past and of no consequence.

116. He is here now, with her; moreover, he loves her, and she loves him.

117. In the present, where life is lived, things couldn't be better.

People in the Park: Story 9

The people you see by the picnic table under the large oak tree are the Traxlers. Despite the fact that Bob and Sue Traxler have been through tough times in recent months, they are grateful for their three healthy children, all of whom are under five years of age. They know that life has its ups and downs, and they try to stay focused on the ups. Last November Bob lost a leg in Baghdad when an IED exploded under his patrol vehicle. Although he was fitted with a prosthesis, he has been unable to return to his job at the Ford factory. Sue, who had wanted to be a stay-at-home mom while her children were young, has had to find employment outside the home. She now works at a motel east of town while continuing to search for a better job. Bob, who had never wanted to be a stay-at-home dad, now finds himself saddled with full daytime responsibility for his children. The new role exacerbates the stress of adapting to life with one leg. It helps that he is taking university extension courses in management, which he hopes will allow him to realize his goal of securing a managerial position in health care.

But today neither Bob nor Sue is thinking about jobs. He is cooking hamburgers and beans, and she is putting plates, potato chips, and large glasses of lemonade on the picnic table, while they keep an eye on the kids, who are doing the fun things that young kids do in the freedom of a park. Amy, the oldest, is kicking a playground ball; Ben, the middle child, is rolling down a small hill; and Christine, a toddler, is playing with a toy truck. In a minute or two, all will sit together at the picnic table, enjoying the food, the fresh air, the sunshine, and each other.

Here the sentences of Story 9. Grammar information about the underlined words is found on the right.

118. The people <u>you see by the picnic table under the large oak tree</u> are the Traxlers.

118. relative clause with unexpressed relative pronoun

119. Despite the fact <u>that Bob and Sue Traxler have been through tough times in recent months</u>, they are grateful for their three healthy children, <u>all</u> of whom are under five years of age.

119. noun clause as appositive / subject of relative clause

120. They know that life has its <u>ups</u> and <u>downs</u>, and they try to stay focused on the <u>ups</u>.

120. adverbs used as nouns

121. <u>Last November</u> Bob lost a leg in Baghdad when an IED exploded under his patrol vehicle.

121. adverbial objective

122. <u>Although</u> he was fitted with a prosthesis, he has been unable to return to his job at the Ford factory.

122. subordinating conjunction

123. Sue, who had wanted to be a stay-at-home mom <u>while her children were young</u>, has had to find employment outside the home.

123. adverb clause within a relative clause

124. She now works at a motel east of town <u>while continuing to search for a better job</u>.

124. elliptical subordinate clause, with infinitive phrase as direct object

125. Bob, who had never wanted to be a stay-at-home dad, now finds himself <u>saddled</u> with full daytime responsibility for his children.

125. past participle as objective complement

126. The new role exacerbates the stress of <u>adapting to life with one leg</u>.

126. gerund phrase as object of preposition

127. It helps <u>that he is taking university extension courses in management,</u> <u>which</u> he hopes will allow him <u>to realize his goal of securing a managerial position in health care</u>.

127. noun clause as appositive / relative pronoun as subject of verb *will allow* / infinitive phrase as objective complement

128. But today <u>neither</u> Bob <u>nor</u> Sue is thinking about jobs.

128. correlative conjunctions

129. He is cooking hamburgers and beans, and she is putting plates, potato chips, and large glasses of lemonade on the picnic table, while they keep an eye on the kids, who are doing the fun things that young kids do in the freedom of a park.

129. two main clauses and three dependent clauses

130. Amy, the <u>oldest</u>, is kicking a playground ball; Ben, the middle child, is rolling down a small hill; and Christine, a toddler, is playing with a toy truck.

130. adjective used as a noun (sentence is a series of independent clauses, each with an appositive

131. In a minute or two, all will sit together at the picnic table, <u>enjoying</u> the food, the fresh air, the sunshine, and each other.

131. present participle as predicate adjective

Diagram the sentences of Story 9.

118. The people you see by the picnic table under the large oak tree are the Traxlers.

119. Despite the fact that Bob and Sue Traxler have been through tough times in recent months, they are grateful for their three healthy children, all of whom are under five years of age.

120. They know that life has its ups and downs, and they try to stay focused on the ups.

121. Last November Bob lost a leg in Baghdad when an IED exploded under his patrol vehicle.

122. Although he was fitted with a prosthesis, he has been unable to return to his job at the Ford factory.

123. Sue, who had wanted to be a stay-at-home mom while her children were young, has had to find employment outside the home.

124. She now works at a motel east of town while continuing to search for a better job.

125. Bob, who had never wanted to be a stay-at-home dad, now finds himself saddled with full daytime responsibility for his children.

126. The new role exacerbates the stress of adapting to life with one leg.

127. It helps that he is taking university extension courses in management, which he hopes will allow him to realize his goal of securing a managerial position in health care.

128. But today neither Bob nor Sue is thinking about jobs.

129. He is cooking hamburgers and beans, and she is putting plates, potato chips, and large glasses of lemonade on the picnic table, while they keep an eye on the kids, who are doing the fun things that young kids do in the freedom of a park.

130. Amy, the oldest, is kicking a playground ball; Ben, the middle child, is rolling down a small hill; and Christine, a toddler, is playing with a toy truck.

131. In a minute or two, all will sit together at the picnic table, enjoying the food, the fresh air, the sunshine, and each other.

People in the Park: Story 10

Now that the regular basketball season is over and only the NCAA tournament remains to be played, Jerome Wilkins, an outstanding collegiate basketball player, is giving more and more thought to entering the NBA draft, which would mean dropping out of college at the end of this year. The tall guy just coming across the foot bridge, that's Jerome. The woman he's talking with is his mother, who would be a major beneficiary of her son's sprint up the ladder of financial success. She has worked hard all her life and given selflessly to Jerome and her other children to help them get a good start in life.

      Jerome is telling his mother that he will eventually have to get an agent and that, when he does this, he will lose his collegiate eligibility. He tells her that he can "test the waters," i.e., talk with NBA representatives to try to get an idea of how high he would be expected to go in the draft. Being drafted in the first round would land him such a lucrative job that he could not afford to pass it up; on the other hand, if his chances of being drafted early do not appear to be good, it might be to his advantage to return to college for his junior year, play even better than this year, and secure for himself a higher place in the draft.

      Jerome's mother is happy that he has thought the matter through. Her advice is that he keep his coach informed no matter what route he decides to take.

Here are the sentences of Story 10. Grammar information about the underlined words is found on the right.

132. <u>Now that</u> the regular basketball season is over and only the NCAA tournament remains to be played, Jerome Wilkins, an outstanding collegiate basketball <u>player</u>, is giving more and more thought to entering the NBA draft, <u>which</u> would mean dropping out of college at the end of this year.

132. phrasal conjunction / appositive / relative pronoun with a gerund phrase as antecedent.

133. The tall guy <u>just coming across the foot bridge</u>, <u>that</u>'s Jerome.

133. participial phrase / pleonastic

134. The woman <u>he's talking with</u> is his mother, who would be a major beneficiary of her son's sprint up the ladder of financial success.

134. relative clause with unexpressed relative pronoun

135. She has worked hard <u>all her life</u> and given selflessly to Jerome and her other children to help them <u>get a good start in life</u>.

135. adverbial objective / "*to*-less" infinitive phrase as objective complement

136. Jerome is telling his mother that he will eventually have to get an agent and that, <u>when he does this</u>, he will lose his collegiate eligibility.

136. adverb clause within second of two noun clauses

137. He tells her that he can "test the waters," <u>i.e.</u>, <u>talk with NBA representatives to try to get an idea of how high he would be expected to go in the draft.</u>

137. expletive / appositive with phrase as antecedent

138. Being drafted in the first round would land him such a lucrative job that he could not afford to pass it up; on the other hand, if his chances of being drafted early do not appear to be good, it might be to his advantage <u>to return to college for his junior year, play even better than this year, and secure for himself a higher place in the draft.</u>

138. compound infinitive phrase as appositive

139. Jerome's mother is happy <u>that he has thought the matter through</u>.

139. noun clause as adverbial objective

140. Her advice is <u>that he keep his coach informed</u> <u>no matter what route he decides to take.</u>

140. noun clause as predicate nominative / preposition with noun clause as its object

Diagram the sentences of Story 10.

132. Now that the regular basketball season is over and only the NCAA tournament remains to be played, Jerome Wilkins, an outstanding collegiate basketball player, is giving more and more thought to entering the NBA draft, which would mean dropping out of college at the end of this year.

133. The tall guy just coming across the foot bridge, that's Jerome.

134. The woman he's talking with is his mother, who would be a major beneficiary of her son's sprint up the ladder of financial success.

135. She has worked hard all her life and given selflessly to Jerome and her other children to help them get a good start in life.

136. Jerome is telling his mother that he will eventually have to get an agent and that, when he does this, he will lose his collegiate eligibility.

137. He tells her that he can "test the waters," i.e., talk with NBA representatives to try to get an idea of how high he would be expected to go in the draft.

138. Being drafted in the first round would land him such a lucrative job that he could not afford to pass it up; on the other hand, if his chances of being drafted early do not appear to be good, it might be to his advantage to return to college for his junior year, play even better than this year, and secure for himself a higher place in the draft.

139. Jerome's mother is happy that he has thought the matter through.

140. Her advice is that he keep his coach informed no matter what route he decides to take.

Sentence 1: 101 Words

With six seconds to play, the Tigers trailing by two points, and the championship on the line, Atkins, who had been a powerful force on the boards all evening, grabbed the rebound of an errant free throw and passed the ball immediately to Brown at mid court, who hauled it in and, dribbling beautifully, wove his way through three opponents, swooped under the basket, and laid the ball gently against the backboard and in the basket, which tied the score, sent the game into overtime, and put the Tigers in an excellent position to realize their goal of becoming conference champions.

Diagram Sentence 1 step by step:

Step 1: *Atkins . . . grabbed the rebound of an errant free throw and passed the ball immediately to Brown at mid court*

Step 2: *With six seconds to play, the Tigers trailing by two points, and the championship on the line*

Step 3: *who had been a powerful force on the boards all evening*

Step 4: *who hauled it in and, dribbling beautifully, wove his way through three opponents, swooped under the basket, and laid the ball gently against the backboard and in the basket*

Step 5: *which tied the score, sent the game into overtime, and put the Tigers in an excellent position to realize their goal of becoming conference champions*

Diagram Sentence 1 by putting the pieces together.

Sentence 2: 109 Words

My family's fifth annual Super Bowl party, which had begun auspiciously with a kickoff return for a touchdown and the arrival of Aunt Mae's delicious apple strudel, suffered a serious setback during the halftime meal, when Uncle Ben, who was notorious among my relatives for his scrupulously healthful eating, put three grapes atop his plate of salmon, red cabbage, Indian cauliflower, and snow peas, tossed one of the grapes into the air and caught it in his mouth and then in his windpipe, causing him to choke, Uncle Will to make an awkward attempt at the Heimlich maneuver, and me to dash to the phone and dial 911.

Diagram the sentence step by step:

Step 1: My family's fifth annual Super Bowl party . . . suffered a serious setback during the halftime meal

Step 2: which had begun auspiciously with a kickoff return for a touchdown and the arrival of Aunt Mae's delicious apple strudel

Step 3: when Uncle Ben . . . put three grapes atop his plate of salmon, red cabbage, Indian cauliflower, and snow peas, tossed one of the grapes into the air, and caught it in his mouth and then in his windpipe

Step 4: who was notorious among my relatives for his scrupulously healthful eating

Step 5: causing him to choke, Uncle Will to make an awkward attempt at the Heimlich maneuver, and me to dash to the phone and dial 911

Diagram Sentence 2 by putting the pieces together.

Sentence 3: 113 Words

If one sets out to write a 100-word sentence that has even a modicum of grammatical complexity, that consists of more than a six-word introduction to 94 appositives, or that is more sophisticated than a subject, a verb, and a series of fifteen infinitive phrases, one will want to consider incorporating into the sentence several challenging constructions such as gerund phrases used as appositives, infinitive phrases used as objective complements, noun clauses used as adverbial objectives, and elliptical adverbial clauses used in equal and unequal comparisons, although it must in fairness be pointed out that no 100-word sentence will ever encompass the wealth of grammatical variation that the English language has to offer.

Step 1: one will want to consider incorporating into the sentence several challenging constructions

Step 2: such as gerund phrases used as appositives, infinitive phrases used as objective complements, noun clauses used as adverbial objectives, and elliptical adverbial clauses used in equal and unequal comparisons

Step 3: although it must in fairness be pointed out that no 100-word sentence will ever encompass the wealth of grammatical variation

Step 4: that the English language has to offer

Step 5: If one sets out to write a 100-word sentence that has even a modicum of grammatical complexity

Step 6: that consists of more than a six-word introduction to 94 appositives

Step 7: or that is more sophisticated than a subject, a verb, and a series of fifteen infinitive phrases

Diagram Sentence 3 by putting the pieces together.

Sentence 4: 114 Words

Because his failure to check the weather forecast before leaving St. Louis on a beguilingly beautiful day had led to his driving through hail storms near Topeka, which left forty or fifty pock marks on the hood, top, and trunk lid of his new Camry, he now sat, a week later, before a computer in Denver diligently checking weather forecasts (all of which promised multiple snowfalls over the next four days), looking and hoping for a window of departure that would allow him to return to St. Louis in time to feed, as promised, the pet raccoons of his neighbor, who was vacationing comfortably aboard a cruise ship on the warm waters of the Caribbean Sea.

Step 1: he now sat, a week later, before a computer in Denver diligently checking weather forecasts

Step 2: (all of which promised multiple snowfalls over the next four days)

Step 3: Because his failure to check the weather forecast before leaving St. Louis on a beguilingly beautiful day had led to his driving through hail storms near Topeka

Step 4: which left forty or fifty pock marks on the hood, top, and trunk lid of his new Camry

Step 5: looking and hoping for a window of departure that would allow him to return to St. Louis in time to feed, as promised, the pet raccoons of his neighbor

Step 6: who was vacationing comfortably aboard a cruise ship on the warm waters of the Caribbean Sea

Diagram Sentence 4 by putting the pieces together.

Sentence 5: 118 Words

The sun had just slipped behind the clouds on the western horizon, and the south wind that had blown all day was beginning its nocturnal slumber when 12-year-old Christopher, dressed only in the short pants that were his everyday summer attire, sculling with his left hand, urged his father's Arkansas Traveler out onto the lake and began casting and retrieving his favorite black-and-white River Runt as he moved the boat slowly toward an old stump around the bend, where a week ago, at about this time of day, he had hooked and then lost the bass of his dreams--a huge fish that he hoped, with a perfect cast and just the right lure action, to hook again.

Step 1: The sun had just slipped behind the clouds on the western horizon

Step 2: and the south wind that had blown all day was beginning its nocturnal slumber

Step 3: when 12-year-old Christopher . . . urged his father's Arkansas Traveler out onto the lake and began casting and retrieving his favorite black-and-white River Runt

Step 4: dressed only in the short pants that were his everyday summer attire, sculling with his left hand

Step 5: as he moved the boat slowly toward an old stump around the bend

Step 6: where a week ago, at about this time of day, he had hooked and then lost the bass of his dreams

Step 7: a huge fish that he hoped, with a perfect cast and just the right lure action, to hook again

Diagram Sentence 5 by putting the pieces together.

Sentence 6: 119 Words

Having sold the family cow for a magic bean, despite the fact that his mother needed and wanted cash for the cow, Jack, who may have lacked prudence but was never without a sense of adventure, took hold of the beanstalk that had grown from the discarded bean and climbed it to the top, where he discovered the giant who had stolen the family goose that laid golden eggs and, by waiting patiently and courageously for the giant to fall asleep, took back the goose; whereupon he scampered down to earth with the giant in pursuit, and chopped down the beanstalk, which brought the life of the giant to an end and ensured his and his mother's future prosperity.

Step 1: Jack . . . took hold of the beanstalk that had grown from the discarded bean and climbed it to the top

Step 2: Having sold the family cow for a magic bean, despite the fact that his mother needed and wanted cash for the cow

Step 3: who may have lacked prudence but was never without a sense of adventure

Step 4: where he discovered the giant who had stolen the family goose that laid golden eggs and, by waiting patiently and courageously for the giant to fall asleep, took back the goose

Step 5: whereupon he scampered down to earth with the giant in pursuit, and chopped down the beanstalk

Step 6: which brought the life of the giant to an end and ensured his and his mother's future prosperity

Diagram Sentence 6 by putting the pieces together.

Sentence 7: 131 Words

Not at all discouraged when, having huffed and puffed and blown down the straw house of the youngest pig, he had allowed its inhabitant to flee to his older brother's house of sticks, nor when, having blown down the stick house, he had missed the two pigs, who found refuge in the brick house of the oldest brother, nor when, having failed to blow down the house of bricks, he had had to endure the laughter of the succulent pigs, the enterprising wolf found a ladder, climbed up on the roof, slid down the chimney, and landed right in a pot of boiling water, where, to add insult to injury, he was serenaded in his final moments on earth by dancing pigs, who sang, "Who's afraid of the big bad wolf?"

Step 1: the enterprising wolf found a ladder, climbed up on the roof, slid down the chimney, and landed right in a pot of boiling water

Step 2: where, to add insult to injury, he was serenaded in his final moments on earth by dancing pigs

Step 3: who sang, "Who's afraid of the big bad wolf?"

Step 4: Not at all discouraged when, having huffed and puffed and blown down the straw house of the youngest pig, he had allowed its inhabitant to flee to his older brother's house of sticks

Step 5: nor when, having blown down the stick house, he had missed the two pigs

Step 6: who found refuge in the brick house of the oldest brother

Step 7: nor when, having failed to blow down the house of bricks, he had had to endure the laughter of the succulent pigs

Diagram Sentence 7 by putting the pieces together.

Sentence 8: 145 Words

While one can subscribe with intellectual sincerity to the ontological proof for the existence of God (according to which God, who is by definition a being than which no more perfect being is able to be conceived, must exist, for--existence being more perfect than non-existence--one can conceive of a being more perfect than an imaginary god), and while many honest, intelligent individuals are moved to assent to God's existence by the argument from intelligent design (which reasons that the world is so complex that it cannot have happened by chance but must have been created by a higher power), it is either disingenuous or stupid (because it involves the use of circular reasoning, in which the conclusion is subsumed in one of the premises) to argue that God exists because the Bible, which was inspired by God and is therefore inerrant, says so.

Step 1: it is either disingenuous or stupid . . . to argue that God exists because the Bible . . . says so

Step 2: (because it involves the use of circular reasoning, in which the conclusion is subsumed in one of the premises)

Step 3: which was inspired by God and is therefore inerrant

Step 4: While one can subscribe with intellectual sincerity to the ontological proof for the existence of God

Step 5: (according to which God, who is by definition a being than which no more perfect being is able to be conceived, must exist, . . .)

Step 6: (. . . for--existence being more perfect than non-existence--one can conceive of a being more perfect than an imaginary god)

Step 7: and while many honest, intelligent individuals are moved to assent to God's existence by the argument from intelligent design

Step 8: (which reasons that the world is so complex that it cannot have happened by chance but must have been created by a higher power)

Diagram Sentence 8 by putting the pieces together.

Sentence 9: 156 Words

As he knelt in the dimly lit convent chapel and thought about his classmates, who even at this moment were being ordained priests in the seminary chapel around the corner, as he ruminated about the months of agonizing uncertainty that had culminated in his last-minute decision to rise above his fears and eschew ordination, as he imagined the surprise and disappointment of his peers upon their becoming aware that he was not among them, and as he wondered how they would greet him when he returned to the seminary later that morning, the young man realized that he would never become what his mother had wanted him to become, would never complete the course he had begun out of fear of damnation, but would follow his heart, which even now was filling with the joy of living and the anticipation of the best that life offers a man: a wife and a family of his own.

Step 1: the young man realized that he would never become what his mother had wanted him to become, would never complete the course he had begun out of fear of damnation, but would follow his heart

Step 2: which even now was filling with the joy of living and the anticipation of the best that life offers a man: a wife and a family of his own

Step 3: As he knelt in the dimly lit convent church and thought about his classmates, who even at this moment were being or-dained priests in the seminary chapel around the corner

Step 4: as he ruminated about the months of agonizing uncertainty that had culminated in his last-minute decision to rise above his fears and eschew ordination

Step 5: as he imagined the surprise and disappointment of his peers upon their becoming aware that he was not among them

Step 6: and as he wondered how they would greet him when he returned to the seminary later that morning

Diagram Sentence 9 by putting the pieces together.

Sentence 10: 165 Words

It is a fact greatly to be wondered at and abundantly to be praised that no man on his wedding day, his mind enraptured by his bride's beauty and filled with thoughts of love, has ever taken a second to consider that, some years hence, he may be standing at the bedside of his dying wife, whose breathing has become erratic and for whom death is only minutes away, and yet, 41 years after his wedding, a grieving husband watches as his wife, the mother of his three children, the anchor of their family, whose cancer has made it necessary for her to receive all nourishment intravenously for the past five months, takes a final deep breath, after which he waits a minute, two minutes for another breath, knowing that none will follow and that he has lost the greatest treasure he has ever had and can ever expect to have--the woman to whom (you may have guessed) this book is gratefully and lovingly dedicated.

Step 1: It is a fact greatly to be wondered at and abundantly to be praised that no man on his wedding day . . . has ever taken a second to consider that, some years hence, he may be standing at the bedside of his dying wife

Step 2: his mind enraptured by his bride's beauty and filled with thoughts of love

Step 3: whose breathing has become erratic and for whom death is only minutes away

Step 4: and yet, 41 years later, a grieving husband now watches as his wife, the mother of his three children, the anchor of their family, . . . takes a final deep breath

Step 5: whose cancer has made it necessary for her to receive all nourishment intravenously for the past five months

Step 6: after which he waits a minute, two minutes for another breath

Step 7: knowing that none will follow and that he has lost the greatest treasure he has ever had and can ever expect to have

Step 8: --the woman to whom (you may have guessed) this book has been gratefully and lovingly dedicated

Diagram Sentence 10 by putting the pieces together.

Tree Diagrams: Lesson 1

Transformational generative grammar, often referred to simply as generative grammar, originated in the 1950s with an MIT professor by the name of Noam Chomsky. Chomsky's goal, and the goal of modern linguists who have subscribed to and built upon his theory of syntax, is to unlock and explain what they call universal grammar: a syntax common to all languages. These scholars represent this syntax graphically in several ways, chiefly perhaps by means of tree diagrams. They proceed scientifically, that is, by means of data-based and data-tested hypotheses. Modern linguists are not at all interested in prescriptive grammar (rules that must be followed if one is to use a particular language correctly); instead, they take a language as they find it and attempt to describe its syntax. In these descriptions, they take what they can use from traditional grammar and discard or replace the rest. For instance, they keep the terms noun, verb, adjective, adverb, preposition, and conjunction, but they lump articles and demonstrative adjectives together, calling them determiners; moreover, of the six traditional tenses, they retain only two (present and past), and they label the expletives *that, if,* and *whether* complementizers.

Syntactical generalizations that modern linguists uncover they call rules; they hope to discover to what extent these rules exist innately in the subconscious minds of all infants. That there should be any such rules at all is based on the belief that young children around the world can use language far beyond the degree possible if they were reliant solely upon modeling. Parents and others, it is claimed, simply do not offer children enough examples of correct syntax; what's more, they do not point out a sufficient number of syntactical errors. In a word, the insufficiency of adult modeling upon a brain that has not been pre-wired can be demonstrated, according to the exponents of generative grammar.

Opponents of generative grammar point out that the human brain excels in the ability to find patterns. How many times, they ask, would a child have to hear sentences like "Eat your peas" and "Drink your milk" to suspect that sentences like *"Your peas eat" and *"Drink milk your" may be wrong? How long would it take a child to learn that if sentences like "Don't throw your toys" and "Don't play with your food" are right, then it may be wrong to say *"Throw don't your toys" and *"Not play with your food"? (It is customary to place an asterisk before an incorrect sentence or phrase.) The most intriguing argument used by modern linguists in support of pre-wired brains is that, languages being infinite systems, one could never arrive at certain competence on the basis of a finite number of models or examples. One proof of the infinite nature of languages is their recursiveness; that is, the same phrases are able to be used over and over again to form infinitely long sentences. Here is an example: "Gayle said that George said that Drew said that Scarlet said that Kate said that Will said that . . . Stella's first word was 'Mama.'"

Because of the widespread acceptance of generative grammar in academic circles, it behooves anyone with a serious interest in grammar to be acquainted with the subject. As an introduction, each of the following 23 lessons will explain one or more aspects of this important discipline. No matter how convinced you are of the merits of Reed & Kellogg diagramming, I think you will agree with me that we can learn much from modern linguists' syntactical analyses and from their presentation of these analyses in tree diagrams. I do hold out one caveat: the material is too difficult for young students. Months of working my way through several books of modern linguistics, including Chomsky's seminal work *Linguistic Structures*, have convinced me that an attempt to teach modern syntax in elementary or middle schools would be futile. Basic ideas like constituency tests, c-command, theta roles, V-to-T movement, and X-bar would pass young students by. The very best high-school students could perhaps handle introductory material in moderation, including some X-bar theory and transformation theory, but the subject seems more appropriate for upper-level undergrads.

Linguists have developed many approaches to generative grammar. Only one of these approaches--Principles and Parameters, which uses tree diagramming--is presented in this book. Alternatives to Principles and Parameters include Relational Grammar, Categorical Grammar, Optimality Theory, Lexical-Functional Grammar, and Head-Driven Phrase Structure Grammar. Some of these approaches make use of graphic analyses that bear no resemblance to tree diagramming.

By including in a book about traditional syntax and Reed & Kellogg diagramming a section about modern syntax and tree diagramming, I hope to introduce you, the reader, to an important area of scholarship. In planning this section of my book, I had to choose between an in-depth presentation of a small number of topics and a more cursory presentation of a substantial number of topics. I think you would have been underwhelmed by the former approach; I hope you don't feel overwhelmed by the latter. In any case, you may be frustrated at times by a minimum of explanatory material and a paucity of diagramming examples. As you read through these pages, you may have unanswered questions. Should you wish to take a closer look at this subject, I would recommend to you the three books that I found most instructive in my own study: *Syntax: A Generative Introduction* by Andrew Carnie (2002), *Syntax: A Minimalist Introduction* by Andrew Radford (1997), and *Syntactic Analysis: The Basics* by Nicholas Sobin (2011).

Tree Diagrams: Lesson 2

For the most part, modern linguists retain the traditional parts of speech; however, they define them differently. Their definitions are based on morphology (the study of the forms of words) and on syntax (the study of the arrangement of words) rather than on semantics (the study of the meanings of words).

The traditional definition of *noun* is "the name of a person, place, or thing." This definition is semantic. *Elizabeth* is the name of a person, *library* is the name of a place (as well as a thing), and *book* is the name of a thing. But what about nouns like *insinuation, allotment*, and *value*? Are these really things? The traditional definition, according to modern linguists, is deficient. They point out that if a word forms its plural by the addition of *-s*, it's a noun. Of course, this morphological test will not identify every noun; words like sheep and deer that have the same singular and plural forms, as well as words like coarseness and traffic that don't have plural forms, would not be identified as nouns if the plural *-s* criterion alone were used. Endings play a role as well. If a word ends in *-ion, -ity, -ment,* or *-ness*, for example, it's probably a noun. Syntax also assists with noun identification. Many nouns are able to be preceded by *a, the, this*, and *my*, for example, without the intervention of an adjective (e.g., *a barn, the wagon, this lesson, my grandfather*). If you can meaningfully fill in the blank in "They have no _____ " with a single word, that word is a noun. Many nouns are count words; that is, they can follow *one, two, three*, etc. Nouns can follow adjectives, e.g., *beautiful day, proud mom, difficult test*. These are the kinds of criteria that modern linguists use to identify nouns.

Verbs, traditionally defined as words expressing actions or states, are identified morphologically and syntactically by modern linguists. Most verbs add *-s* in the third person singular, that is, when they are preceded by *he, she, it*, or a singular noun (*she runs, Audrey listens*). Verbs also add *-ing* in their progressive forms (*are traveling, am wondering, will be visiting*). The past tense of most verbs is different from the presents tense (*see, saw; is, was; play, played*); *put* and *let* are exceptions. If a word fits in the following blank, it is a verb: *They can _____.* Verbs typically follow subjects. Auxiliary verbs (*be, have, do*, and the modals) are quite different from others verbs. They are placed first in yes/no questions, and they can be negated with *-n't*.

Modern linguists have no argument with the traditional definition of adjectives (modifiers of nouns, pronouns, and equivalent expressions). Adjectives are often found between what modern linguists call "determiners"--words like *a, the, this*, and *my* (more about this in the next paragraph)--and nouns (*a little house, the friendly dog, this old document, my sore back*). Thus, only an adjective can be used to complete the sentence *I liked the _____ movie*. Also, only an adjective fits in the following blank: *We are very _____.* Adjectives follow *very*, but so do adverbs (which modify verbs, adjectives, other adverbs, etc.). So how does one tell the difference? For starters, most words ending in *-ly* are adverbs (among a handful of exceptions are *wily, holy, jolly*, and *surly*). If answers are limited to one word, only an adverb can fill the following blank: *The governor handled the matter _____.*

Traditionalists' articles (*a, an, the*), demonstrative adjectives (*this, that, these, those*), and possessive pronouns (*my, your, his, her, its, our, their*) are lumped together in modern linguistics into a class called determiners. Perhaps you are asking yourself why. What's different about possessive pronouns, say, and adjectives? Don't they all modify nouns? Yes, they do, but they really are different. And they're different in three ways. First, in a series of modifiers, determiners always come first (e.g., *his beautiful young wife*, not **beautiful young his wife*, for example). Secondly, whereas several adjectives can be strung together before a noun, only one determiner can be so used (e.g., *narrow, hilly, windy roads*, but not **the this road* or **a my bicycle*). And, thirdly, a determiner always modifies the entire noun phrase that it precedes. For example, in the phrase *an ancient red barn, an* does not modify only *barn*, as it is traditionally said to do, but the entire phrase *ancient red bard*. This is an important point; it will be discussed at greater length later.

In traditional grammar, the word *that* in a sentence like "Kevin heard that Ellie is sick today" and the word *if* (or *whether*) in a sentence like "He wonders if she will be in school tomorrow" are called expletives. Modern linguistics calls them (and the word *for* in a sentence like "For him to say something like that is ridiculous") complementizers. Complementizer phrases (CPs) play a prominent role in tree diagrams.

You may have never heard of transitive prepositions and intransitive prepositions, but some modern linguists use these terms to distinguish between prepositions that have objects (transitive prepositions) and prepositions that don't (intransitive prepositions). An example of the former is *outside* in the sentence "Many fans were gathered outside the arena"; an example of the latter is *outside* in the sentence "Many fans were left standing outside."

Finally, some modern linguists consider pronouns to be determiners. They see no need for the word *pronoun* as a part of speech.

Tree Diagrams: Lesson 3

Syntacticians seek to discover how groups of words fit together to form sentences. These groups of words, traditionally called phrases, are also called constituents in modern linguistics. Tree diagramming is used to show sentence structure.

Traditionally, a sentence consists of a subject and a predicate. Modern linguists prefer to say that a sentence consists of a noun phrase and a verb phrase. In linguistic shorthand, this can be expressed as follows: S → NP VP (→ means "consists of"). In a tree diagram, it looks like this:

The most basic noun phrase (NP) is simply a noun. A two-word noun phrase consists of a determiner (an article or a demonstrative adjective, for example) and a noun (NP → D N) or an adjective and a noun (NP → A N). A three-word noun phrase could consist of a determiner, an adjective, and a noun (NP→ D A N).

A verb phrase (VP) consists of a verb and its modifiers and complements. For now, we will consider only verb phrases in which the verb is modified by a single adverb (Adv). There are two possibilities: VP → Adv V and VP → V Adv.

Tree diagrams of the sentences "That woman sang" and "The happy man whistled pleasantly" would be as follows:

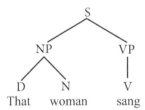   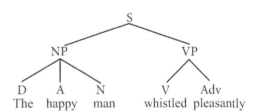

The determiner *the* modifies the expression *happy man*, not just the noun *man*. This relationship, which is not shown in Reed & Kellogg diagrams, is also not expressed in the preliminary tree diagram above. Later, you will see how more sophisticated tree diagramming overcomes this weakness.

Diagram the following sentences using tree diagrams.

1. Content cats purr.

2. This old house often squeaks.

Tree Diagrams: Lesson 4

Let's bring in direct objects and also extend our scope to adverbs that modify adjectives. In tree diagramming, direct objects, like subjects, are given the label NP (noun phrase). To be able to diagram adverbs that modify adjectives, we will have to use the label AP (adjective phrase). A noun phrase consisting of a determiner, an adverb, an adjective, and a noun can be described this way: NP → D AP N, where AP → AdvP A and AdvP → Adv. Likewise, a verb phrase consisting of a verb, a determiner, and a noun is expressed symbolically as VP → V NP, where NP → D N. Shorthand for a verb phrase consisting of an adverb, a verb, and an unmodified noun used as a direct object is VP → AdvP V NP, where AdvP → Adv and NP → N. Here is a succinct symbolic representation of the syntax of some basic structures: S → NP VP, NP → (D) (AP) N, VP → (AdvP) V (AdvP) (NP) (AdvP), NP → (D) (AP) N, AP → (AdvP) A, AdvP → (AdvP) Adv. Parentheses mean the enclosed item is optional. As you can see, a noun phrase can consist simply of a noun; or its noun can be preceded by a determiner and/or modified by an adjective or adjectives. Similarly, a VP can consist of nothing more than a verb, or it can take modifiers and complements. An adjective phrase can consist of an adjective alone, or the adjective can be modified by an adverb. Symbolic expressions of phrases list the constituents in the order in which they are found in the language being described. We are considering only the English language in our brief examination of tree diagramming.

Here is a tree diagram of the sentence "The very kind volunteers gladly helped the unfortunate victims."

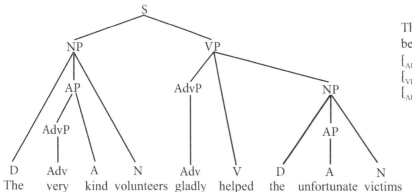

The syntax of this sentence can also be represented as follows: $[_S[_{NP}[_D$The$]$ $[_{AP}[_{AdvP}[_{Adv}$very$]][_A$kind$]][_N$volunteers$]]$ $[_{VP}[_{AdvP}[_{Adv}$gladly$]][_V$helped$][_{NP}[_D$the$]$ $[_{AP}[_A$unfortunate$]][_N$victims$]]]$.

You probably noticed that the phrase labels AP and AdvP, unused in the diagrams of the preceding page, appear in this diagram. Henceforth, we will never use a single-letter label unless it is preceded in its diagram by its phrase label. Thus NP, VP, AP, and AdvP will always appear above N, V, A, and Adv, respectively. D has a special status for now; it is immediately preceded by NP. More about D later.

Diagram the following sentence using a tree diagram: Those workers built these very nice homes quickly.

Tree Diagrams: Lesson 5

A preposition carries the label P, while PP is used for a prepositional phrase. If the verb is modified by a prepositional phrase, we could have, for example, VP → (AdvP) V (NP) (AdvP) PP (AdvP), where parentheses indicate that the enclosed item may or may not occur. If the prepositional phrase modifies a noun, you would have NP → (D) (AP) N PP. In this book, the following is true: PP → P NP. It should be noted that some linguists refer to words like *on, out,* and *up* as prepositions even when they do not have an object (e.g., *run on, go out, jump up*); for them , PP → P (NP); that is, the object is optional. Here is a tree diagram of the sentence "The spectators ran onto the field," in which the prepositional phrase *onto the field* is a verbal modifier.

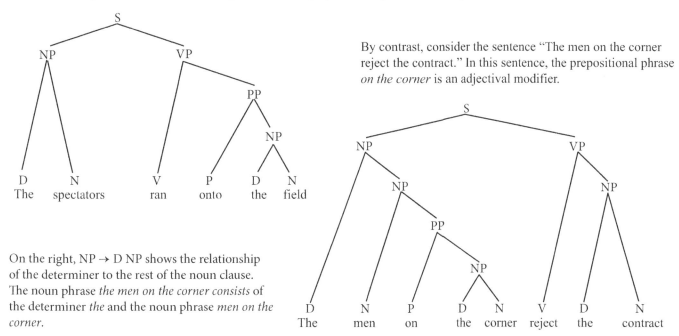

By contrast, consider the sentence "The men on the corner reject the contract." In this sentence, the prepositional phrase *on the corner* is an adjectival modifier.

On the right, NP → D NP shows the relationship of the determiner to the rest of the noun clause. The noun phrase *the men on the corner consists* of the determiner *the* and the noun phrase *men on the corner*.

Diagram the following sentence using a tree diagram: The women on that team worked at night.

Tree Diagrams: Lesson 6

According to modern linguists, there are only two tenses: present and past. These scholars maintain that English has no future tense and no perfect tenses. What traditional linguists call the future tense, modern linguists see as the present tense of the modal auxiliary verb *will* with a *to*-less infinitive. In deep structure, the tense indicators -*s* and -*ed* precede their verbs. In a process called affix-hopping, these endings hop onto their verbs when the deep structure is transformed to surface structure. Since modern linguists find that verb affixes function much like modal auxiliary verbs, they label both affixes and modals with a T (tense) in tree diagrams. Here is a diagram of the sentence "The first group moved to a new position."

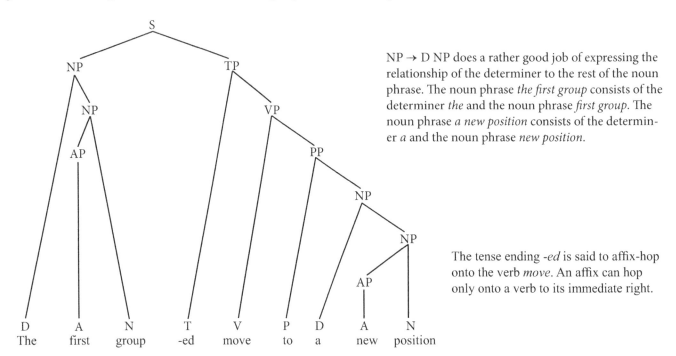

NP → D NP does a rather good job of expressing the relationship of the determiner to the rest of the noun phrase. The noun phrase *the first group* consists of the determiner *the* and the noun phrase *first group*. The noun phrase *a new position* consists of the determiner *a* and the noun phrase *new position*.

The tense ending -*ed* is said to affix-hop onto the verb *move*. An affix can hop only onto a verb to its immediate right.

Diagram the following sentence using a tree diagram: Tired shoppers staggered through the aisles of the grocery store.

Tree Diagrams: Lesson 7

Generative grammar uses the term "perfect aspect" to refer to the traditional present-perfect, past-perfect, and future-perfect tenses. The traditional present-perfect and past-perfect tenses are seen as the present and past tenses, respectively, of the auxiliary verb *have* with a past participle; the traditional future-perfect tense consists of the present tense of *will* with the *to*-less infinitive *have* and a past participle. For example, the tenses ascribed to the forms *has seen*, *had seen*, and *will have seen* are present (*has* and *will*) and past (*had*). Here is how the sentence "Their guest has arrived" is diagrammed.

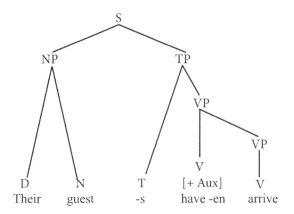

The tense ending *-s* (which also indicates person and number) affix-hops onto *have*. [+Aux] says that *have* is used as an auxiliary verb. The *-en* following *have* indicates that the following verb is a past participle.

Here is a more challenging sentence: The companies had been wasting too much money.

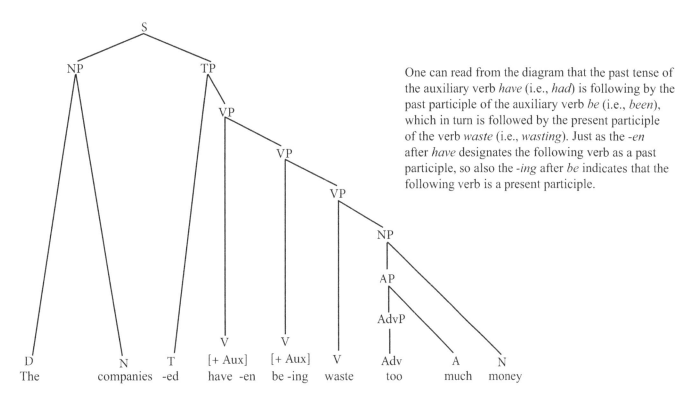

One can read from the diagram that the past tense of the auxiliary verb *have* (i.e., *had*) is following by the past participle of the auxiliary verb *be* (i.e., *been*), which in turn is followed by the present participle of the verb *waste* (i.e., *wasting*). Just as the *-en* after *have* designates the following verb as a past participle, so also the *-ing* after *be* indicates that the following verb is a present participle.

Diagram the following sentence using a tree diagram: Felix was jogging at the beach.

Tree Diagrams: Lesson 8

In tree diagramming, affixes of deep structures are able to hop onto the verb to their immediate right, producing surface structure. An affix cannot jump over a word. In this lesson you will see the kind of movement used in generative grammar to unite an affix with its verb despite an intervening word. It's called V to T movement. The diagram of the sentence "My dog was not standing in your yard" will illustrate this point.

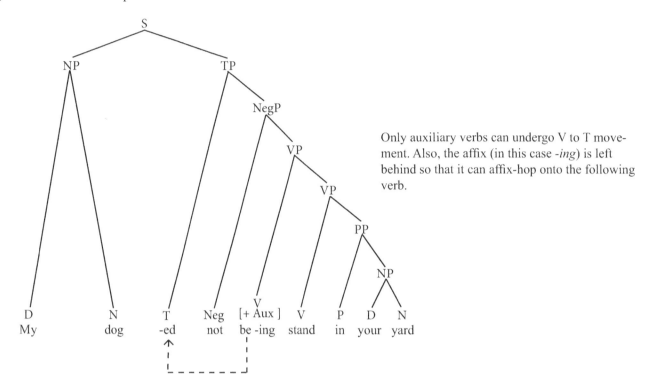

Only auxiliary verbs can undergo V to T movement. Also, the affix (in this case *-ing*) is left behind so that it can affix-hop onto the following verb.

Diagram the following sentence using a tree diagram: The immensely talented dancer has not won a contest.

Tree Diagrams: Lesson 9

Compounds are easy to diagram with trees. In this lesson you will see how compound nouns are diagrammed. Just follow the patterns NP → NP Conj NP and N → N Conj N. Here's the diagram of the sentence "Danny and Sam have not met your brother or my sister." The symbol Ø under T means that that there is no verb affix; in other words, the base form *have* is uninflected. The *-en* to the right of *have* indicates that the next word is a past participle. The broken-line arrow shows the movement necessary to get from deep structure to surface structure. This V to T movement is an example of head movement. A head is the word represented by the capital letter to the left of P in NP, TP, VP, PP, etc.

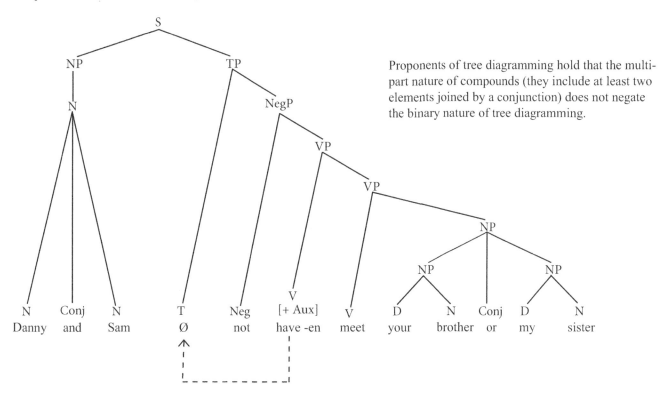

Proponents of tree diagramming hold that the multipart nature of compounds (they include at least two elements joined by a conjunction) does not negate the binary nature of tree diagramming.

Diagram the following sentence using a tree diagram: Sara and Bob have not played cards with Phyllis and her friend.

Tree Diagrams: Lesson 10

Conjunctions are also used to form compound verbs and compound verb phrases. The syntactic patterns are VP → VP Conj VP and V → V Conj V. Here is a sentence that contains a compound verb phrase: "The winds toppled trees and destroyed homes."

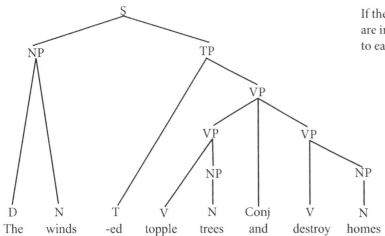

If the tense of the two verbs were different, as they are in the sentence "We have been and will be nice to each other," one would use TP → TP Conj TP.

Some of the branches of a tree diagram must be diagonal; the rest can be vertical, according to personal preference.

Diagram the following sentence using a tree diagram: Our Hugo plays in the sand and wades in the water.

Tree Diagrams: Lesson 11

Conjunctions also connect adjectives, adjective phrases, prepositions, and prepositional phrases: AP → AP Conj AP (also A → A Conj A) and PP → PP Conj PP (also P → P Conj P). Objects of prepositions can also be compound, according to the familiar pattern NP → NP Conj NP (also N → N Conj N). Here is the diagram of the sentence "Large and small drones can fly through deep canyons and over tall mountains."

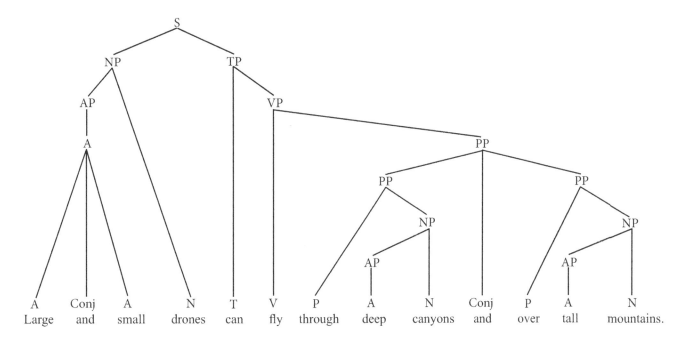

Diagram the following sentence using a tree diagram: The mayor noticed enthusiastic conversations between and among council members and their guests.

Tree Diagrams: Lesson 12

Modern linguists distinguish between adjuncts and complements. The difference between the two is hard to define. It helps to keep in mind that a word or phrase is more closely connected with its complement than with its adjunct. To differentiate adjuncts and complements in tree diagrams, modern linguists use a system called X-bar (X'). Limiting our present scope to nouns, the following rules apply: N' → N' (PP) and N' → N (PP). Both adjuncts and complements are daughters of N'. A complement is the sister of N, while an adjunct is the sister of N'. Sisters are two members of the same constituent that have the same mother. In a diagram, a single line connects each of the sisters with the shared mother. Notice how this works out in the diagram of this sentence: "They examined the large boxes of books in the attic."

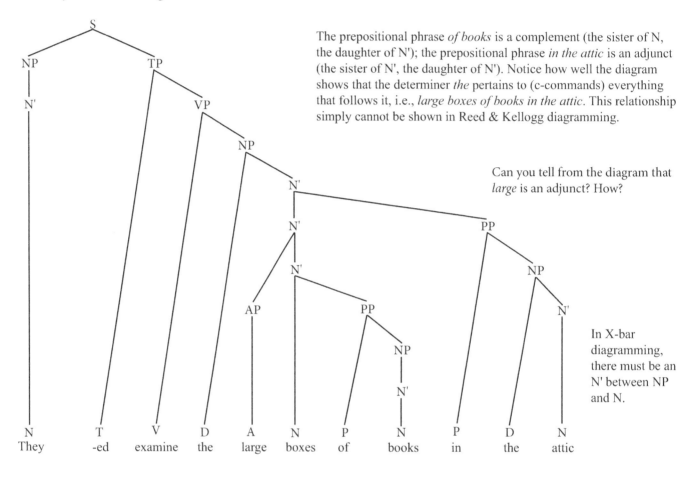

The prepositional phrase *of books* is a complement (the sister of N, the daughter of N'); the prepositional phrase *in the attic* is an adjunct (the sister of N', the daughter of N'). Notice how well the diagram shows that the determiner *the* pertains to (c-commands) everything that follows it, i.e., *large boxes of books in the attic*. This relationship simply cannot be shown in Reed & Kellogg diagramming.

Can you tell from the diagram that *large* is an adjunct? How?

In X-bar diagramming, there must be an N' between NP and N.

Diagram the following sentence using a tree diagram: The cartons of food from America will arrive tomorrow.

Tree Diagrams: Lesson 13

Verbs can also have adjuncts and complements: V' → V' (PP), V' → V (NP) What's more, the objects of prepositions are the complements of their prepositions: P' → P NP. In the sentence "My daughters fly kites in the park with their friends," *kites* is a complement of the verb while the two prepositional phrases are adjuncts. *The park* and *their friends* are the complements of the prepositions *in* and *with*, respectively. Notice how these relationships are expressed in the following tree diagram.

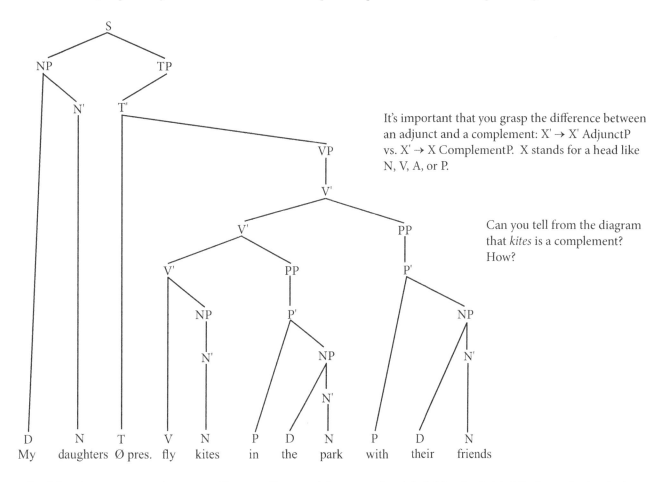

It's important that you grasp the difference between an adjunct and a complement: X' → X' AdjunctP vs. X' → X ComplementP. X stands for a head like N, V, A, or P.

Can you tell from the diagram that *kites* is a complement? How?

Diagram the following sentence using a tree diagram: Steve and Annette painted their bicycles behind the house in the shade.

Tree Diagrams: Lesson 14

Adjectives can also be complements; however, most are adjuncts. In the sentence "Those large water birds will not make their nest in a small peach tree," the adjectives *large* and *small* are adjuncts while the adjectives (nouns used as adjectives) *water* and *peach* are complements. In N' → (AP) N', the AP is an adjunct; in N' → (AP) N, the AP is a complement.

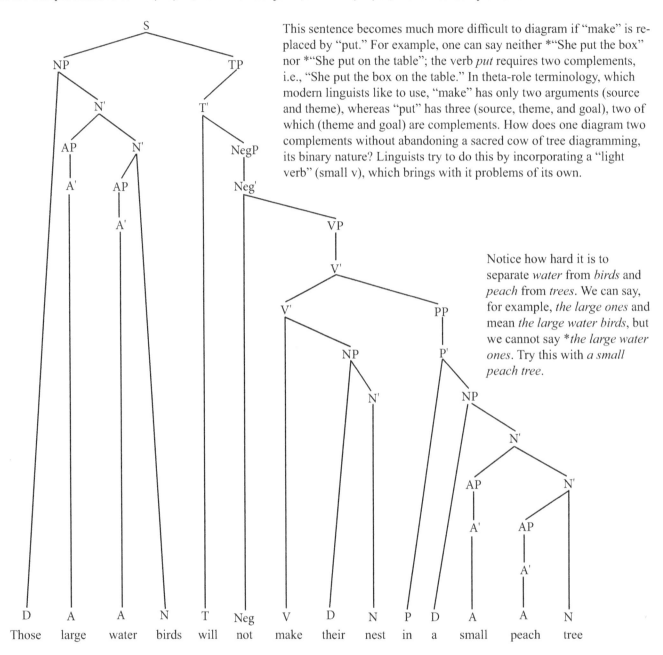

This sentence becomes much more difficult to diagram if "make" is replaced by "put." For example, one can say neither *"She put the box" nor *"She put on the table"; the verb *put* requires two complements, i.e., "She put the box on the table." In theta-role terminology, which modern linguists like to use, "make" has only two arguments (source and theme), whereas "put" has three (source, theme, and goal), two of which (theme and goal) are complements. How does one diagram two complements without abandoning a sacred cow of tree diagramming, its binary nature? Linguists try to do this by incorporating a "light verb" (small v), which brings with it problems of its own.

Notice how hard it is to separate *water* from *birds* and *peach* from *trees*. We can say, for example, *the large ones* and mean *the large water birds*, but we cannot say *the large water ones*. Try this with *a small peach tree*.

Diagram the following noun phrase using a tree diagram: a very old anatomy book

Tree Diagrams: Lesson 15

Modern linguists distinguish between regular pronouns and special pronouns called anaphors. An anaphor must get its meaning from another noun, noun phrase, or pronoun in the same sentence. Anaphors include what traditionalists call reflexive pronouns (*himself, herself, itself, themselves*) and reciprocal pronouns like *each other* or *one another*. An anaphor is c-commanded by its antecedent; that is, it is the sister of the antecedent or a daughter, granddaughter, etc. of the sister. Other pronouns (*he, she, it, they*) may have an antecedent in the same sentence, or they may not. In the sentence "The brother of the president hurt himself," *president* does not c-command *himself*, but the noun phrase *the brother of the president* does. Note how this is shown in the tree diagram that follows.

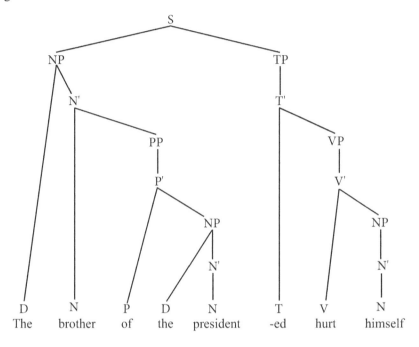

*"The brother of the Queen hurt herself" is an unsuccessful sentence because *herself* is not c-commanded by *Queen*.

Diagram the following sentence using a tree diagram: A friend of my sister wrote a story about herself.

Tree Diagrams: Lesson 16

Traditionally, adverbs are thought to modify prepositions as well as prepositional phrases. In the sentence "We arrived exactly on time," the adverb *exactly* modifies the prepositional phrase *on time*; in the phrase "right after the intermission," the adverb *right* modifies the preposition *after*. Tree diagramming does a good job with *exactly on time*; *right after the intermission*, on the other hand, doesn't seem to work. In order for the adverb *right* to be an adjunct (which it is), P' must have a P' as a constituent (P' → AdvP P'). In order for the noun phrase *the intermission* to be a complement (which it is), P' must have P (may not have P') as a constituent (P' → P NP). In diagram (a) below, *right* is an adjunct (as it should be), and *the intermission* is a complement (as it should be), but *right* modifies the prepositional phrase *after the intermission* instead of the preposition *after*. In diagram (b), *right* is an adjunct modifying the preposition *after* (as it should), but *the intermission* is also an adjunct (it should be a complement). If there is an answer to this dilemma in tree diagramming, I haven't found it.

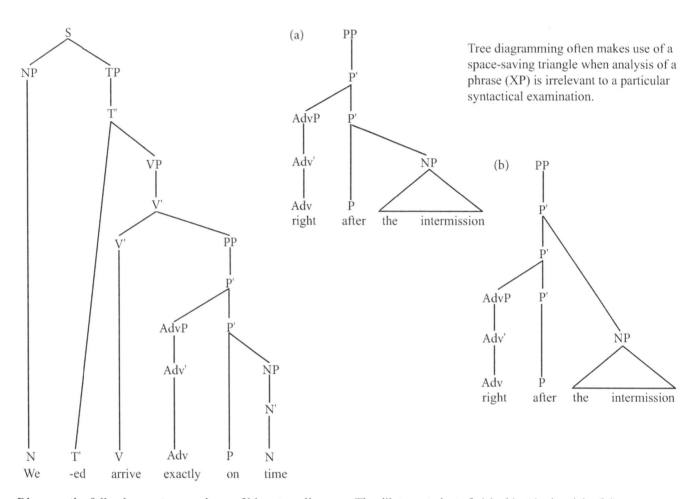

Tree diagramming often makes use of a space-saving triangle when analysis of a phrase (XP) is irrelevant to a particular syntactical examination.

Diagram the following sentence using an X-bar tree diagram: The dilatory students finished just in the nick of time.

Tree Diagrams: Lesson 17

In traditional grammar, the word *that* can be used as an expletive (a word that has a function but little or no meaning). Modern linguists call such a word a complementizer. The sentence "Kelly knew that Tom liked her" uses the complementizer *that*.

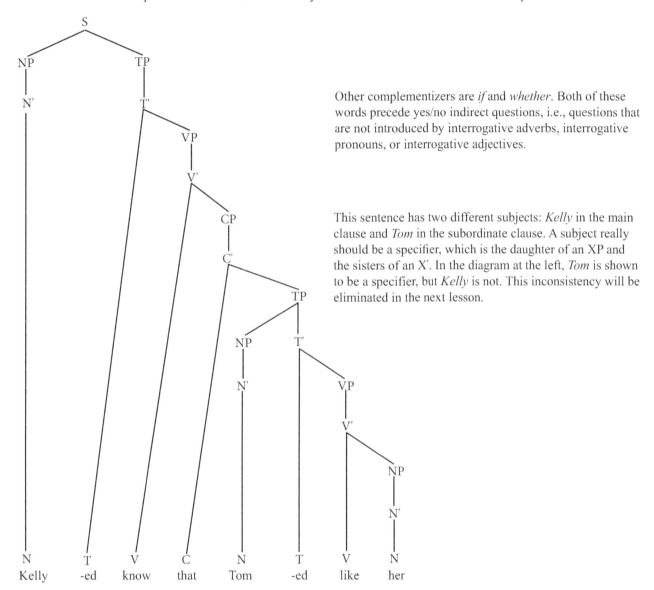

Other complementizers are *if* and *whether*. Both of these words precede yes/no indirect questions, i.e., questions that are not introduced by interrogative adverbs, interrogative pronouns, or interrogative adjectives.

This sentence has two different subjects: *Kelly* in the main clause and *Tom* in the subordinate clause. A subject really should be a specifier, which is the daughter of an XP and the sisters of an X'. In the diagram at the left, *Tom* is shown to be a specifier, but *Kelly* is not. This inconsistency will be eliminated in the next lesson.

Diagram the following sentence using an X-bar tree diagram: The neighbors will think that we moved.

Tree Diagrams: Lesson 18

The complementizer *that* is actually used twice in the sentence "Eric hoped Melissa knew that he liked her"; its first use (after *hoped*) is unexpressed. The replacement of S with CP will be explained in Lesson 20. The use of CP makes it possible to diagram the subject of the sentence as a specifier, which it is: TP→NP T'.

Diagram the following sentence using a tree diagram:
Christie thought that Kent said he had time.

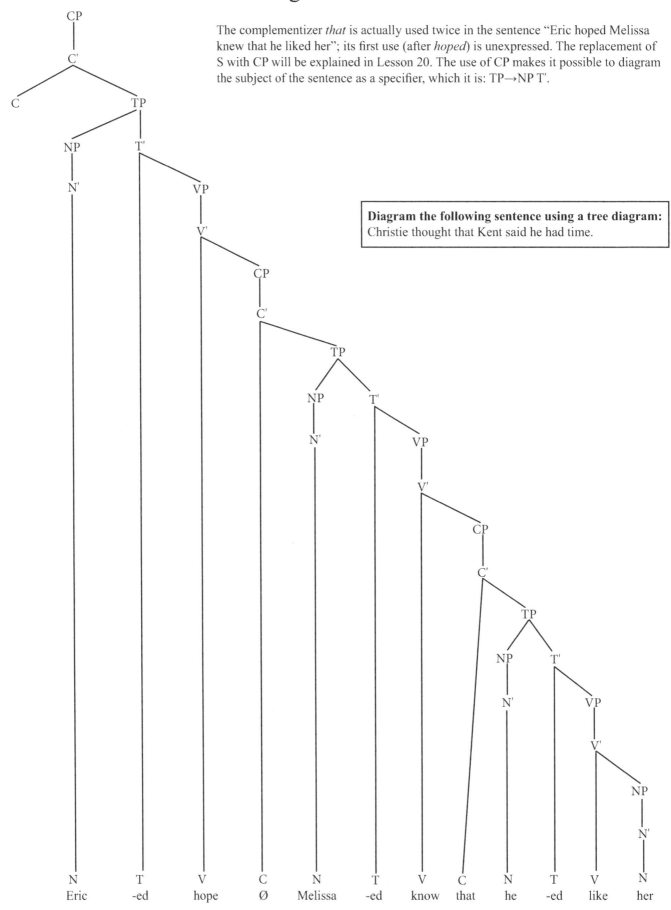

Tree Diagrams: Lesson 19

In this lesson, we will consider the quantifiers *all, each,* and *both.* You will see how the quantifier *all* is diagrammed in the sentence "The guests will all enter the house." Deep structure's NP *the guests* is moved from the specifier position of VP to the specifier position of TP to get the surface structure. Small t stands for "trace." Some linguists think that all subjects originate in VP and are moved to TP. For better visualization of movement, a triangle is used, which keeps the analysis of the subject at the NP level.

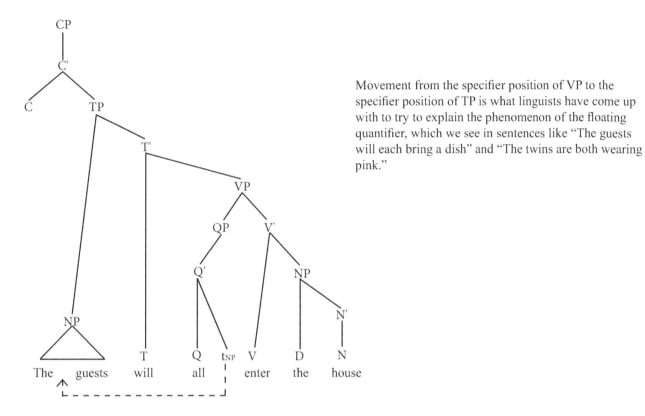

Movement from the specifier position of VP to the specifier position of TP is what linguists have come up with to try to explain the phenomenon of the floating quantifier, which we see in sentences like "The guests will each bring a dish" and "The twins are both wearing pink."

Diagram the following sentence using an X-bar tree diagram: The brothers will both vacation with their parents.

~ 233 ~

Tree Diagrams: Lesson 20

Modern linguists argue that complementizers (Cs) exist not only in subordinate clauses but even as null elements in main clauses. Some languages use a special particle to introduce yes/no questions. English has no such particle; the claim is that it has a null complementizer instead. This null complementizer can provide a suitable destination for moved auxiliary verbs. Since CP fits better than S into the X-bar system, S is replaced by CP. The null complementizer is designated as [+Q] if it introduces a question or as [-Q] is it introduces a non-question. You can see how this works in the diagram of the following yes/no question: "Will the critics read the latest issue of your journal?" Linguists also argue for the existence of determiner phrases (DPs), which fit well into the X-bar system.

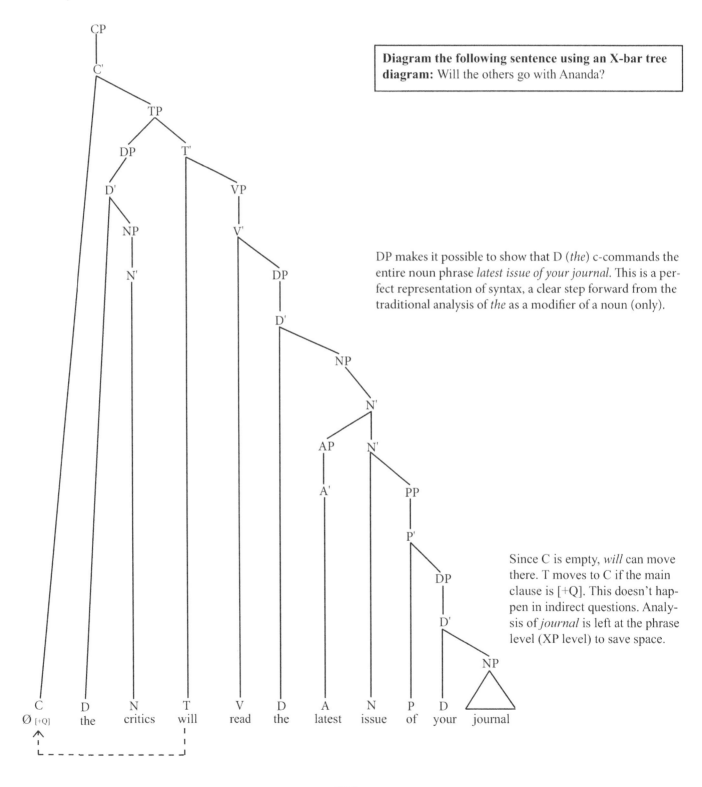

Diagram the following sentence using an X-bar tree diagram: Will the others go with Ananda?

DP makes it possible to show that D (*the*) c-commands the entire noun phrase *latest issue of your journal*. This is a perfect representation of syntax, a clear step forward from the traditional analysis of *the* as a modifier of a noun (only).

Since C is empty, *will* can move there. T moves to C if the main clause is [+Q]. This doesn't happen in indirect questions. Analysis of *journal* is left at the phrase level (XP level) to save space.

Tree Diagrams: Lesson 21

The verb *do* introduces many yes/no questions, e.g., "Does Anson know Matt?" "Do Milo and Emi have time?" "Does Aubrey visit often?" These forms of *do* are not found in equivalent statements: "Anson knows Matt," "Milo and Emi have time," "Aubrey visits often." Thus, *do* must be inserted in deep structure and then moved to surface structure, as you will see in the diagram of the sentence "Did the cheerleaders practice after school?"

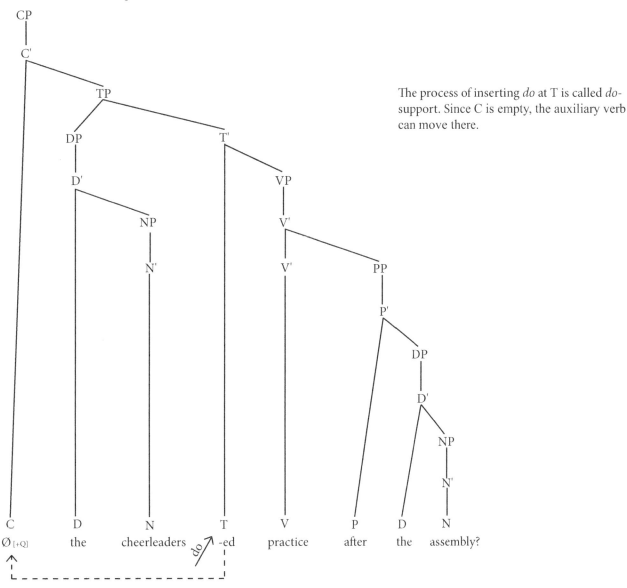

The process of inserting *do* at T is called *do-support*. Since C is empty, the auxiliary verb can move there.

Diagram the following sentence using an X-bar tree diagram: Do the leaders understand the problem?

Tree Diagrams: Lesson 22

By moving one or more words, modern linguists show how questions involving *wh*-words, i.e., words that begin with *wh* (*who, whom, what, why, when,* etc.) get from deep structure to surface structure. We will focus on a simple example: "What are the workers building?" (You can imagine how much more complex the tree diagram of a sentence like "What do the children think that the women know about what the workers are building?" would be.) Notice that this is the first diagram in this book that makes use of the empty specifier component of CP.

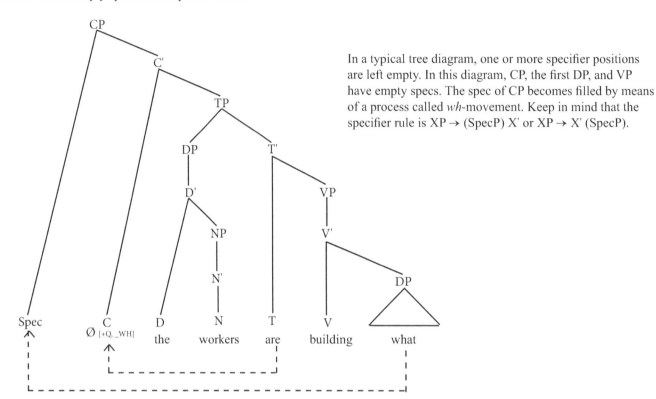

In a typical tree diagram, one or more specifier positions are left empty. In this diagram, CP, the first DP, and VP have empty specs. The spec of CP becomes filled by means of a process called *wh*-movement. Keep in mind that the specifier rule is XP → (SpecP) X' or XP → X' (SpecP).

Diagram the following sentence using an X-bar tree diagram: Whom will the president meet there?

Tree Diagrams: Lesson 23

Relative clauses (adjective clauses introduced by *who, whom, which, that,* or an unexpressed relative pronoun) are adjunct clauses. If the relative pronoun is not the subject of its clause, a transformation is required to get it from deep structure to surface structure. The following sentence contains both an interrogative *wh*-word and a relative clause: "What is the guy who you invited to the party bringing?" (Modern analysts take the language as they find it. *Who* is common as an objective form these days.)

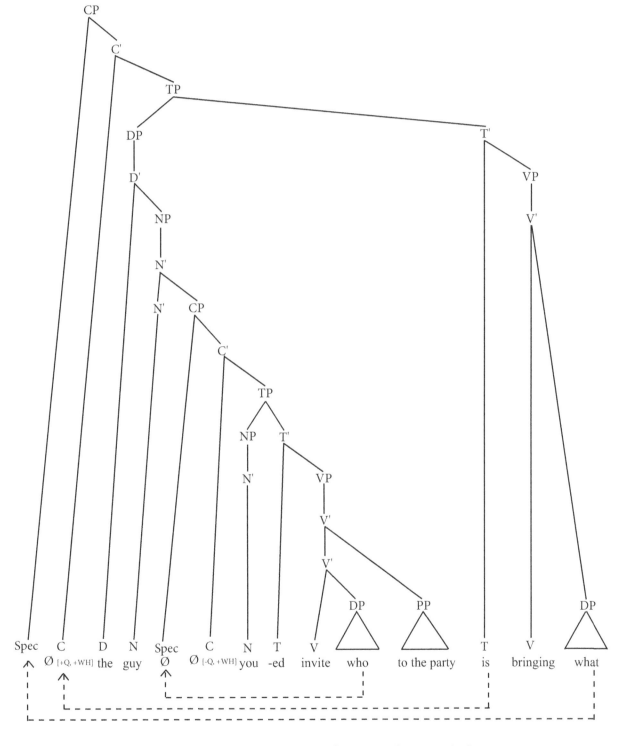

Diagram the following phrase using an X-bar tree diagram: the person whom your Andrew met.

Tree Diagrams: Lesson 24

Modern linguists go to some lengths to fit the passive voice into their X-bar system. In brief, they argue that the verb of a sentence in the passive voice is in the passive voice already in deep structure. Likewise, the agent of a passive-voice sentence does not begin as a subject in deep structure but as the object of the preposition *by*. Only one movement is then necessary to get from deep structure to surface structure: movement from VP to TP. Let's see how that looks with the sentence "The nominee was chosen by a committee." I will use triangles in the tree diagram for simplification and clarity.

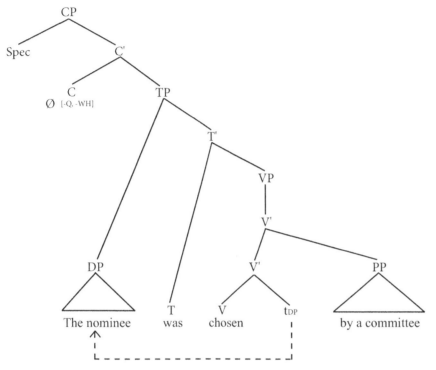

Diagram the following sentence using an X-bar tree diagram:
This information was gathered by the police.

Exercise 1: Subjects and Verbs

1. Ducks | quack

The subject of the sentence is *ducks*. The verb *quack* is in the present tense. In Reed & Kellog diagrams, a vertical line passing through the main horizontal line (called the base line) always separates the subject from its verb.

2. Mosquitoes | are buzzing

The verb *are buzzing* is a progressive form of the present tense.

3. People | have been talking

The verb *have been talking* is present-perfect progressive.

4. They | will be captured

The subject of the sentence is *they*, a personal pronoun. The verb *will be captured* is in the future tense, passive voice.

5. Money | had been collected

Had been collected is in the past-perfect tense, passive voice.

6. That | will have changed

The subject is *that*, a demonstrative pronoun. The verb *will have changed* is in the future-perfect tense.

7. fish | Do fly

Do fly is present emphatic. Notice that the first word of the sentence is capitalized in the diagram.

8. What | happened

The subject *what* is an interrogative pronoun. The verb *happened* is in the simple past tense.

9. Who | was talking

An interrogative pronoun, *who*, is the subject of the sentence. The verb *was talking* is past progressive.

10. I | did study

Did study is a past-tense verb in the emphatic form.

Exercise 2: Modal Auxiliary Verbs

11. You | may stay

The verb consists of the present modal auxiliary verb *may* and the basic present-tense form *stay*.

12. We | must go

The present modal auxiliary verb *must* is used with the basic present-tense form *go*.

13. elephants | Can jump

The present modal auxiliary verb *can* is used here with the basic present-tense form *jump* to ask a question.

14. They | should be scolded

The present modal auxiliary verb *should* is used with the basic present passive form of the verb *scold.*

15. I | Should have asked

The verb consists of the present modal auxiliary verb *should* and the basic present-perfect active form of the verb *ask.*

16. Carolyn | must have been delayed

The present modal auxiliary verb *must* is used with the basic present-perfect passive form of the verb *delay.*

17. That | could have been done

The present subjunctive of the modal auxiliary verb *can* is used here with the basic present-perfect passive form of the verb *do.*

18. She | may have been asked

The present modal auxiliary verb *may* is used with the basic present-perfect passive form of the verb *ask.*

19. They | might be coming

The present subjunctive form of the modal auxiliary verb *may* is used with the basic present progressive form of the verb *come.*

20. we | Might have succeeded

The verb consists of the present subjunctive of *may* and the basic present-perfect form of the verb *succeed.*

Exercise 3: Imperatives, Vocatives, Contractions and Coordinating Conjunctions

21. x | Run

The subject, *you*, is unexpressed. An unexpressed word is represented in a diagram by an *x*.

22. Dave

    x | hurry

Dave is a vocative (i.e., a noun of direct address). Vocatives are diagrammed on a separate line above the subject.

23. x | Don't worry

Contractions involving a verb and a contracted form of *not* are kept as a single word in diagrams. Other such contractions are *isn't, can't, won't, shouldn't, couldn't, isn't, aren't*, etc.

24. I | 'm trying

24. Contractions involving a subject (often a personal pronoun) and a contracted verb form are separated in diagrams. Other such contractions are *I'll, they're, it's, I've*, etc. (also *that's*).

25. Gentlemen

    we | cannot leave

The word *cannot* is kept as a single word. *Gentlemen* is a vocative.

26. Doctors

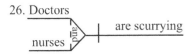

    nurses   are scurrying

Doctors and nurses is a compound subject. The coordinating conjunction *and* joins the two nouns. Two other important coordinating conjunctions are *or* and *but*.

27. Buses   come / and \ go

Come and go is a compound verb. Since it constitutes the entire predicate, it is also a compound predicate.

28. Deer | were   runnning / and \ jumping

Together with the helping verb *were*, the compound present participle *running and jumping* forms the past progressive.

29. Children | run / jump / and / play

This compound predicate consists of three verbs.

30. Teachers

    x | 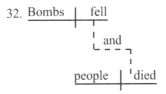 travel / and / learn

Travel and learn is a compound imperative.

31. boys

    girls / and

    x | Listen

Boys and girls is a compound vocative.

32. Bombs | fell

          and

    people | died

This is a compound sentence: two independent clauses joined by a coordinating conjunction.

Exercise 4: Articles, Attributive Adjectives, and Direct Objects

33.

You is a direct object in this sentence. In diagramming, a direct object follows a vertical line that rests on the base line.

34.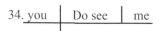

A direct object can be identified by asking *whom?* or *what?* after a non-linking verb. Not all sentences have direct objects.

35.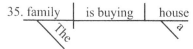

The and *a* are articles, the former definite, the latter indefinite.

36.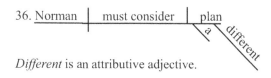

Different is an attributive adjective.

37.

Basketball is a noun used here as an attributive adjective.

38.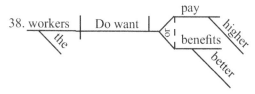

Pay or benefits is the compound direct object of the verb *do want*. The attributive adjectives *higher* and *better* modify *pay* and *benefits*, respectively.

39.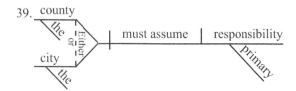

Either . . . or is called a correlative conjunction.

40.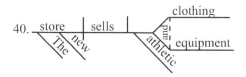

Since athletic modifies both *clothing* and *equipment*, its line is attached to the part of the direct-object line that belongs to both objects.

41.

The verbs *buys* and *restores* have the same direct object: *furniture*.

42.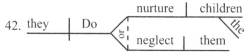

Except for the shared helping verb *do*, this sentence has a compound predicate. Its coordinating conjunction is *or*. The verbs *nurture* and *neglect* have different direct objects.

43. he | does want | What

Even though it comes first in the sentence, *what* is a direct object.

44. we | can send | Whom

Because it is a direct object, *whom* is correct (*who*, although a nominative form, is often used in informal English).

45.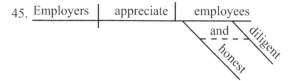

Honest and diligent is a compound attributive adjective.

Exercise 5: Adverbs

46.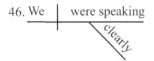

Clearly is an adverb modifying the verb *were speaking*.

47.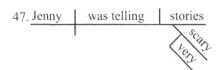

The adverb *very* modifies the attributive adjective *scary*.

48.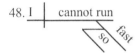

The adverb *so* modifies the adverb *fast*.

49.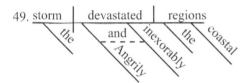

Angrily and inexorably is a compound adverb.

50.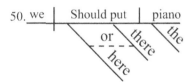

The coordinating conjunction *or* connects the adverbs *here* and *there*.

51.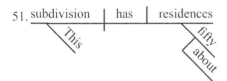

This is callled a demonstrative adjective. *About* is an adverb modifying the adjective *fifty*.

52.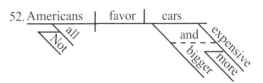

The adverbs *not* and *more* modify the attributive adjectives *all* and *expensive*, respectively. *Bigger and more expensive* is a compound attributive adjective.

53.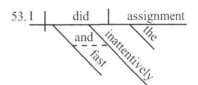

Fast and inattentively is a compound adverb.

54.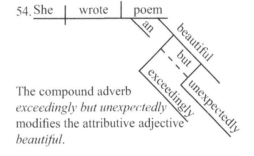

The compound adverb *exceedingly but unexpectedly* modifies the attributive adjective *beautiful*.

55.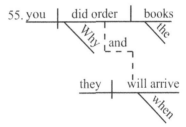

The interrogative adverb *why* modifies the verb *did order*, and the interrogative adverb *when* modifies the verb *will arrive* in this compound sentence.

56.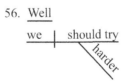

Well is an independent adverb: it modifies nothing at all.

Exercise 6: Predicate Nominatives and Predicate Adjectives

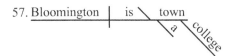

57. Bloomington | is \ town

As a predicate nominative, *town* is preceded by a backslash. The noun *college* is used in this sentence as an adjective.

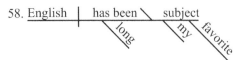

58. English | has been \ subject

Has been is a present-perfect form of *be*; thus, *subject* is a predicate nominative. *My* is a possessive pronoun. Possessives are diagrammed like adjectives.

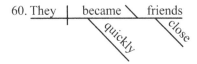

59. She | was feeling \ happy
    but
    he | was feeling \ sad

This is a compound sentence whose two main clauses are joined by the coordinating conjunction *but. Was feeling* is a linking verb. *Happy* and *sad* are predicate adjectives.

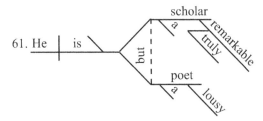

60. They | became \ friends

Became is a linking verb, *friends* a predicate nominative.

61. He | is \ scholar but poet

This sentence features a compound predicate nominative.

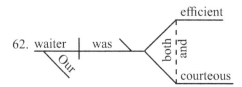

62. waiter | was \ efficient both and courteous

Our is a possessive pronoun (more about this later). *Both* and *and* are correlative coordinating conjunctions.

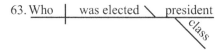

63. Who | was elected \ president

The passive verb *was elected* functions as a linking verb. *Class* is a noun used as an adjectrive.

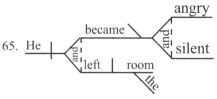

64. x | Be \ good and stay \ healthy

This imperative sentence has a compound predicate. *Good* and *healthy* are predicate adjectives. When *stay* means "continue to be," it is a linking verb.

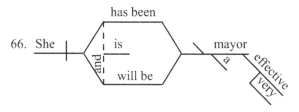

65. He | became \ angry and silent left | room the

The first branch of the compound predicate contains a compound predicate adjective (*angry and silent*), the second a direct object (*room*).

66. She | has been is will be \ mayor

The compound, tripartite verb *has been, is, and will be* has *mayor* as its predicate nominative.

Exercise 7: Possessives, Appositives, and Expletives

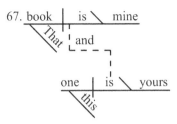

67.

That and *this* are demonstrative adjectives. *Mine* and *yours* are called absolute possessive pronouns. Like *hers, ours,* and *theirs,* they indicate the possessor and take the place of the thing possessed. They cannot be used attributively.

68.

The passive voice of the factitive verb *appoint* is used here as a linking verb. *Representative* is a predicate nominative. *As* is an expletive (a word with a function but with little or no meaning).

69.

Dave's is a possessive noun. The first *friends* is a subject, the second a predicate nominative.

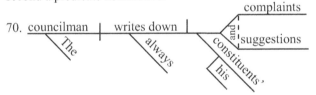

70.

Constituents', a possessive noun, pertains to both components of the compound direct object. *Writes down* is a phrasal verb.

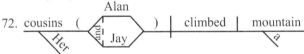

71.

Marcy is a restrictive appositive. It is in apposition with the direct object, *friend.*

72.

Brian and Jay is a compound restrictive appositive. It is in apposition with the subject, *cousins.*

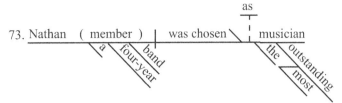

73.

Member, a nonrestrictive appositive, is in apposition with the subject *Nathan*. The passive verb *was chosen* functions as a linking verb. *Musician* is a predicate nominative and *as* is an expletive.

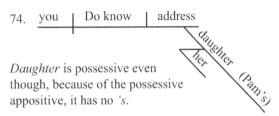

74.

Daughter is possessive even though, because of the possessive appositive, it has no *'s.*

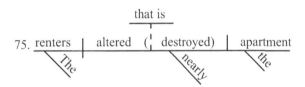

75.

The verb phrase *nearly destroyed* is in apposition with the main verb, *altered.* *That is* is an expletive. Other such function words and phrases, which are sometimes called appositive conjunctions because they are not entirely devoid of meaning, are *especially, for example, in other words,* and *or.*

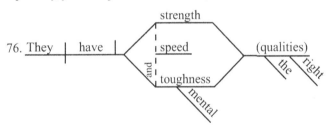

76.

Qualities is in apposition with the compound direct object *strength, speed, and mental toughness.*

Exercise 8: Prepositional Phrases

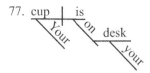

77.

On your desk is a prepositional phrase modifying the verb *is*; it is, therefore, adverbial.

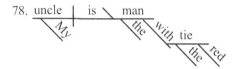

78.

The prepositional phrase *with the red tie* modifies the noun *man*; thus it is adjectival.

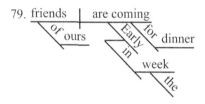

79.

In the week and *for dinner* are adverbial prepositional phrases. The former modifies the adverb *early*, the latter the verb *are coming*. *Ours* is an absolute possessive.

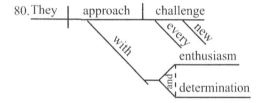

80.

With enthusiasm and determination is a prepositional phrase containing a compound object.

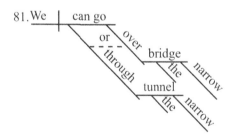

81.

Through the narrow tunnel or over the narrow bridge is a compound prepositional phrase.

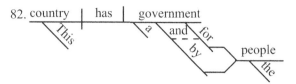

82.

The adjectival prepositional phrase *by and for the people* has a compound preposition but a single object, *people*.

83.

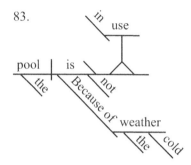

Because of is a phrasal preposition. The prepositional phrase *in use* functions as a predicate adjective.

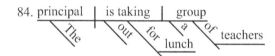

84.

Out for is not a phrasal preposition. *Out* is an adverb in this sentence.

85.

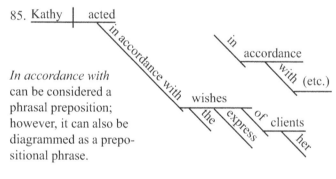

In accordance with can be considered a phrasal preposition; however, it can also be diagrammed as a prepositional phrase.

86.

The adverb *just* modifies the preposition *before*. Adverbs can modify not only verbs, adjectives, and other adverbs, but also prepositions.

87.

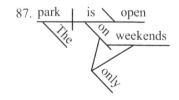

The adverb *only* modifies the prepositional phrase *on weekends*. Adverbs can modify both prepositions and prepositional phrases.

Exercise 9: Indirect Objects and Objective Complements

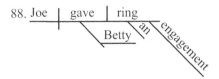

88. Joe | gave | ring

Betty (the person to whom something was given) is an indirect object. *Engagement* is a noun used as an adjective.

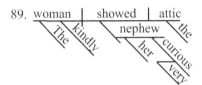

89. woman | showed | attic

In this sentence, the indirect object is *nephew* (the person to whom something was shown).

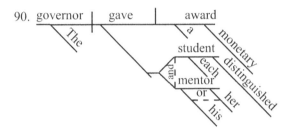

90. governor | gave | award

Student and *mentor* constitute a compound indirect object.

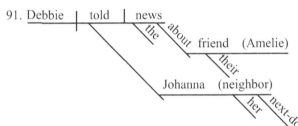

91. Debbie | told | news

Neighbor is in apposition with *Johanna*, an indirect object, while *Amelie* is in apposition with *friend*, the object of the preposition *about*.

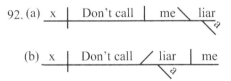

92. (a) x | Don't call | me \ liar

(b) x | Don't call / liar | me

Liar is an objective complement. The first diagram shows the modern way of diagramming an objective complement. The second diagram shows the traditional way.

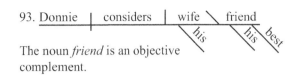

93. Donnie | considers | wife \ friend

The noun *friend* is an objective complement.

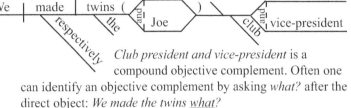

94. We | made | twins (Jim / Joe) club president and vice-president

Club president and vice-president is a compound objective complement. Often one can identify an objective complement by asking *what?* after the direct object: *We made the twins what?*

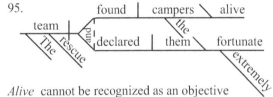

95. team | found | campers \ alive; declared | them \ fortunate

Alive cannot be recognized as an objective complement by asking *what?* Like all objective complements, it completes the action of the verb with respect to the direct object.

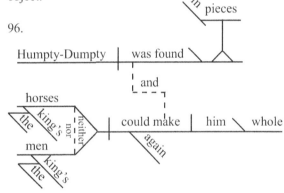

96. Humpty-Dumpty | was found \ in pieces; and horses | could make | him \ whole

The passive verb *was found* functions here as a linking verb, and the prepositional phrase *in pieces* serves as a predicate adjective. If the first main clause were active (*they found him in pieces*), *in pieces* would be an objective complement, like *alive* in Sentence 95.

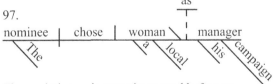

97. nominee | chose | woman \ as manager

The expletive *as* is sometimes used before an objective complement.

Exercise 10: Adverbial Objectives, Retained Objects, and the Expletive *There*

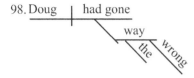

The noun *way* modifies the verb *had gone*. Nouns that modify the kinds of words that adverbs modify are called adverbial objectives.

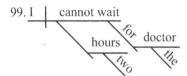

Like *way* in the previous sentence, *hours* is an adverbial objective. Most transitive verbs can be used passively. *Two hours were waited for the doctor* doesn't work.

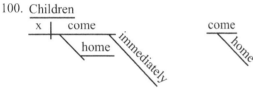

Children is a noun of direct address (a vocative). *Home* can be construed as an adverbial objective or as a pure adverb.

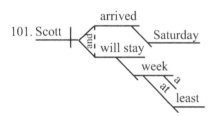

Both *Saturday* and *week* are adverbial objectives.

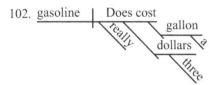

Although we say colloquially *What does gas cost?*, what we mean is *How much does gas cost? Dollars* is an adverbial objective. On the other hand, in the sentence *Gas costs money*, *money* is a direct object even though the sentence has no passive equivalent (more about this in Lesson 24).

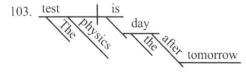

Day, an adverbial objective, is modified by the prepositional phrase *after tomorrow*.

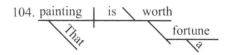

The noun *fortune*, an adverbial objective, modifies the predicate adjective *worth*.

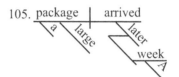

The adverbial objective *week* modifies the adverb *later*.

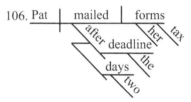

Two days does not tell how long she mailed her tax forms, but how long after the deadline she mailed them. Thus the adverbial objective *days* modifies the preposition *after*.

The subject of this passive-voice sentence, *Sandy*, is the indirect object in an equivalent sentence in the active voice (see Ecercise 9, Sentence 88). The direct object of the active sentence (*ring*), which is retained in the passive sentence, is called a retained object.

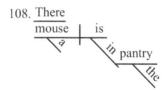

The expletive *there* announces that the subject will follow the verb.

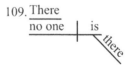

The second *there* is not an expletive but an adverb meaning "at that place."

Exercise 11: Infinitives

110.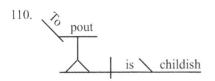

The infinitive *to pout* is the subject of the sentence.

111.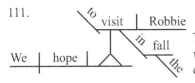

The infinitive phrase *to visit Robbie in the fall* is the direct object.

112.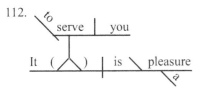

The infinitive phrase *to serve you* is in apposition with the subject of the sentence, *it*.

113.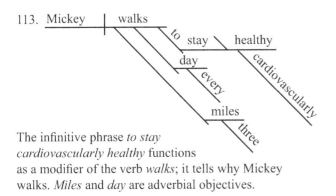

The infinitive phrase *to stay cardiovascularly healthy* functions as a modifier of the verb *walks*; it tells why Mickey walks. *Miles* and *day* are adverbial objectives.

114.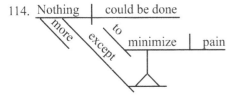

The infinitive phrase *to minimize pain* is the object of the preposition *except*.

115.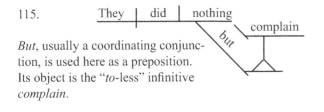

But, usually a coordinating conjunction, is used here as a preposition. Its object is the "*to*-less" infinitive *complain*.

116.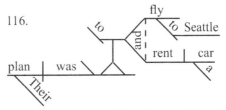

The compound infinitive phrase *to fly to Seatle and rent a car* serves as a predicate nominative.

117.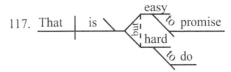

The infinitives *to promise* and *to do* function here as adverbial modifiers. They modify the predicate adjectives *easy* and *hard*, respectively.

118.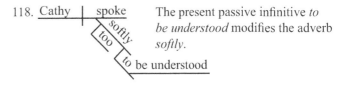

The present passive infinitive *to be understood* modifies the adverb *softly*.

119.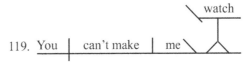

The "*to*-less" infinitive *watch* is used as an objective complement. Sentences 119 and 120 demonstrate the two acceptable ways of diagramming objective complements.

120.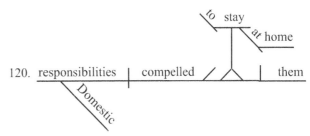

The infinitive phrase *to stay at home* functions here as an objective complement.

121.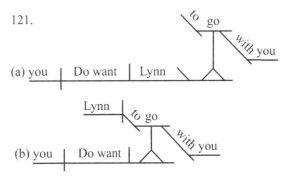

Lynn can be construed (a) as a direct object or (b) as the subject of an infinitive phrase.

Exercise 12: Infinitives (2)

122.

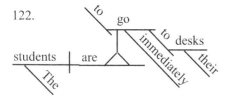

To go is a complementary infinitive. A verb and its complementary infinitive are, taken together, often equivalent to a verb phrase using a modal auxiliary verb or to a future-tense verb form. In this case, *are to go* can be expressed as *must go*.

123.

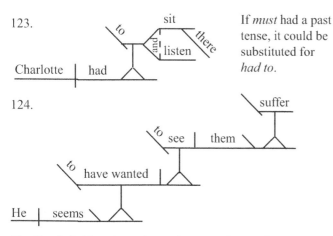

If *must* had a past tense, it could be substituted for *had to*.

124.

The first infinitive phrase is used as a predicate adjective and the second as a direct object. The *to*-less infinitive *suffer* is an objective complement.

125.

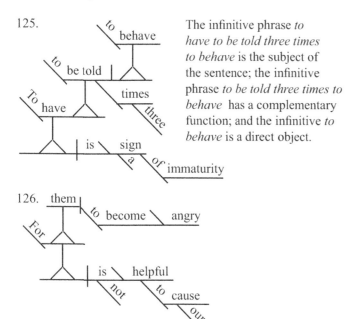

The infinitive phrase *to have to be told three times to behave* is the subject of the sentence; the infinitive phrase *to be told three times to behave* has a complementary function; and the infinitive *to behave* is a direct object.

126.

The word *for* as used in this sentence can be called an expletive. It has has no meaning but only the function of introducing an infinitive phrase and its objective-case subject. If the sentence were expressed as *It is not helpful to our cause for them to become angry*, the *for*-phrase would be in apposition with the subject *it*.

127.

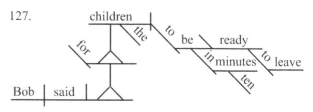

The infinitive phrase introduced by the expletive *for* is the direct object of *said*. *Children* is the subject of the infinitive *to be*.

128. Students

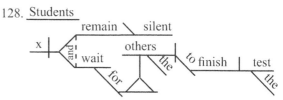

This imperative sentence has a compound predicate. The word *for* in this sentence is a preposition, not an expletive. *Students* is a vocative.

129.

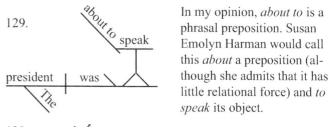

In my opinion, *about to* is a phrasal preposition. Susan Emolyn Harman would call this *about* a preposition (although she admits that it has little relational force) and *to speak* its object.

130.

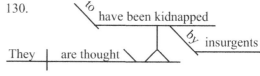

The present-perfect passive infintive *to have been kidnapped*, along with its modifying prepositional phrase, functions here as a predicate adjective. The passive verb *are thought* acts as a linking verb.

131.

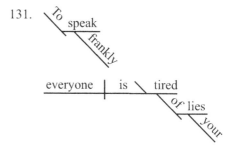

To speak frankly is an independent phrase.

Exercise 13: Gerunds

132.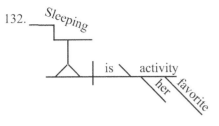

The gerund *sleeping* is the subject of the sentence.

133.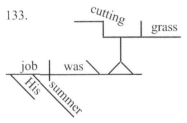

The gerund phrase *cutting grass* functions as the predicate nominative.

134.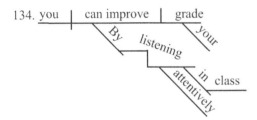

The gerund phrase *listening attentively in class* is the object of the preposition *by*.

135.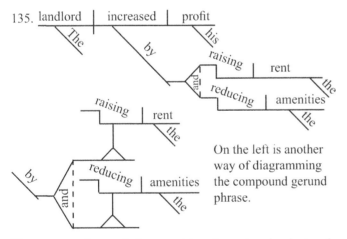

On the left is another way of diagramming the compound gerund phrase.

The compound gerund phrase *raising the rent and reducing the amenities* is the object of the preposition *by*.

136.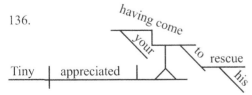

The gerund phrase introduced by the present-perfect gerund *having come* functions as the dierct object. Adjectival modifiers of gerunds are placed under the upper horizontal line, adverbial modifiers under the lower line.

137.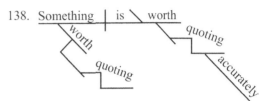

The gerund phrase *fraternizing with the enemy* is an objective complement, which is diagrammed here in the traditional manner.

138.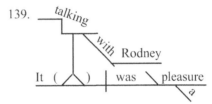

Each *quoting* is an adverbial objective. The first modifies an attributive adjective, the second a predicate adjective.

139.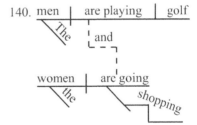

The gerund phrase *talking with Rodney* is in apposition with the subject of the sentence, *it*.

140.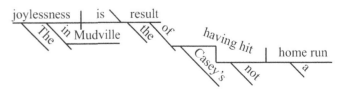

Shopping is a gerund used as an adverbial objective. It tells where the women are going. *Playing* and *going* are participial components of progressive verb forms.

141.

joylessness | is \ result ... The ... in Mudville ... the ... of ... having hit | home run ... Casey's ... not ... a

The gerund phrase *Casey's not having hit a home* contains the adjectival modifier *Casey's* and the adverbial modifier *not*. *Having hit* is a present-perfect active gerund.

Exercise 14: Participles

142.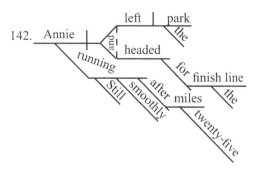

Running is a present participle. It introduces a participial phrase that modifies the subject of the sentence, *Annie*. The sentence has a compound predicate.

143.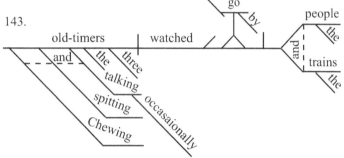

A compound participial phrase featuring three present participles modifies the subject of the sentence, *old-timers*. *Go by* is a "*to*-less" infinitive phrase used as an objective complement. It is diagrammed here the traditional way.

144.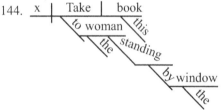

Take is an imperative. The subject *you* is understood. The present participle *standing* modifies *woman*, the object of the preposition *to*.

145.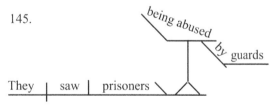

The present passive participle *being abused* introduces a participial phrase that functions as an objective complement.

146.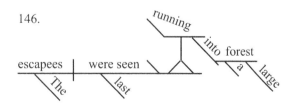

Were seen acts here as a linking verb; the participial phrase *running into a large forest* is used as a predicate adjective.

147.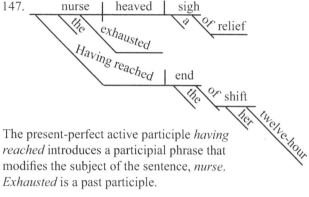

The present-perfect active participle *having reached* introduces a participial phrase that modifies the subject of the sentence, *nurse*. *Exhausted* is a past participle.

148.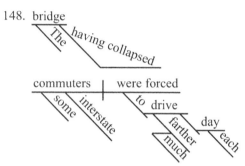

The bridge having collapsed is a nominative absolute. *Having collapsed* is a present-perfect participle.

149.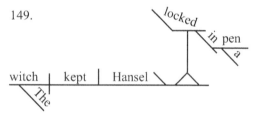

The participial phrase *locked in a pen* functions here as an objective complement. *Locked* is a past participle.

150.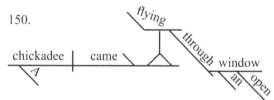

Came functions here as a linking verb. *Flying through an open window* is a participial phrase used as a predicate adjective.

151.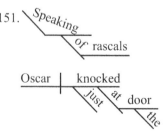

Speaking of rascals is an independent participial phrase.

Exercise 15: Adverb Clauses

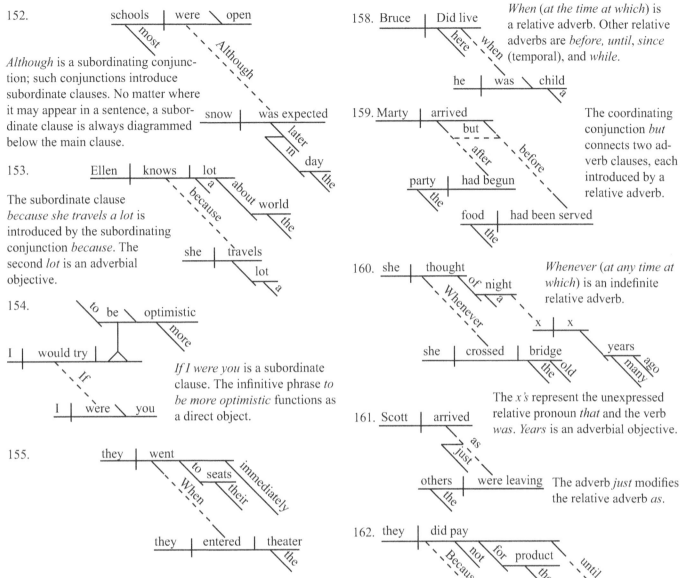

152.

Although is a subordinating conjunction; such conjunctions introduce subordinate clauses. No matter where it may appear in a sentence, a subordinate clause is always diagrammed below the main clause.

153.

The subordinate clause *because she travels a lot* is introduced by the subordinating conjunction *because*. The second *lot* is an adverbial objective.

154.

If I were you is a subordinate clause. The infinitive phrase *to be more optimistic* functions as a direct object.

155.

When is equivalent to two prepositional phrases: *at the time* and *at which*, the second of which includes a relative pronoun. *When's* modification of both *went* and *entered* is shown in the diagram by the solid ends of the line upon which *when* rests.

156.

As is also a relative adverb. Some scholars make no distinction between subordinating conjunctions and relative adverbs, using the former term for both.

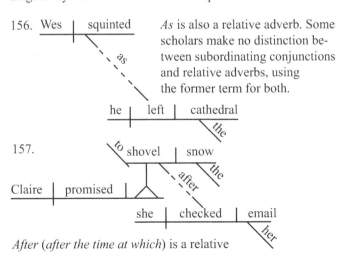

157.

After (after the time at which) is a relative adverb.

158.

When (at the time at which) is a relative adverb. Other relative adverbs are *before, until, since* (temporal), and *while*.

159.

The coordinating conjunction *but* connects two adverb clauses, each introduced by a relative adverb.

160.

Whenever (at any time at which) is an indefinite relative adverb.

The *x's* represent the unexpressed relative pronoun *that* and the verb *was. Years* is an adverbial objective.

161.

The adverb *just* modifies the relative adverb *as*.

162.

This sentence has two subordinate clauses, the first introduced by a subordinating conjunction, *because*, the second by a relative adverb, *until* (the equivalent of *until the time at which*).

163.

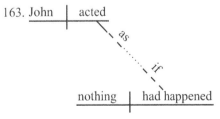

As if is a compound conjunction consisting of a relative adverb and a subordinating conjunction (*John acted in the way in which he would have acted if nothing had happened*). The dots represent the ellipsis between *as* and *if*.

Exercise 16: Adverb Clauses (2)

164.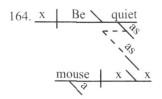

In an equal comparison, the second *as* is a relative adverb. Think: *Be quiet in the degree in which a mouse is quiet.*

165.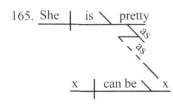

The elliptical subordinate clause can be expanded to *as she can be pretty* or *as anyone can be pretty*. Once again, the second *as* is a relative adverb.

166.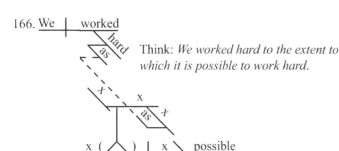

Think: *We worked hard to the extent to which it is possible to work hard.*

167.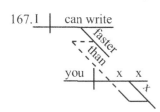

The relative advverb *than* is used in an unequal comparison. Think: *I can write fast beyond the degree in which you can write fast.*

168.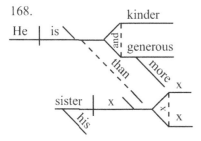

This comparative sentence contains a compound comparative adjective. The relative adverb is *than*.

169.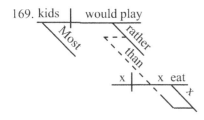

Think: *Most kids would play gladly beyond the degree in which they would eat gladly.*

170.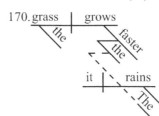

This sentence features the correlatives *the . . . the*. Think: *The grass grows faster according to the extent to which it rains more.* The first correlative *the* is an ordinary adverb, the second a relative adverb.

171.

Think: *It is merrier according to the extent to which there are more.*

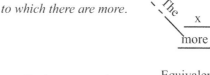

The exact expansion of this elliptical sentence depends on its context. It could be *The more there are, the merrier it is.*

172.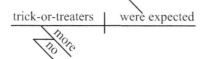

Equivalent expression: *It was late in a degree in which no more trick-or-treaters were expected.*

173.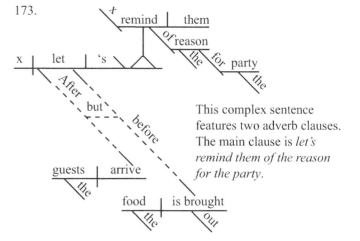

This complex sentence features two adverb clauses. The main clause is *let's remind them of the reason for the party.*

174.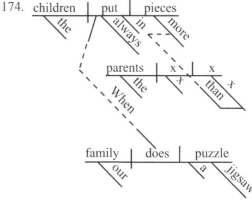

This sentence has two subordinate clauses: one introduced by *when*, a relative adverb of time, the other by *than*, a relative adverb of comparison. The *x*'s stand for *put in many pieces*.

Exercise 17: Adjective Clauses

175.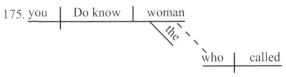

The relative pronoun *who* is the subject of the relative clause *who called*. Its antecedent is the direct object of the main clause, *woman*.

176.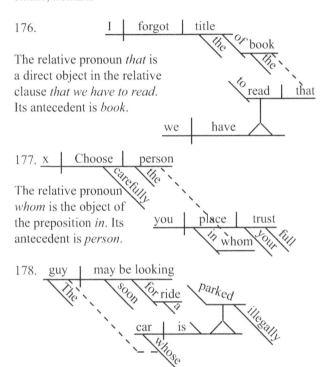

The relative pronoun *that* is a direct object in the relative clause *that we have to read*. Its antecedent is *book*.

177.

The relative pronoun *whom* is the object of the preposition *in*. Its antecedent is *person*.

178.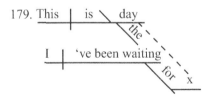

The relative pronoun *whose*, a possessive modifier of the noun *car*, has *guy* as its antecedent.

179.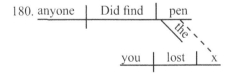

The relative pronoun *that*, the object of the preposition *for*, is unexpressed. Its antecedent is *day*.

180.

The relative pronoun *that*, the direct object of *lost*, is unexpressed. Its antecedent is *pen*.

181.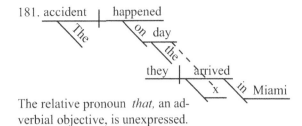

The relative pronoun *that,* an adverbial objective, is unexpressed.

182.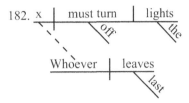

The indefinite relative pronoun *whoever* is the subject of the relative clause *whoever leaves last*. Its antecedent is the unexpressed subject of the main clause.

183.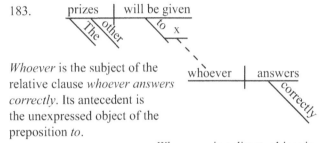

Whoever is the subject of the relative clause *whoever answers correctly*. Its antecedent is the unexpressed object of the preposition *to*.

Whomever is a direct object in the relative clause *whomever she likes best*. Its antecedent is the object of the preposition *with*.

184.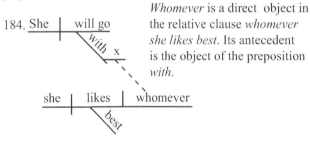

185.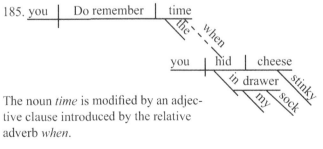

The noun *time* is modified by an adjective clause introduced by the relative adverb *when*.

186.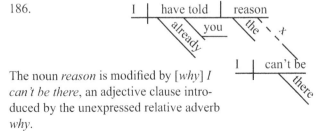

The noun *reason* is modified by [*why*] *I can't be there*, an adjective clause introduced by the unexpressed relative adverb *why*.

Exercise 18: Noun Clauses

187.

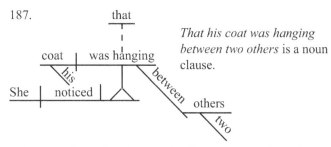

That his coat was hanging between two others is a noun clause.

This noun clause functions as the direct object of the verb *noticed*. It is introduced by the expletive *that*.

188.

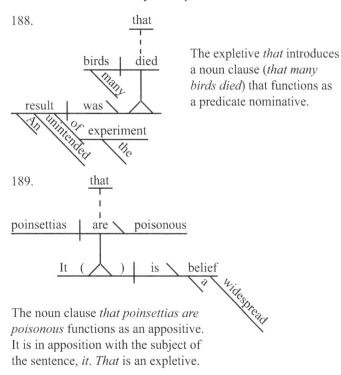

The expletive *that* introduces a noun clause (*that many birds died*) that functions as a predicate nominative.

189.

The noun clause *that poinsettias are poisonous* functions as an appositive. It is in apposition with the subject of the sentence, *it. That* is an expletive.

190.

The noun clause *when the game starts* is the direct object of the verb *know.*

191.

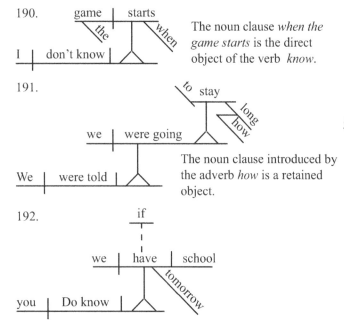

The noun clause introduced by the adverb *how* is a retained object.

192.

The noun clause *if we have school tomorrow* functions as the direct object of *know. If* is an expletive.

193.

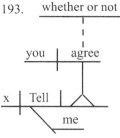

The phrasal expletive *whether or not* introduces a noun clause that functions as a direct object. In this imperative sentence, *x* represents the unexpressed subject *you.*

194.

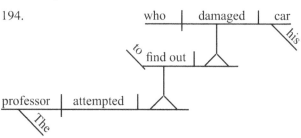

The interrogative pronoun *who* introduces a noun clause that functions as the direct object of the phrasal verb *find out.*

195.

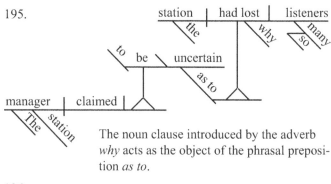

The noun clause introduced by the adverb *why* acts as the object of the phrasal preposition *as to.*

196.

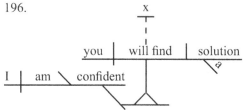

The noun clause introduced by the unexpressed expletive *that* functions as an adverbial objective.

197.

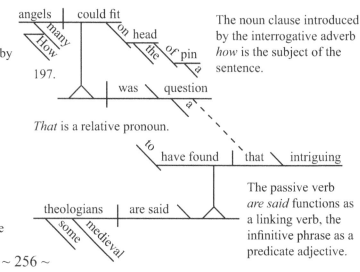

The noun clause introduced by the interrogative adverb *how* is the subject of the sentence.

That is a relative pronoun.

The passive verb *are said* functions as a linking verb, the infinitive phrase as a predicate adjective.

Exercise 19: Compound-Complex Sentences

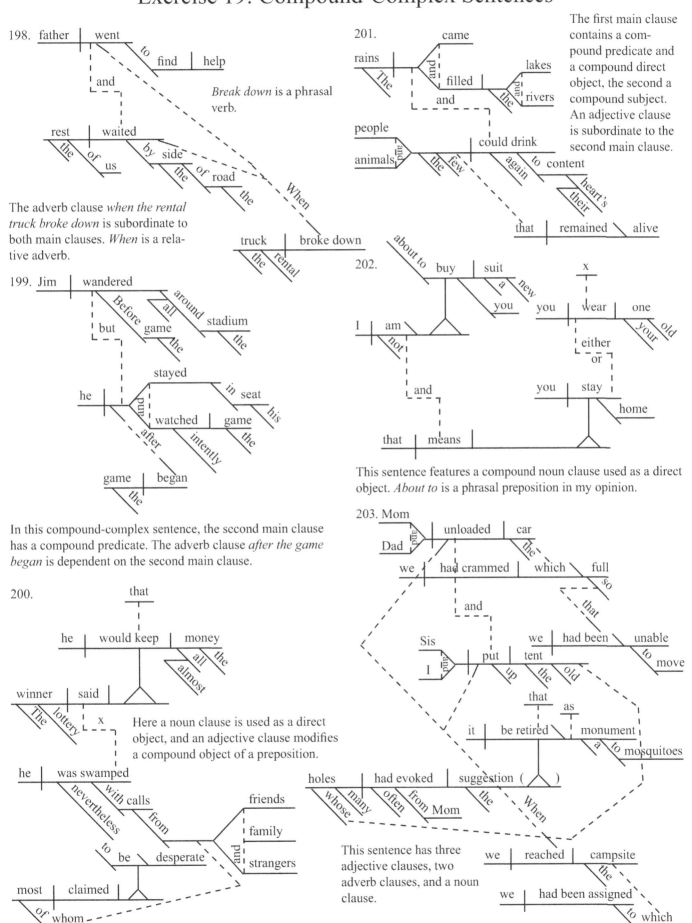

198.

Break down is a phrasal verb.

The adverb clause *when the rental truck broke down* is subordinate to both main clauses. *When* is a relative adverb.

199. Jim

In this compound-complex sentence, the second main clause has a compound predicate. The adverb clause *after the game began* is dependent on the second main clause.

200.

Here a noun clause is used as a direct object, and an adjective clause modifies a compound object of a preposition.

201.

The first main clause contains a compound predicate and a compound direct object, the second a compound subject. An adjective clause is subordinate to the second main clause.

202.

This sentence features a compound noun clause used as a direct object. *About to* is a phrasal preposition in my opinion.

203. Mom

This sentence has three adjective clauses, two adverb clauses, and a noun clause.

~ 257 ~

Exercise 20: Prepositional Phrases (2)

204.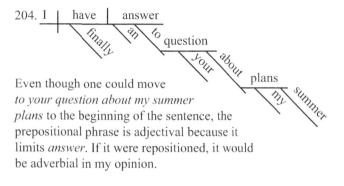

Even though one could move *to your question about my summer plans* to the beginning of the sentence, the prepositional phrase is adjectival because it limits *answer*. If it were repositioned, it would be adverbial in my opinion.

205.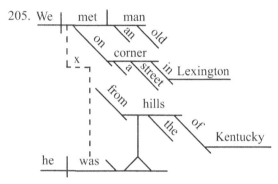

On a street corner in Lexington tells where the meeting occurred. *From the hills of Kentucky* expresses a characteristic of the man. Because of its position, *in Lexington* is adjectival (a Lexington street corner). If the sentence read *In Lexington we met a man . . . on a street corner*, *in Lexington* would be adverbial.

206.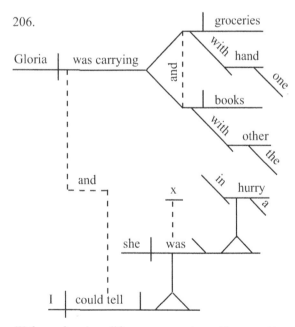

With one hand modifies *was carrying* with respect to *groceries*, and *with the other* modifies the same verb with respect to *books*. The prepositional phrase *in a hurry* functions as a predicate adjective; it expresses a quality of the subject at that particular time.

207.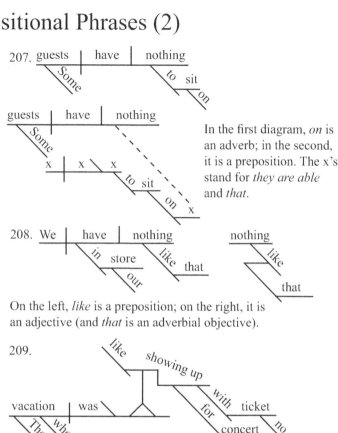

In the first diagram, *on* is an adverb; in the second, it is a preposition. The x's stand for *they are able* and *that*.

208.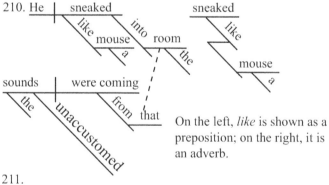

On the left, *like* is a preposition; on the right, it is an adjective (and *that* is an adverbial objective).

209.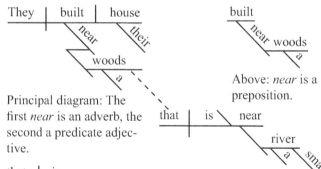

In the first analysis, *like* is a preposition; in the second, it is a predicate adjective. *Showing up* is a phrasal gerund.

210.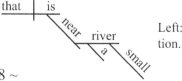

On the left, *like* is shown as a preposition; on the right, it is an adverb.

211.

Principal diagram: The first *near* is an adverb, the second a predicate adjective.

Above: *near* is a preposition.

Left: *near* is a preposition.

Exercise 21: Participles (2)

212.
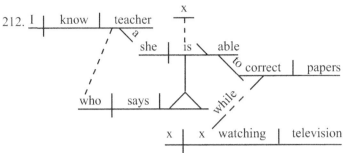

While watching television is an elliptical subordinate clause. The unexpressed words, represented in the diagram by *x*'s, are *she* and *is*.

213.
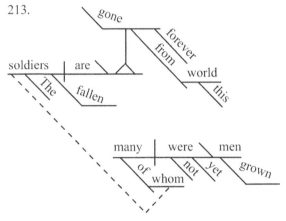

Most past participles are passive; however, *fallen, gone,* and *grown* (past participles of intransitive verbs) are not passive.

214.
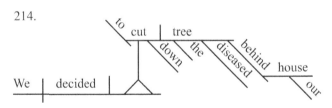

Don't let words like *diseased* fool you. Since *disease* is not a verb, *diseased* cannot be a participle. It's just a regular adjective.

215.
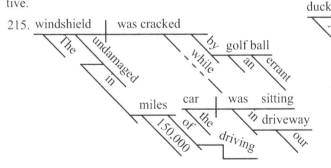

Undamaged is not a participle because *undamage* is not a verb. *Cracked* and *sitting* are participial components of finite verbs.

216.
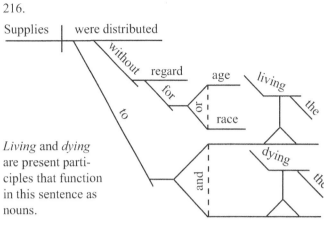

Living and *dying* are present participles that function in this sentence as nouns.

217.
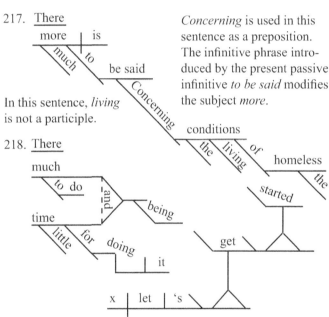

In this sentence, *living* is not a participle.

Concerning is used in this sentence as a preposition. The infinitive phrase introduced by the present passive infinitive *to be said* modifies the subject *more*.

218.

Being is a present participle used in a nominative absolute. *Started* is a past participle used as a predicate adjective.

219.
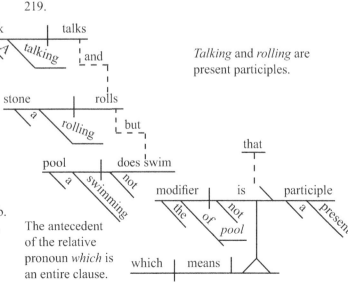

Talking and *rolling* are present participles.

The antecedent of the relative pronoun *which* is an entire clause.

Exercise 22: Adverbs (2), Adverbial objectives (2)

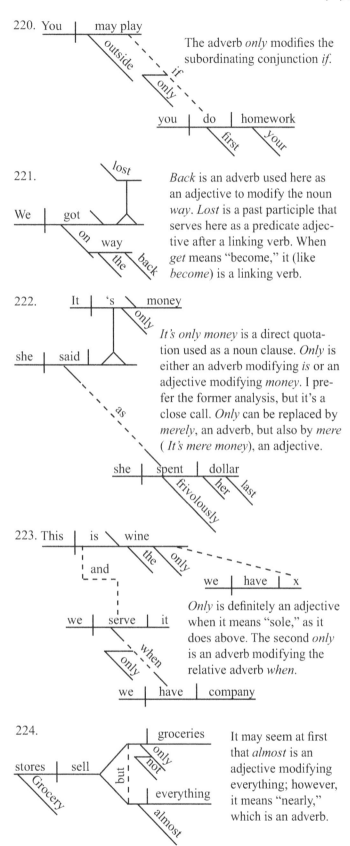

220. You | may play

The adverb *only* modifies the subordinating conjunction *if*.

221.

Back is an adverb used here as an adjective to modify the noun *way*. *Lost* is a past participle that serves here as a predicate adjective after a linking verb. When *get* means "become," it (like *become*) is a linking verb.

222.

It's only money is a direct quotation used as a noun clause. *Only* is either an adverb modifying *is* or an adjective modifying *money*. I prefer the former analysis, but it's a close call. *Only* can be replaced by *merely*, an adverb, but also by *mere* (*It's mere money*), an adjective.

223. This | is \ wine

Only is definitely an adjective when it means "sole," as it does above. The second *only* is an adverb modifying the relative adverb *when*.

224.

It may seem at first that *almost* is an adjective modifying everything; however, it means "nearly," which is an adverb.

Two delayed direct-object lines are used, which makes it possible to show that *not only* modifies the verb with respect to the first direct object, and *almost* modifies the verb with respect to the second direct object.

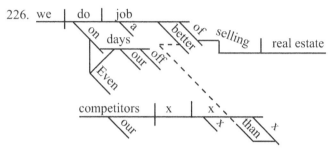

Few is an interesting word. It can be a pronoun (*Few came to the performance*), a noun (*A few came to the performance*), and an adjective (*Few people came to the performance*). See Sentence 246 in Exercise 24 for an explanation of *quite a few*.

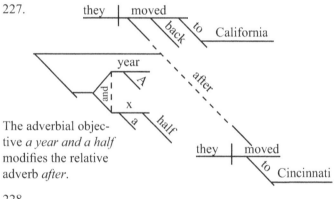

Off is an adverb used as an adjective to modify the noun *days*. The adverb *even* modifies the prepositional phrase *on our off days*. The x's in the elliptical clause stand for *do a good job*.

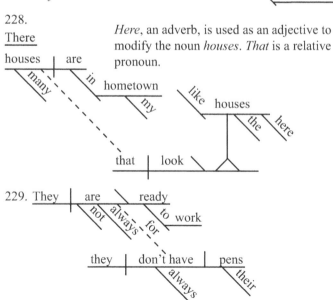

The adverbial objective *a year and a half* modifies the relative adverb *after*.

228.

Here, an adverb, is used as an adjective to modify the noun *houses*. *That* is a relative pronoun.

229. They | are \ ready

The contraction *don't* implies that *not* modifies the verb (and not *always*), even when *not* is not contracted.

~ 260 ~

Exercise 23: Gerunds (2)

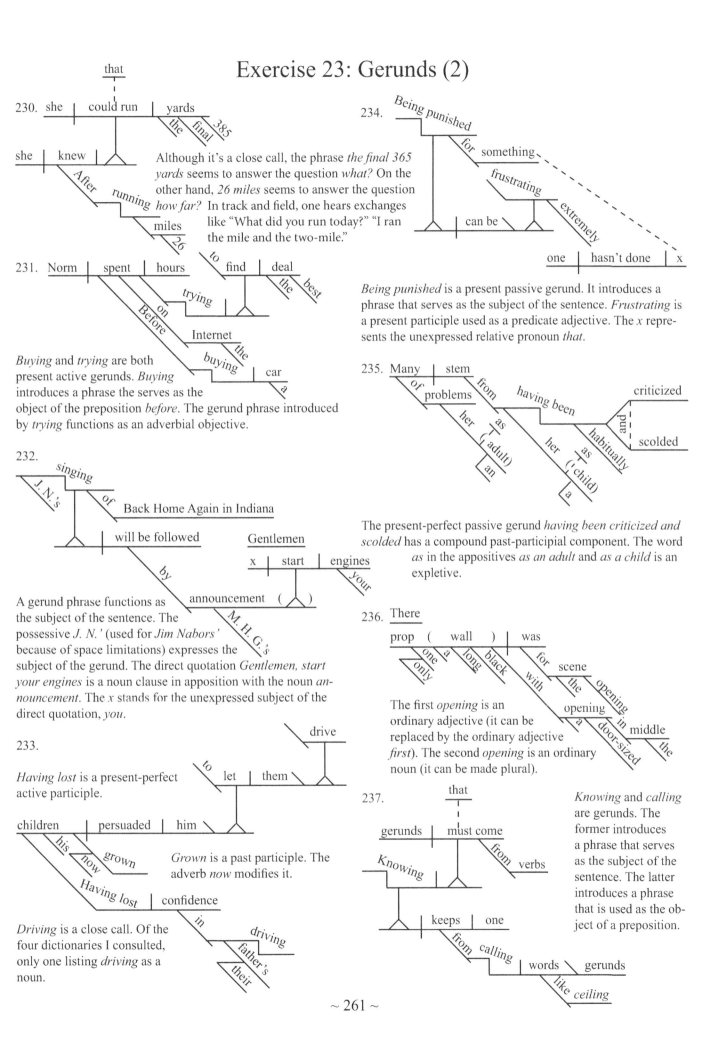

230.

Although it's a close call, the phrase *the final 365 yards* seems to answer the question *what?* On the other hand, *26 miles* seems to answer the question *how far?* In track and field, one hears exchanges like "What did you run today?" "I ran the mile and the two-mile."

231.

Buying and *trying* are both present active gerunds. *Buying* introduces a phrase the serves as the object of the preposition *before*. The gerund phrase introduced by *trying* functions as an adverbial objective.

232.

A gerund phrase functions as the subject of the sentence. The possessive *J. N. '* (used for *Jim Nabors'* because of space limitations) expresses the subject of the gerund. The direct quotation *Gentlemen, start your engines* is a noun clause in apposition with the noun *announcement*. The *x* stands for the unexpressed subject of the direct quotation, *you.*

233.

Having lost is a present-perfect active participle.

Grown is a past participle. The adverb *now* modifies it.

Driving is a close call. Of the four dictionaries I consulted, only one listing *driving* as a noun.

234.

Being punished is a present passive gerund. It introduces a phrase that serves as the subject of the sentence. *Frustrating* is a present participle used as a predicate adjective. The *x* represents the unexpressed relative pronoun *that.*

235.

The present-perfect passive gerund *having been criticized and scolded* has a compound past-participial component. The word *as* in the appositives *as an adult* and *as a child* is an expletive.

236.

The first *opening* is an ordinary adjective (it can be replaced by the ordinary adjective *first*). The second *opening* is an ordinary noun (it can be made plural).

237.

Knowing and *calling* are gerunds. The former introduces a phrase that serves as the subject of the sentence. The latter introduces a phrase that is used as the object of a preposition.

~ 261 ~

Exercise 24: Miscellaneous

238.

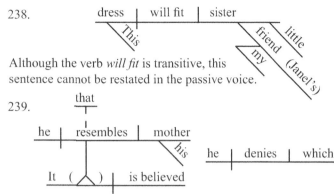

Although the verb *will fit* is transitive, this sentence cannot be restated in the passive voice.

239.

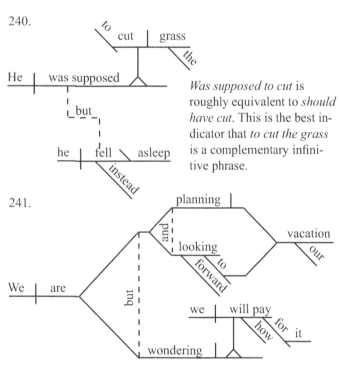

The antecedent of the relative pronoun *which* is the noun clause *that he resembles his mother.* When the antecedent is a phrase or a clause, no line is drawn between it and the relative pronoun. *Resembles* is a "middle verb."

240.

Was supposed to cut is roughly equivalent to *should have cut.* This is the best indicator that *to cut the grass* is a complementary infinitive phrase.

241.

Vacation is both the direct object of *are planning* and the object of the preposition *to.*

242.

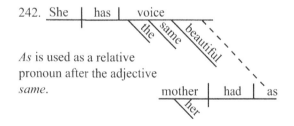

As is used as a relative pronoun after the adjective *same.*

243.

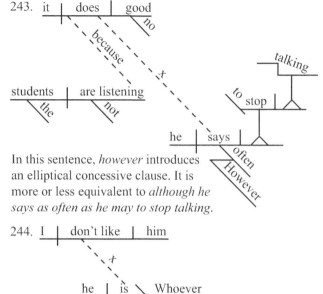

In this sentence, *however* introduces an elliptical concessive clause. It is more or less equivalent to *although he says as often as he may to stop talking.*

244.

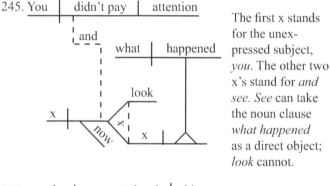

The *x* stands for the unexpressed subordinating conjunction *although. Whoever he is,* an elliptical clause, is roughly equivalent to *although he may be anyone you please.*

245.

The first x stands for the unexpressed subject, *you.* The other two x's stand for *and* and *see. See* can take the noun clause *what happened* as a direct object; *look* cannot.

246.

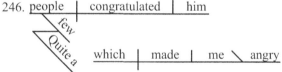

It seems that *quite a* must be construed as a phrasal modifier of *few*; otherwise we are left with *quite* modifying the noun *few* or the article *a,* neither of which is possible.

247.

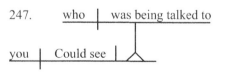

If the noun clause were expressed actively, it would be *whom they (he, she) were (was) talking to,* in which *whom* is the object of the preposition *to.* In the passive rendition, *whom* is replaced by *who* (now the the subject of the clause), and *to* ceases to be a preposition. In my opinion, *to* becomes part of the verb.

People in the Park: Story 1

1.

The *x* represents the unexpressed subject *you.*

2.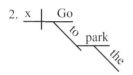

To the park is an adverbial preposi-tional phrase modifying the verb *go.* It consists of the preposition *to,* the object *park,* and the article *the.*

3.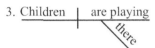

Children is the subject of the sentence. *Are playing* is a present-progressive verb. *There,* an adverb, modifies the verb.

4.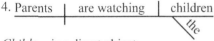

Children is a direct object.

5.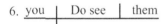

The personal pronoun *they* is the subject of the sentence, and the adjective *proud* is a predicate adjective. The linking verb *are* is a present-tense form of the verb *be.*

6.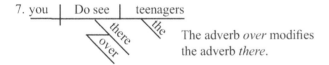

Since *do* is the first word of the sentence, it is capitalized.

7.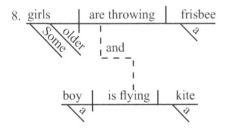

The adverb *over* modifies the adverb *there.*

8.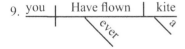

Some and *older* are attributive adjectives modifying *girls.* The coordinating conjunction *and* joins the two main clauses of this compound sentence.

9.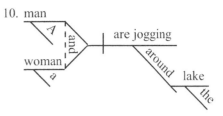

The verb *have flown* is in the present-perfect tense.

10.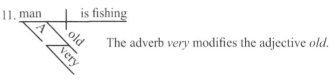

A man and a woman is a compound subject. *Man* and *woman* are joined by the coordinating conjunction *and.*

11.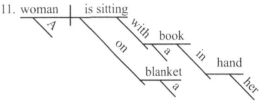

The adverb *very* modifies the adjective *old.*

11.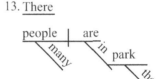

The prepositional phrase *in her hand* is adjectival; it modifies *book.* The other two prepositional phrases in this sentence are adverbial.

13.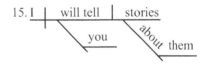

There is often an adverb; how-ever, in this sentence, it is an expletive. It announces that the subject will follow the verb.

14.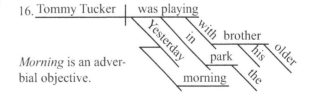

Storyteller is a predicate nominative. The linking verb *am* is a present-tense form of the verb *be.*

15.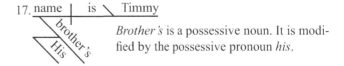

You is an indirect object. It tells *to whom* the stories will be told.

People in the Park: Story 2

16. Tommy Tucker | was playing

Morning is an adver-bial objective.

17. name | is \ Timmy

Brother's is a possessive noun. It is modi-fied by the possessive pronoun *his.*

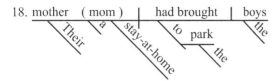

18.

Mom, an appositive, is in apposition with the subject of the sentence, *mother*.

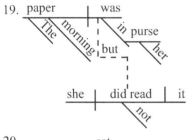

19.

This compound sentence consists of two main clauses joined by the coordinating conjunction *but*.

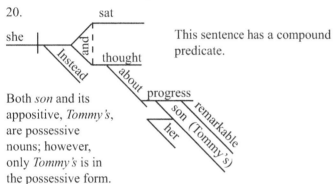

20.

This sentence has a compound predicate.

Both *son* and its appositive, *Tommy's*, are possessive nouns; however, only *Tommy's* is in the possessive form.

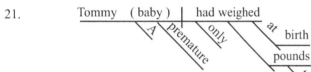

21.

One expects an appositive to follow the word or words with which it is in apposition; however, *baby*, an appositive, precedes *Tommy*, the noun with which it is in apposition. *Only*, an adverb, modifies the verb *had weighed*; it means "this much and no more" here.

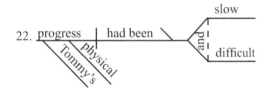

22.

Slow and difficult is a compound predicate adjective.

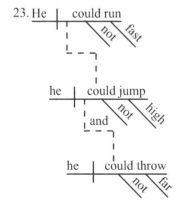

23.

This compound sentence consists of three main clauses. The coordinating conjunction is *and*.

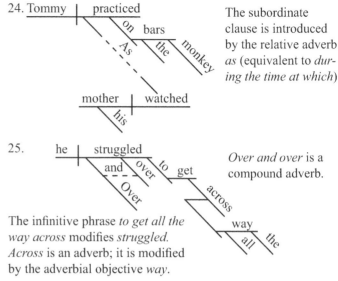

24.

The subordinate clause is introduced by the relative adverb *as* (equivalent to *during the time at which*)

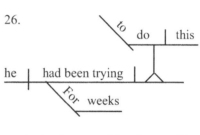

25.

Over and over is a compound adverb.

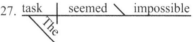

The infinitive phrase *to get all the way across* modifies *struggled*. *Across* is an adverb; it is modified by the adverbial objective *way*.

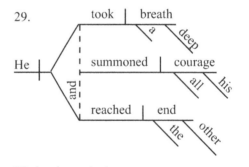

26.

The infinitive phrase *to do this* is the direct object of the verb *had been trying*. The demonstrative pronoun *this* is the direct object of the infinitive *to do*.

27. task | seemed \ impossible

Seemed is a linking verb. *Impossible* is a predicate adjective.

28. Tommy | did do | What

What, an interrogative pronoun, comes first in the sentence, but it isn't the subject of the sentence; it's a direct object.

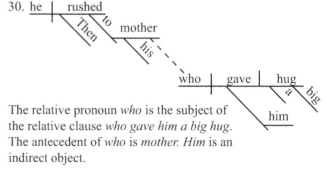

29.

Each part of the tripartite compound predicate includes a direct object with two modifiers.

30.

The relative pronoun *who* is the subject of the relative clause *who gave him a big hug*. The antecedent of *who* is *mother*. *Him* is an indirect object.

People in the Park: Story 3

31.

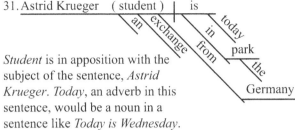

Astrid Krueger (student) | is
an exchange
in
from
today
park
the
Germany

Student is in apposition with the subject of the sentence, *Astrid Krueger. Today*, an adverb in this sentence, would be a noun in a sentence like *Today is Wednesday.*

32.

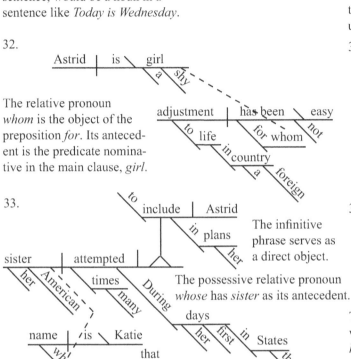

Astrid | is \ girl
a
shy
adjustment | has been \ easy
to life
in country
a
foreign
for whom
not

The relative pronoun *whom* is the object of the preposition *for*. Its antecedent is the predicate nominative in the main clause, *girl.*

33.

to include | Astrid
in plans
her

The infinitive phrase serves as a direct object.

sister | attempted
her
American
times
many
During
days
her
first
in States
the
name | is \ Katie
whose
that

The possessive relative pronoun *whose* has *sister* as its antecedent.

she | had | something
to do

34.

Astrid | would say |
ashamed
of
English
her
imperfect

The prepositional phrase *of her imperfect English* modifies the adjective *ashamed.*

The noun clause *that she had something to do* functions as the direct object of the verb *would say; that* is an expletive.

35.

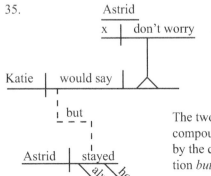

Astrid
x | don't worry
Katie | would say
but
Astrid | stayed
always
home

Astrid is a vocative (a.k.a. nominative of direct address). The *x* represents the unexpressed subject *you.*

The two main clauses of this compound sentence are joined by the coordinating conjunction *but. Home* could be construed also as an adverbial objective.

36.

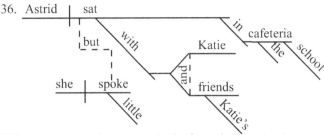

Astrid | sat
but
she | spoke
little
with
Katie
and
friends
Katie's
in cafeteria
the
school

This is a compound sentence. In the first of two main clauses, the preposition *with* has a compound object. The noun *school* is used here as an adjective.

37.

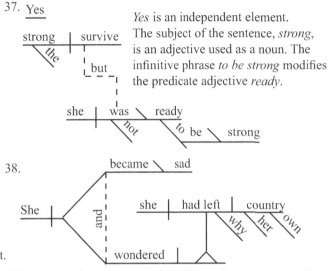

Yes

strong | survive
the
but

she | was \ ready
not
to be \ strong

Yes is an independent element. The subject of the sentence, *strong*, is an adjective used as a noun. The infinitive phrase *to be strong* modifies the predicate adjective *ready.*

38.

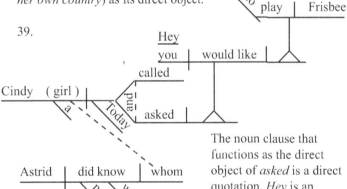

She
became \ sad
and
she | had left | country
why
her
own
wondered

This sentence has a compound predicate, the second part of which has a noun clause (the indirect question *why she had left her own country*) as its direct object.

39.

Hey
you | would like
to play | Frisbee
called
Cindy (girl) |
a
Today
and
asked
Astrid | did know | whom
not
well

The relative pronoun *whom* is the direct object of its relative clause. Its antecedent is *girl*, an appositive.

The noun clause that functions as the direct object of *asked* is a direct quotation. *Hey* is an exclamation, an independent element.

40.

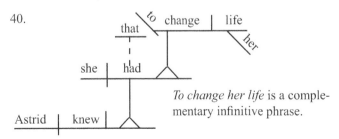

to change | life
that
her
she | had
Astrid | knew

To change her life is a complementary infinitive phrase.

The noun clause *that she had to change her life* is the direct object of the verb *knew. That* is an expletive.

41.

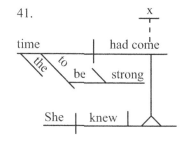

The noun clause *the time to be strong had come* is the direct object of *knew*. The *x* represents the unexpressed expletive *that*. The infinitive phrase *to be strong* modifies the subject of the noun clause, *time*.

42. There

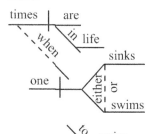

The relative adverb *when* (here equivalent to *at which*) modifies the compound verb *either sinks or swims*. The dependent clause *when one either sinks or swims* functions as an adjective modifying *times*.

43.

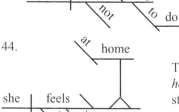

The antecedent of the relative pronoun *which* is the phrase *chose to swim*. This cannot be shown precisely in a Reed and Kellogg diagram. No broken line is drawn because there is no noun or pronoun antecedent.

44.

The prepositional phrase *at home*, which denotes a mental state and not a location, is a predicate adjective. *Feels* is a linking verb.

45.

A contraction consisting of a subject and a verb (e.g., *we're, that's, who's*), an expletive and a verb (*there's*), or an adverb and a verb (e.g., *where's, how's*), is separated in a sentence diagram.

Because is a subordinating conjunction.

People in the Park: Story 4

46. Rodney

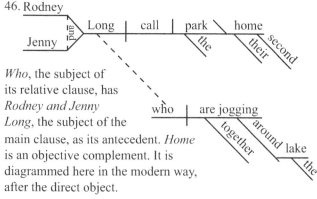

Who, the subject of its relative clause, has *Rodney and Jenny Long*, the subject of the main clause, as its antecedent. *Home* is an objective complement. It is diagrammed here in the modern way, after the direct object.

47.

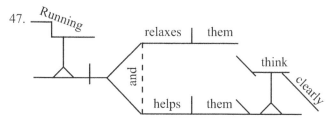

Running, a gerund, is the subject of the sentence. The "to-less" infinitive phrase *think clearly* is an objective complement.

48.

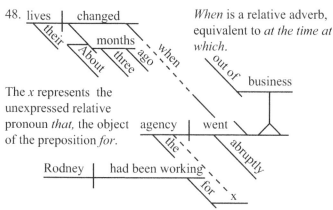

When is a relative adverb, equivalent to *at the time at which.*

The *x* represents the unexpressed relative pronoun *that*, the object of the preposition *for*.

In previous books, I analyzed similar *ago*-expressions differently. If *three months ago* in this sentence were analyzed in that manner, *ago* would be construed as an adverb modifying the verb *changed*, with *months* as an adverbial objective modifying *ago*. What I like better about the present analysis is that it does justice to dictionaries, which agree among themselves that *ago*, so used, is a postpositive attributive adjective.

49. He

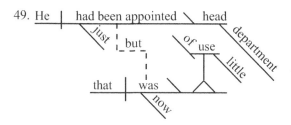

In this compound sentence, *department* is a noun used as an adjective. The prepositional phrase *of little use* functions as a predicate adjective.

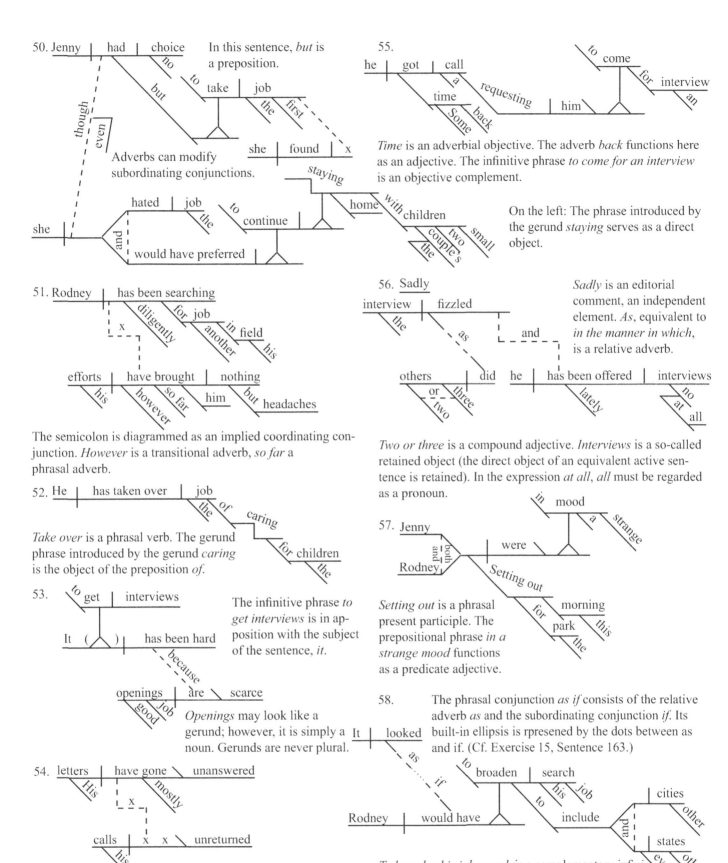

50. Jenny had choice no *but* to take the first job she found x

In this sentence, *but* is a preposition.

Adverbs can modify subordinating conjunctions.

though even she hated the job *and* would have preferred to continue staying home *with* children small two the couple's

51. Rodney has been searching diligently *for* another job *in* his field x

efforts his have brought nothing *but* headaches however so far him

The semicolon is diagrammed as an implied coordinating conjunction. *However* is a transitional adverb, *so far* a phrasal adverb.

52. He has taken over the job *of* caring *for* the children

Take over is a phrasal verb. The gerund phrase introduced by the gerund *caring* is the object of the preposition *of.*

53. to get interviews It ( ) has been hard because openings are scarce good job

The infinitive phrase *to get interviews* is in apposition with the subject of the sentence, *it.*

Openings may look like a gerund; however, it is simply a noun. Gerunds are never plural.

54. letters His have gone unanswered mostly x calls his x x unreturned

His calls unreturned is an elliptical clause; the full clause is *his calls have gone unreturned.* The x's in the diagram represent the unexpressed words *and, have,* and *gone. Unanswered* and *unreturned* are not participles but mere adjectives. Participles are verb forms, and there are no verbs *unanswer* and *unreturn.*

55. he got call a time Some back requesting him to come *for* an interview

Time is an adverbial objective. The adverb *back* functions here as an adjective. The infinitive phrase *to come for an interview* is an objective complement.

On the left: The phrase introduced by the gerund *staying* serves as a direct object.

56. Sadly interview the fizzled as *and* others did or three two he has been offered lately interviews no at all

Sadly is an editorial comment, an independent element. *As,* equivalent to *in the manner in which,* is a relative adverb.

Two or three is a compound adjective. *Interviews* is a so-called retained object (the direct object of an equivalent active sentence is retained). In the expression *at all, all* must be regarded as a pronoun.

57. Jenny both *and* Rodney were in mood a strange Setting out *for* the park this morning

Setting out is a phrasal present participle. The prepositional phrase *in a strange mood* functions as a predicate adjective.

58. It looked as if to broaden his search job to include cities other states even other

The phrasal conjunction *as if* consists of the relative adverb *as* and the subordinating conjunction *if.* Its built-in ellipsis is rpresened by the dots between as and if. (Cf. Exercise 15, Sentence 163.)

Rodney would have

To broaden his job search is a complementary infinitive phrase. The second infinitive phrase, *to include . . . other states* is adverbial; it modifies the infinitive *broaden.* Notice that the direct object indicator that normally would appear between *include* and the bracket is delayed to allow the diagram to show that *even* modifies *include* with respect to *states* only.

~ 267 ~

59.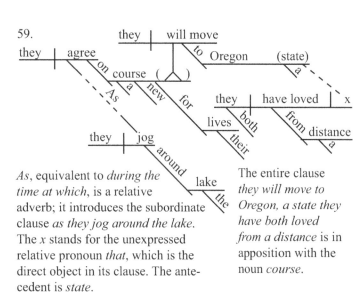

As, equivalent to *during the time at which*, is a relative adverb; it introduces the subordinate clause *as they jog around the lake*. The *x* stands for the unexpressed relative pronoun *that*, which is the direct object in its clause. The antecedent is *state*.

The entire clause *they will move to Oregon, a state they have both loved from a distance* is in apposition with the noun *course*.

60.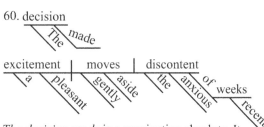

The decision made is a nominative absolute. It is not connected grammatically to the rest of the sentence. *Made* is a past participle.

People in the Park: Story 5

61.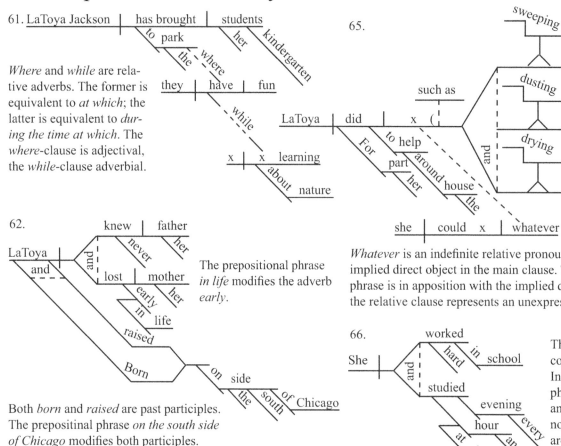

Where and *while* are relative adverbs. The former is equivalent to *at which*; the latter is equivalent to *during the time at which*. The *where*-clause is adjectival, the *while*-clause adverbial.

62.

The prepositional phrase *in life* modifies the adverb *early*.

Both *born* and *raised* are past participles. The prepositinal phrase *on the south side of Chicago* modifies both participles.

63.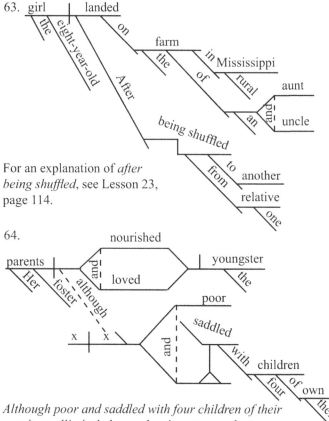

For an explanation of *after being shuffled*, see Lesson 23, page 114.

64.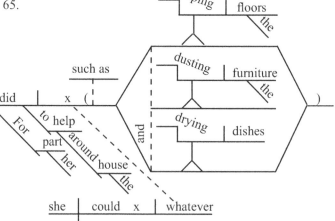

Although poor and saddled with four children of their own is an elliptical clause; the *x*'s represent the unexpressed words *they were*. *Of their own* is an idiomatic expression. The adjective *own* is used as a noun.

65.

Whatever is an indefinite relative pronoun. Its antecedent is an implied direct object in the main clause. The tripartite gerund phrase is in apposition with the implied direct object. The *x* in the relative clause represents an unexpressed *do*.

66.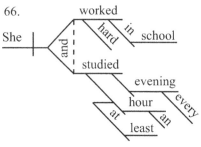

This sentence has a compound predicate. In the prepositional phrase *at least*, *least* is an adjective used as a noun. *Hour* and *evening* are adverbial objectives.

67.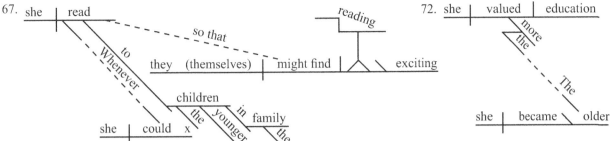

Whenever, equivalent to *at any time at which*, is an indefinite relative adverb. *So that* is a phrasal subordinating conjunction. The intensive pronoun *themselves*, like all intensive pronouns, is an appositive. *Reading* is a gerund; however, *exciting* is a simple adjective, since it can be replaced by an adjective like *fun*. *Exciting* is an objective complement. The *x* represents the unexpressed verb *read*.

68.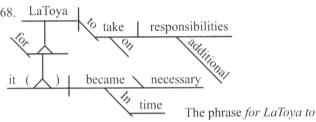

The phrase *for LaToya to take on additional responsibilities* is in apposition with the subject of the sentence, *it*. *LaToya* is the subject of the infinitive *to take*. *For*, an expletive, has little or no prepositional force.

69.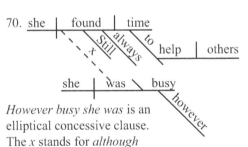

The "to-less" infinitive phrase *use every minute productively* functions as an objective complement.

70.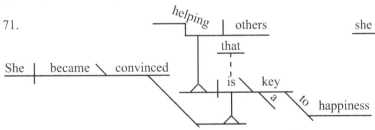

However busy she was is an elliptical concessive clause. The *x* stands for *although* (*Although she was busy to whatever degree, she still found time . . . .*).

71.

She | became \ convinced — helping | others — that | is | key | a | to happiness

The noun clause introduced by the expletive *that* is used here as an adverbial objective. The gerund phrase *helping others* is the subject of the noun clause. *Convinced* is a simple adjective.

72. she | valued | education — more — the — The — she | became \ older

Of the correlatives *the . . . the* (equivalent to *in the degree in which*), one is a simple adverb, the other a relative adverb. The sentence could be rephrased (awkwardly, to be sure, but as a means of showing what is happening grammatically in the sentence) as *She valued education more in the degree in which she became older.*

73.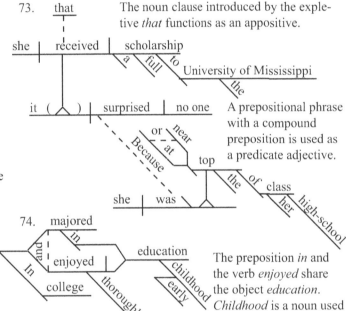

The noun clause introduced by the expletive *that* functions as an appositive.

A prepositional phrase with a compound preposition is used as a predicate adjective.

74.

she | majored / enjoyed | education — In college — thoroughly — childhood — early

The preposition *in* and the verb *enjoyed* share the object *education*. *Childhood* is a noun used here as an adjective.

75.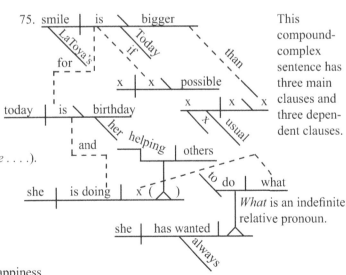

This compound-complex sentence has three main clauses and three dependent clauses.

What is an indefinite relative pronoun.

The clause implied by *than usual* is *than her usual smile is big*; the *x*'s represent the unexpressed words. The unexpressed words in *if possible* are *it is*, also represented by *x*'s.

~ 269 ~

People in the Park: Story 6

76.

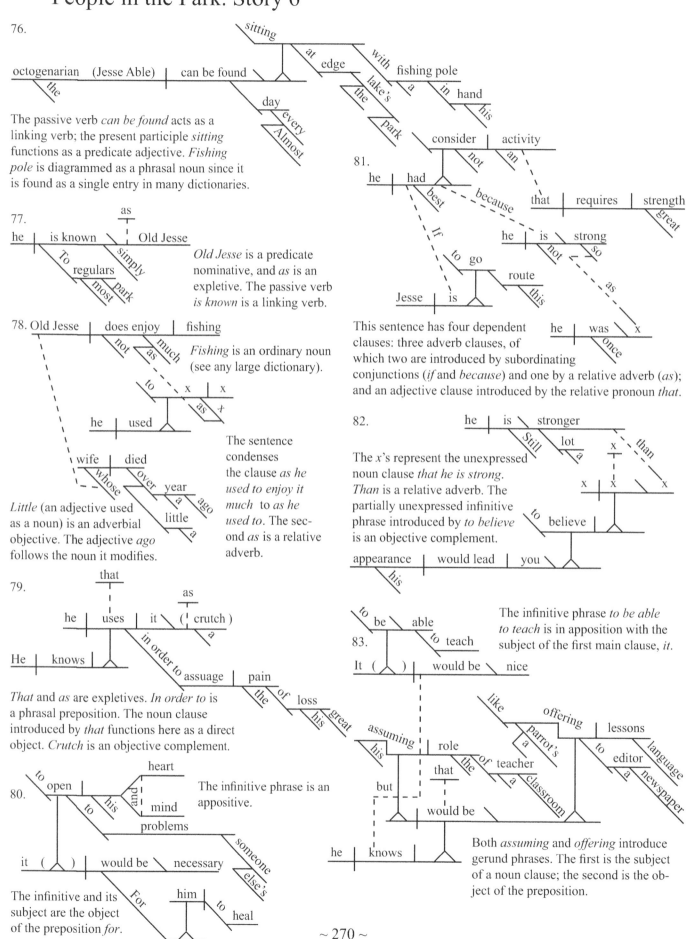

The passive verb *can be found* acts as a linking verb; the present participle *sitting* functions as a predicate adjective. *Fishing pole* is diagrammed as a phrasal noun since it is found as a single entry in many dictionaries.

77.

Old Jesse is a predicate nominative, and *as* is an expletive. The passive verb *is known* is a linking verb.

78.

Fishing is an ordinary noun (see any large dictionary).

The sentence condenses the clause *as he used to enjoy it much* to *as he used to*. The second *as* is a relative adverb.

Little (an adjective used as a noun) is an adverbial objective. The adjective *ago* follows the noun it modifies.

79.

That and *as* are expletives. *In order to* is a phrasal preposition. The noun clause introduced by *that* functions here as a direct object. *Crutch* is an objective complement.

80.

The infinitive phrase is an appositive.

The infinitive and its subject are the object of the preposition *for*.

81.

This sentence has four dependent clauses: three adverb clauses, of which two are introduced by subordinating conjunctions (*if* and *because*) and one by a relative adverb (*as*); and an adjective clause introduced by the relative pronoun *that*.

82.

The *x*'s represent the unexpressed noun clause *that he is strong. Than* is a relative adverb. The partially unexpressed infinitive phrase introduced by *to believe* is an objective complement.

83.

The infinitive phrase *to be able to teach* is in apposition with the subject of the first main clause, *it*.

Both *assuming* and *offering* introduce gerund phrases. The first is the subject of a noun clause; the second is the object of the preposition.

~ 270 ~

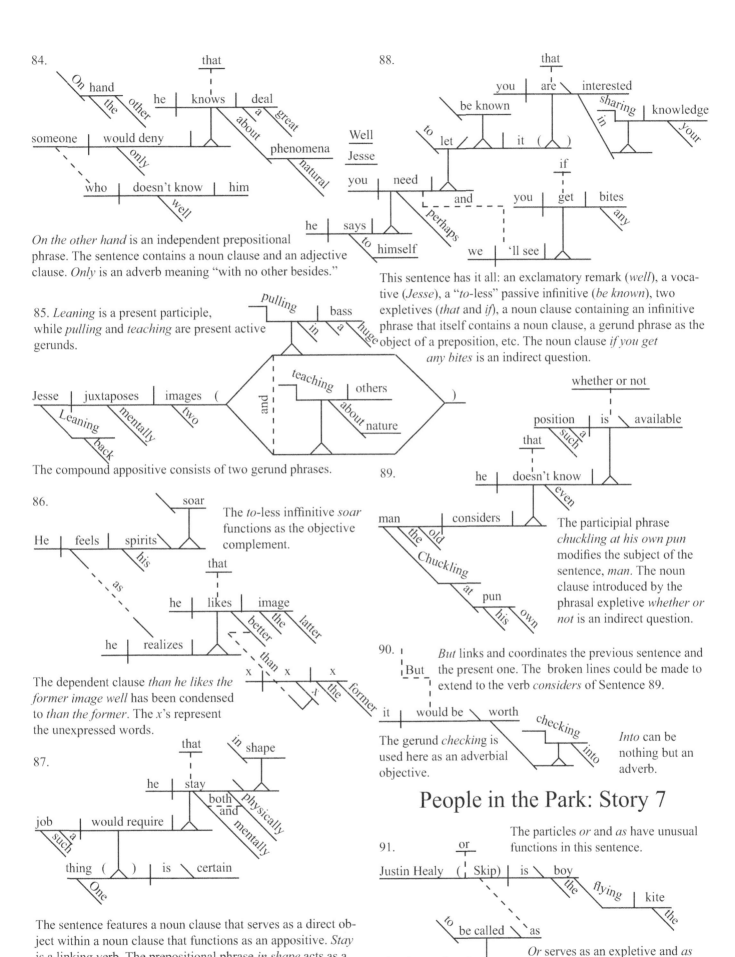

84.

On the other hand is an independent prepositional phrase. The sentence contains a noun clause and an adjective clause. *Only* is an adverb meaning "with no other besides."

85. *Leaning* is a present participle, while *pulling* and *teaching* are present active gerunds.

The compound appositive consists of two gerund phrases.

86.

The *to*-less inffinitive *soar* functions as the objective complement.

The dependent clause *than he likes the former image well* has been condensed to *than the former*. The *x*'s represent the unexpressed words.

87.

The sentence features a noun clause that serves as a direct object within a noun clause that functions as an appositive. *Stay* is a linking verb. The prepositional phrase *in shape* acts as a predicate adjective. *Both* and *and* are correlative coordinating conjunctions.

88.

This sentence has it all: an exclamatory remark (*well*), a vocative (*Jesse*), a "*to*-less" passive infinitive (*be known*), two expletives (*that* and *if*), a noun clause containing an infinitive phrase that itself contains a noun clause, a gerund phrase as the object of a preposition, etc. The noun clause *if you get any bites* is an indirect question.

89.

The participial phrase *chuckling at his own pun* modifies the subject of the sentence, *man*. The noun clause introduced by the phrasal expletive *whether or not* is an indirect question.

90.

But links and coordinates the previous sentence and the present one. The broken lines could be made to extend to the verb *considers* of Sentence 89.

The gerund *checking* is used here as an adverbial objective.

Into can be nothing but an adverb.

People in the Park: Story 7

91.

The particles *or* and *as* have unusual functions in this sentence.

Or serves as an expletive and *as* as a relative pronoun.

92.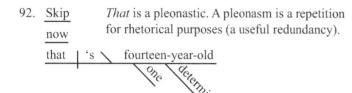

That is a pleonastic. A pleonasm is a repetition for rhetorical purposes (a useful redundancy).

Since *that* is the subject of the sentence, *Skip* is an independent element. *Now*, as used here, is an interjection (like *well*, for example), which is also an independent element.

93.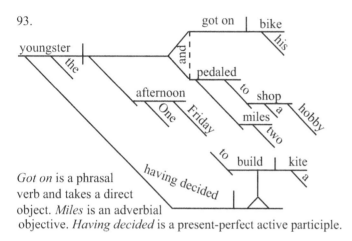

Got on is a phrasal verb and takes a direct object. *Miles* is an adverbial objective. *Having decided* is a present-perfect active participle.

94.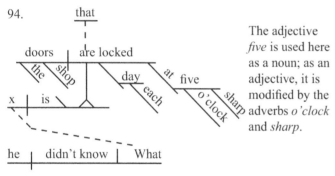

The adjective *five* is used here as a noun; as an adjective, it is modified by the adverbs *o'clock* and *sharp*.

The subject of the sentence is the unexpressed antecedent of the indefinite relative pronoun *what*.

95.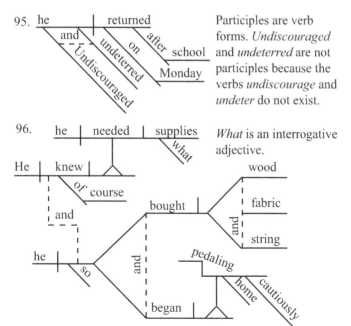

Participles are verb forms. *Undiscouraged* and *undeterred* are not participles because the verbs *undiscourage* and *undeter* do not exist.

96.

What is an interrogative adjective.

97.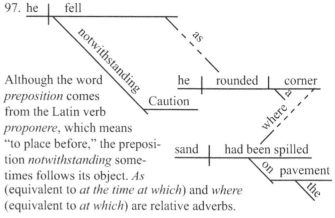

Although the word *preposition* comes from the Latin verb *proponere*, which means "to place before," the preposition *notwithstanding* sometimes follows its object. *As* (equivalent to *at the time at which*) and *where* (equivalent to *at which*) are relative adverbs.

98.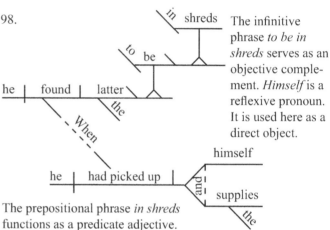

The infinitive phrase *to be in shreds* serves as an objective complement. *Himself* is a reflexive pronoun. It is used here as a direct object.

The prepositional phrase *in shreds* functions as a predicate adjective.

99.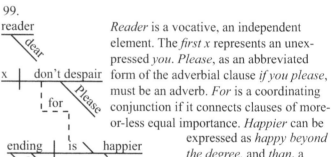

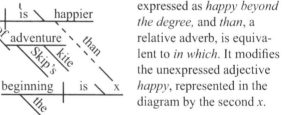

Reader is a vocative, an independent element. The *first x* represents an unexpressed *you*. *Please*, as an abbreviated form of the adverbial clause *if you please*, must be an adverb. *For* is a coordinating conjunction if it connects clauses of more-or-less equal importance. *Happier* can be expressed as *happy beyond the degree,* and *than*, a relative adverb, is equivalent to *in which*. It modifies the unexpressed adjective *happy*, represented in the diagram by the second *x*.

100.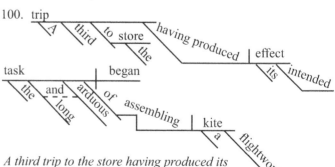

A third trip to the store having produced its intended effect is a nominative absolute. The participle *having produced* is present-perfect active.

The gerund phrase *assembling a flightworthy kite* is the object of the preposition *of*.

101.

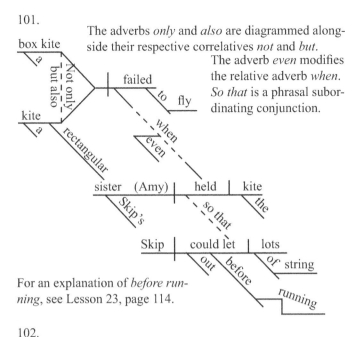

The adverbs *only* and *also* are diagrammed alongside their respective correlatives *not* and *but*.

The adverb *even* modifies the relative adverb *when*. *So that* is a phrasal subordinating conjunction.

For an explanation of *before running*, see Lesson 23, page 114.

102.

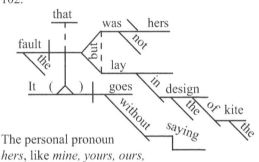

The personal pronoun *hers*, like *mine, yours, ours,* and *theirs*, is called an absolute possessive because it always stands alone, never with a noun. The absolute possessives signify both the thing possessed and the possessor.

103.

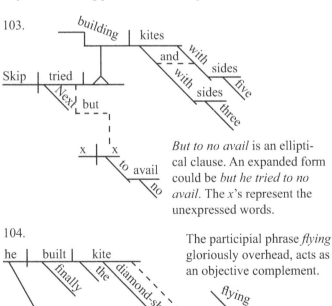

But to no avail is an elliptical clause. An expanded form could be *but he tried to no avail*. The *x*'s represent the unexpressed words.

104.

The participial phrase *flying gloriously overhead*, acts as an objective complement.

Become is a linking verb, *conventional* a predicate adjective.

105.

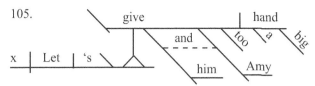

The subject of the sentence is an unexpressed *you*, represented in the diagram by an *x*. *Let's*, a contraction consisting of a verb and a personal-pronoun direct object, must be separated in a sentence diagram. The *to*-less infinitive phrase introduced by *give* serves as an objective complement. *Him and Amy* is a compound indirect object.

People in the Park: Story 8

106.

The compound direct object consists of two gerund phrases.

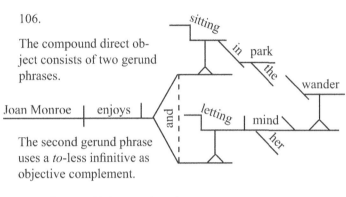

The second gerund phrase uses a *to*-less infinitive as objective complement.

107.

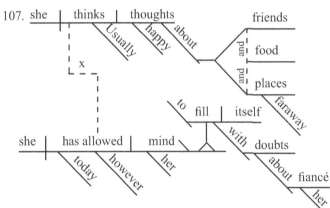

Transitional adverbs like *however* are diagrammed like regular adverbs. The transition from the one main clause to the other is shown by an *x* representing an unexpressed coordinating conjunction. An infinitive phrase serves as an objective complement.

108.

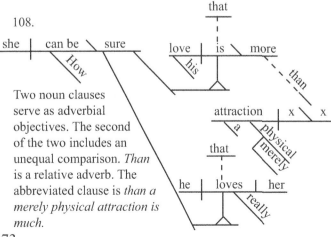

Two noun clauses serve as adverbial objectives. The second of the two includes an unequal comparison. *Than* is a relative adverb. The abbreviated clause is *than a merely physical attraction is much.*

~ 273 ~

109.

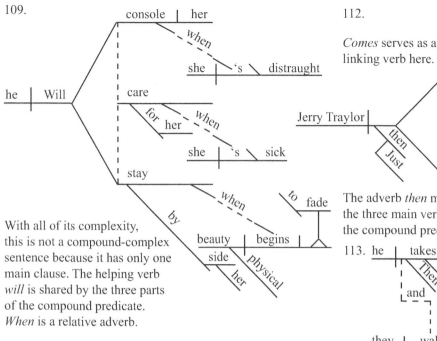

With all of its complexity, this is not a compound-complex sentence because it has only one main clause. The helping verb *will* is shared by the three parts of the compound predicate. *When* is a relative adverb.

110.

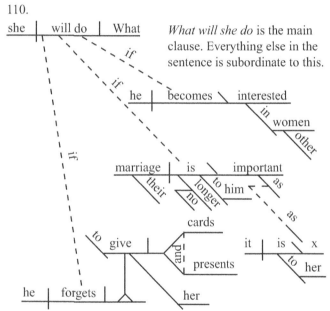

What will she do is the main clause. Everything else in the sentence is subordinate to this.

The sentence has four subordinate clauses: three introduced by the subordinating conjunction *if* and one by the relative adverb *as*. The *x* in the *as*-clause stands for the word *important*.

111.

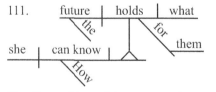

The direct object of the sentence is a noun clause, specifically, an indirect question. *What* is an interrogative pronoun here.

112.

Comes serves as a linking verb here.

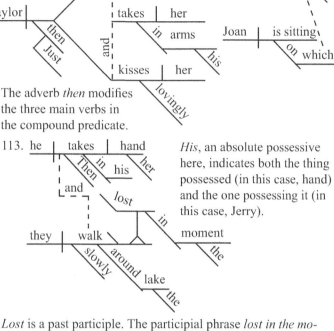

The adverb *then* modifies the three main verbs in the compound predicate.

113.

His, an absolute possessive here, indicates both the thing possessed (in this case, hand) and the one possessing it (in this case, Jerry).

Lost is a past participle. The participial phrase *lost in the moment* functions as a predicate adjective. In this sentence, *walk* is a linking verb.

114.

There is an expletive. It announces that the subject will follow the verb.

115.

The compound predicate adjective consists of two prepositional phrases.

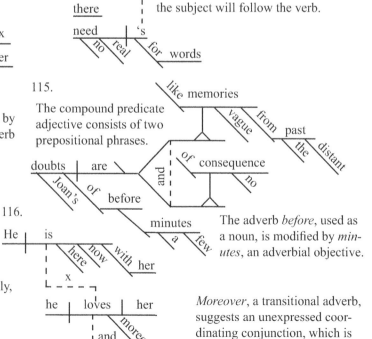

The adverb *before*, used as a noun, is modified by *minutes*, an adverbial objective.

116.

Moreover, a transitional adverb, suggests an unexpressed coordinating conjunction, which is represented in the diagram by an *x*.

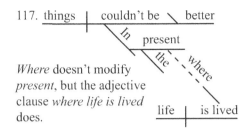

117. things | couldn't be \ better
In present the where
life | is lived

Where doesn't modify *present*, but the adjective clause *where life is lived* does.

Where, a relative adverb, is equivalent to *in which*; thus, it modifies the verb *is lived* while referring to the noun *present*.

People in the Park: Story 9

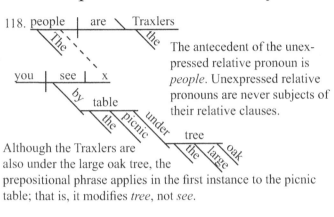

118. people | are \ Traxlers
The you | see | x
by table the picnic under tree the large oak

The antecedent of the unexpressed relative pronoun is *people*. Unexpressed relative pronouns are never subjects of their relative clauses.

Although the Traxlers are also under the large oak tree, the prepositional phrase applies in the first instance to the picnic table; that is, it modifies *tree*, not *see*.

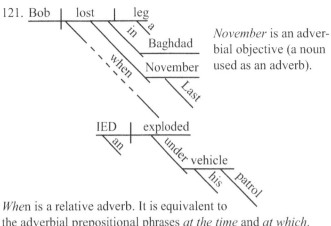

121. Bob | lost | leg
in a Baghdad when November Last
IED | exploded
an under vehicle his patrol

November is an adverbial objective (a noun used as an adverb).

When is a relative adverb. It is equivalent to the adverbial prepositional phrases *at the time* and *at which*.

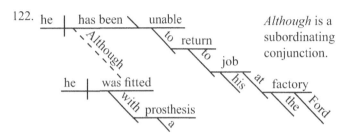

122. he | has been \ unable
Although to return to job
he | was fitted his at factory the Ford
with prosthesis a

Although is a subordinating conjunction.

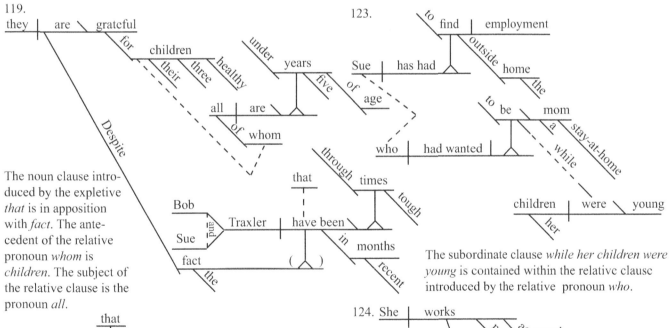

119.
they | are \ grateful
for children their three healthy
under years
all | are five
of whom of age
Despite
Sue | has had

123.
to find | employment
outside home the
to be | mom
a stay-at-home
who | had wanted while
children | were \ young
her

The subordinate clause *while her children were young* is contained within the relative clause introduced by the relative pronoun *who*.

The noun clause introduced by the expletive *that* is in apposition with *fact*. The antecedent of the relative pronoun *whom* is *children*. The subject of the relative clause is the pronoun *all*.

that
Bob and Traxler | have been
Sue
fact
the
through times tough
in months recent

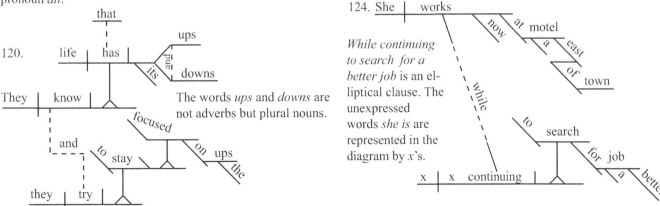

120.
that
life | has ups
its and downs
They | know
focused
and on ups
to stay the
they | try

The words *ups* and *downs* are not adverbs but plural nouns.

A participial phrase introduced by the past participle *focused* serves as a predicate adjective following the linking verb *stay*.

124. She | works
now at motel a east of town
while
to search for job a better
x | x continuing

While continuing to search for a better job is an elliptical clause. The unexpressed words *she is* are represented in the diagram by *x*'s.

The infinitive phrase *to search for a better job* functions as a direct object.

~ 275 ~

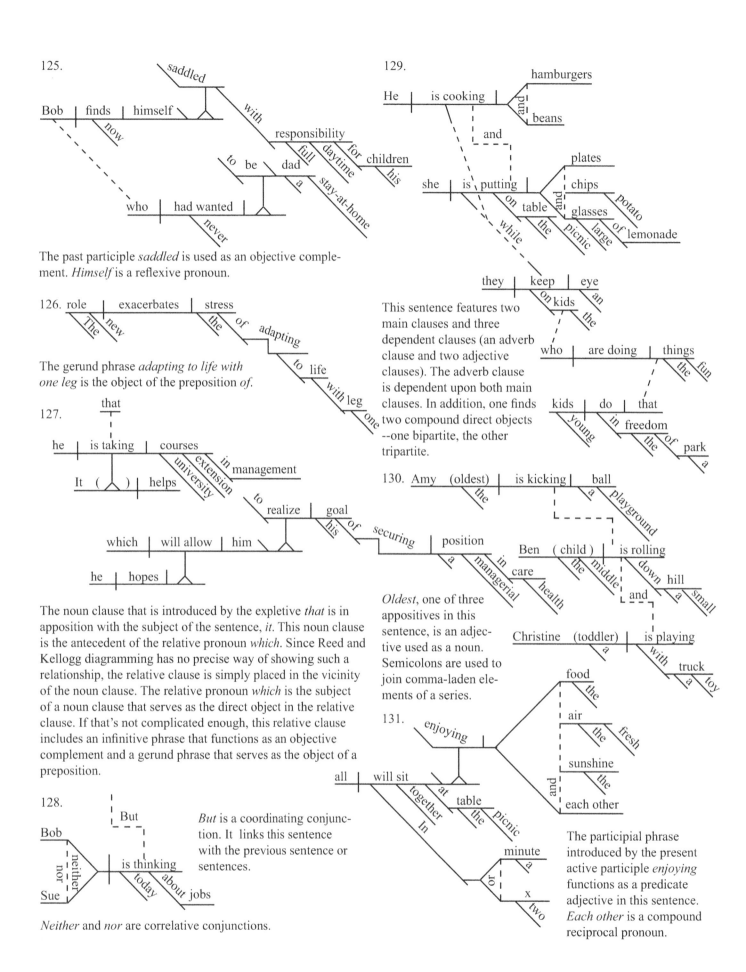

125.

The past participle *saddled* is used as an objective complement. *Himself* is a reflexive pronoun.

126.

The gerund phrase *adapting to life with
one leg* is the object of the preposition *of*.

127.

The noun clause that is introduced by the expletive *that* is in
apposition with the subject of the sentence, *it*. This noun clause
is the antecedent of the relative pronoun *which*. Since Reed and
Kellogg diagramming has no precise way of showing such a
relationship, the relative clause is simply placed in the vicinity
of the noun clause. The relative pronoun *which* is the subject
of a noun clause that serves as the direct object in the relative
clause. If that's not complicated enough, this relative clause
includes an infinitive phrase that functions as an objective
complement and a gerund phrase that serves as the object of a
preposition.

128.

But is a coordinating conjunction. It links this sentence
with the previous sentence or
sentences.

Neither and *nor* are correlative conjunctions.

129.

This sentence features two
main clauses and three
dependent clauses (an adverb
clause and two adjective
clauses). The adverb clause
is dependent upon both main
clauses. In addition, one finds
two compound direct objects
--one bipartite, the other
tripartite.

130.

Oldest, one of three
appositives in this
sentence, is an adjec-
tive used as a noun.
Semicolons are used to
join comma-laden ele-
ments of a series.

131.

The participial phrase
introduced by the present
active participle *enjoying*
functions as a predicate
adjective in this sentence.
Each other is a compound
reciprocal pronoun.

People in the Park: Story 10

132. Jerome Wilkins (player) is giving thought

Now that, equivalent to *because*, is a phrasal subordinating conjunction. It introduces two coordinate adverb clauses.

Over, often a preposition or an adverb, is used here as a predicate adjective.

The passive infinitive *to be played* serves as a predicate adjective. *Remains* is a linking verb.

133. guy coming

Just coming across the bridge is a participial phrase. *Coming* is a present participle.

That is pleonastic; that is, it involves a redundancy used for rhetorical purposes.

134. woman is mother

The *x* represents the unexpressed relative pronoun *that* or *whom*.

Her modifies the possessive noun *son's*. It is not her sprint but his.

135.

The first *life* is an adverbial objective. The infinitive phrase introduced by *to help* is adverbial; it modifies the verb *has given*. The other infinitive phrase in this sentence is introduced by the *to*-less infinitive *get* and functions as an objective complement.

There are two gerund phrases in this sentence. The first is the object of the preposition *to*, and the second is a direct object.

136.

To get an agent is a complementary infinitive phrase.

Mother is an indirect object. The relative adverb *when* introduces the subordinate clause *when he does this*. The compound direct object consists of two noun clauses, each introduced by the expletive *that*.

137 and 138. (on the next page)

139. mother is happy

The noun clause introduced by the expletive *that* functions as an adverbial objective. One is tempted to call *through* a postpositive preposition such that *think the matter through* is really just an inverted *think through the matter*. If it were, *see something through* could be expressed, without a change in meaning, as *see through something*.

140.

No matter is a phrasal preposition (like *regardless of*). The noun clause *what route he decides to take* is its object. The past participle *informed* is an objective complement.

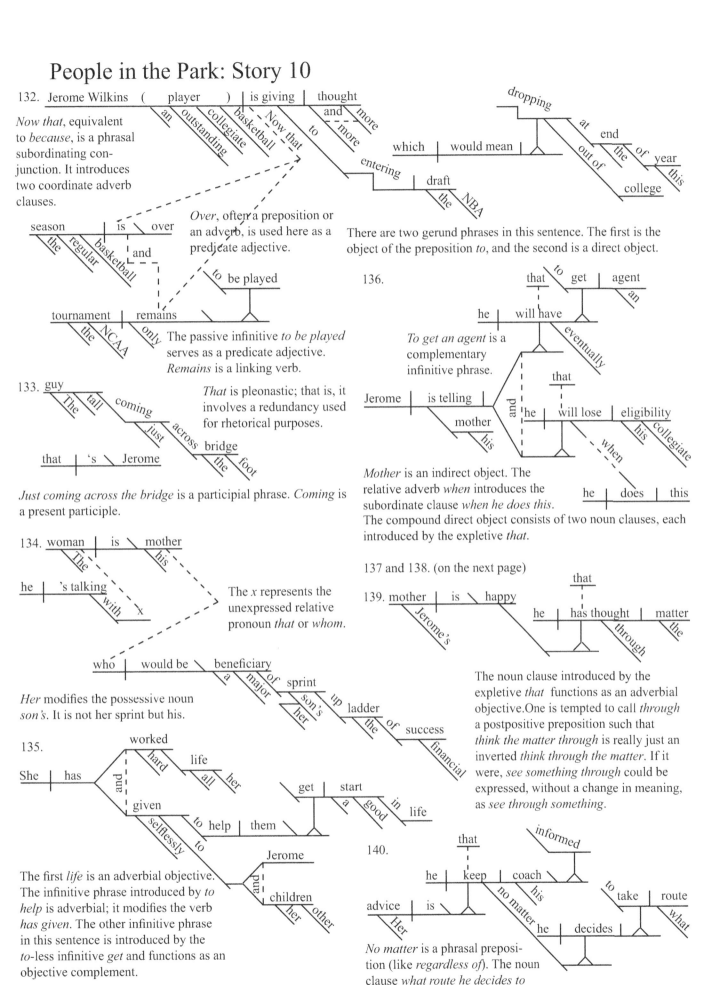

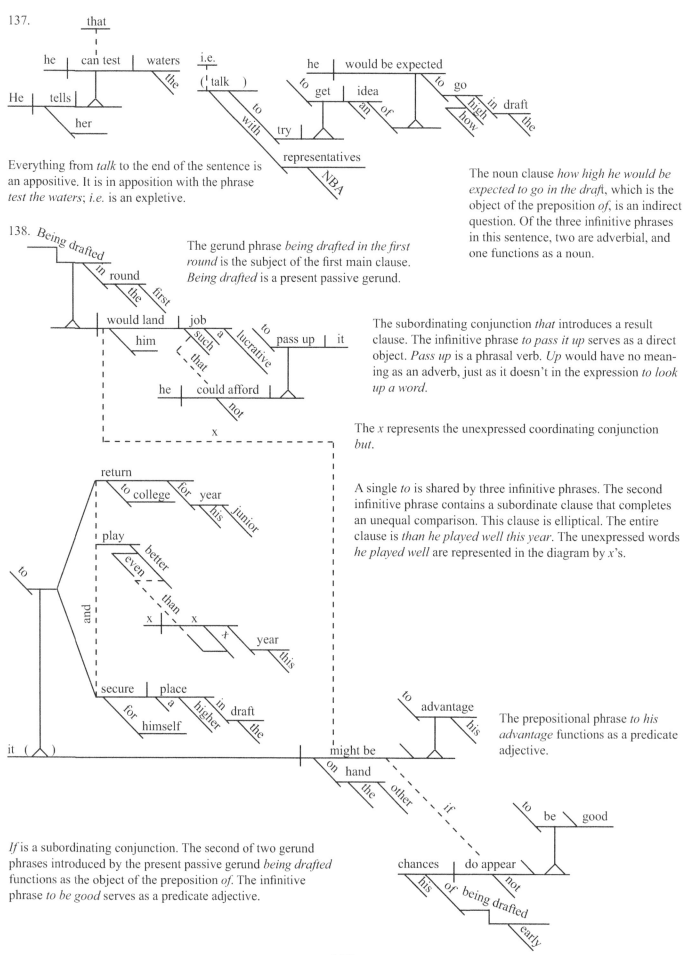

137.

Everything from *talk* to the end of the sentence is an appositive. It is in apposition with the phrase *test the waters*; *i.e.* is an expletive.

The noun clause *how high he would be expected to go in the draft*, which is the object of the preposition *of*, is an indirect question. Of the three infinitive phrases in this sentence, two are adverbial, and one functions as a noun.

138.

The gerund phrase *being drafted in the first round* is the subject of the first main clause. *Being drafted* is a present passive gerund.

The subordinating conjunction *that* introduces a result clause. The infinitive phrase *to pass it up* serves as a direct object. *Pass up* is a phrasal verb. *Up* would have no meaning as an adverb, just as it doesn't in the expression *to look up a word*.

The *x* represents the unexpressed coordinating conjunction *but*.

A single *to* is shared by three infinitive phrases. The second infinitive phrase contains a subordinate clause that completes an unequal comparison. This clause is elliptical. The entire clause is *than he played well this year*. The unexpressed words *he played well* are represented in the diagram by *x*'s.

The prepositional phrase *to his advantage* functions as a predicate adjective.

If is a subordinating conjunction. The second of two gerund phrases introduced by the present passive gerund *being drafted* functions as the object of the preposition *of*. The infinitive phrase *to be good* serves as a predicate adjective.

Sentence 1: 101 Words

Step 1: Atkins . . . grabbed the rebound of an errant free throw and passed the ball immediately to Brown at mid court

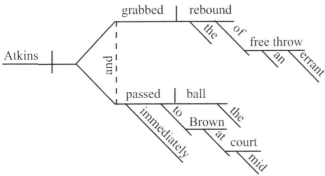

Step 2: With six seconds to play, the Tigers trailing by two points, and the championship on the line

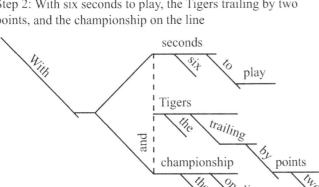

Step 3: who had been a poweerful force on the boards all evening

Step 4: who hauled it in and, dribbling beautifully, wove his way through three opponents, swooped under the basket, and laid the ball gently against the backboard and in the basket

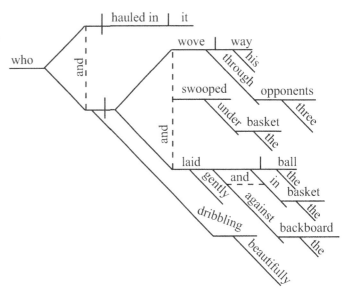

Step 5: which tied the score, sent the game into overtime, and put the Tigers in an excellent position to realize their goal of becoming conference champions

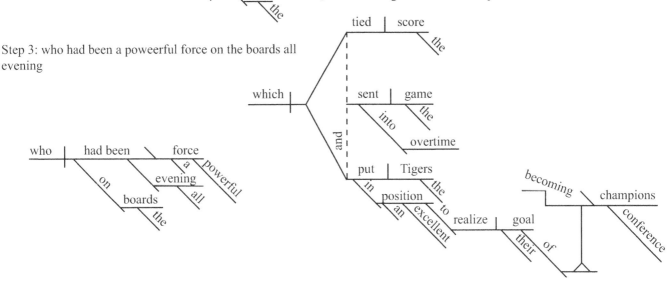

~ 279 ~

Sentence 1: With six seconds to play, the Tigers trailing by two points, and the championship on the line, Atkins, who had been a poweerful force on the boards all evening, grabbed the rebound of an errant free throw and passed the ball immediately to Brown at midcourt, who hauled it in and, dribbling beautifully, wove his way through three opponents, swooped under the basket, and laid the ball gently against the backboard and in the basket, which tied the score, sent the game into overtime, and put the Tigers in an excellent position to realize their goal of becoming conference champions.

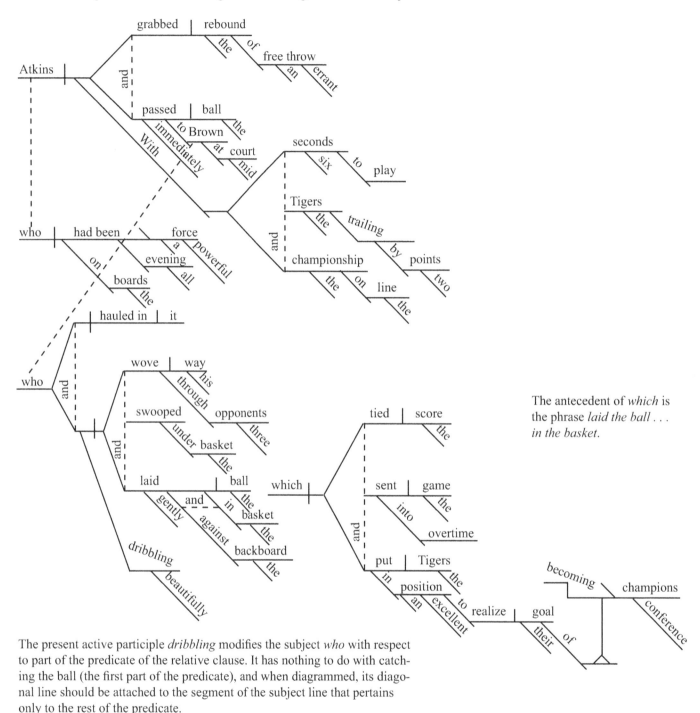

The antecedent of *which* is the phrase *laid the ball . . . in the basket.*

The present active participle *dribbling* modifies the subject *who* with respect to part of the predicate of the relative clause. It has nothing to do with catching the ball (the first part of the predicate), and when diagrammed, its diagonal line should be attached to the segment of the subject line that pertains only to the rest of the predicate.

Sentence 2: 109 Words

Step 1: My family's fifth annual Super Bowl party . . . suffered a serious setback during the halftime meal

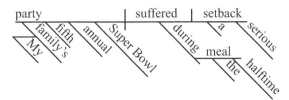

Step 2: which had begun auspiciously with a kickoff return for a touchdown and the arrival of Aunt Mae's delicious apple strudel

Step 3: when Uncle Ben . . . put three grapes atop his plate of salmon, red cabbage, Indian cauliflower, and snow peas, tossed one of the grapes into the air, and caught it in his mouth and then in his windpipe

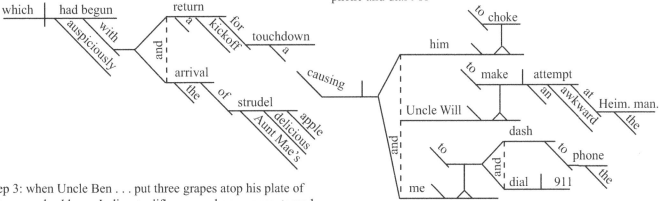

Step 4: who was notorious among my relatives for his scrupulously healthful eating

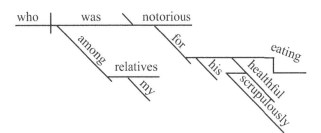

Step 5: causing him to choke, Uncle Will to make an awkward attempt at the Heimlich maneuver, and me to dash to the phone and dial 911

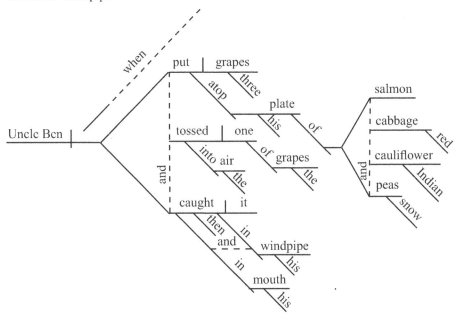

Sentence 2: My family's fifth annual Super Bowl party, which had begun auspiciously with a kickoff return for a touchdown and the arrival of Aunt Mae's delicious apple strudel, suffered a serious setback during the halftime meal, when Uncle Ben, who was notorious among my relatives for his scrupulously healthful eating, put three grapes atop his plate of salmon, red cabbage, Indian cauliflower, and snow peas, tossed one of the grapes into the air and caught it in his mouth and then in his throat, causing him to choke, Uncle Will to make an awkward attempt at the Heimlich maneuver, and me to dash to the phone and dial 911.

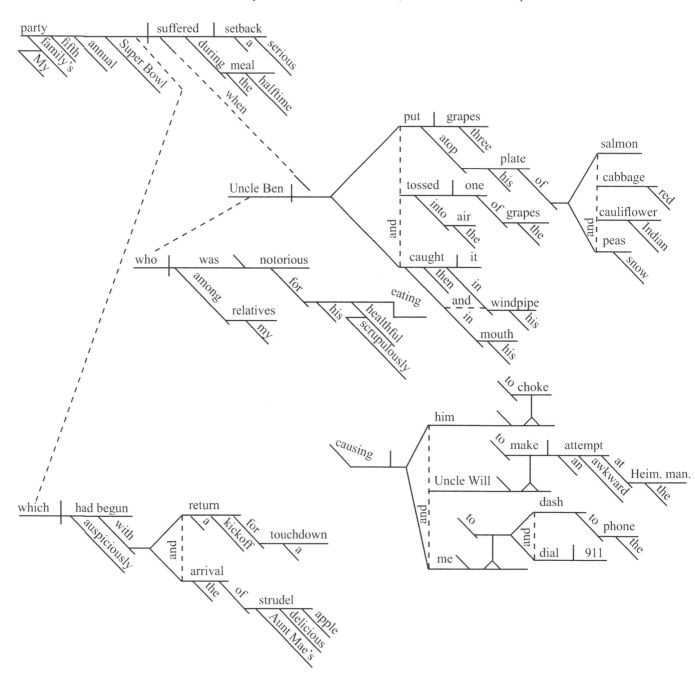

Both the possessive pronoun *his* and the adjective *healthful* are adjectival modifiers of the gerund *eating*; therefore, these two words are placed under the upper horizontal line of the gerund.

The present active participle *causing* modifies the phrase *caught it . . . in his windpipe*.

Within the tripartite compound, one infinitive (*to choke*) and two infinitive phrases function as objective complements.

Sentence 3: 113 Words

Step 1: one will want to consider incorporating into the sentence several challenging constructions

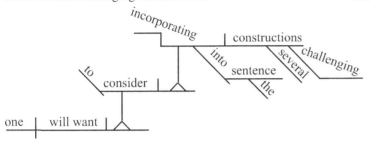

Step 2: such as gerund phrases used as appositives, infinitive phrases used as objective complements, noun clauses used as adverbial objectives, and elliptical adverbial clauses used in equal and unequal comparisons

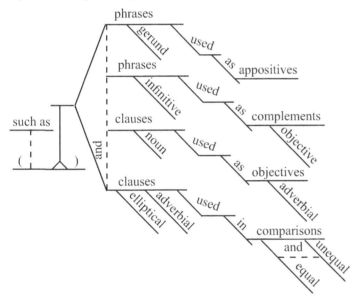

Step 3: although it must in fairness be pointed out that no 100-word sentence will ever encompass the wealth of grammatical variation

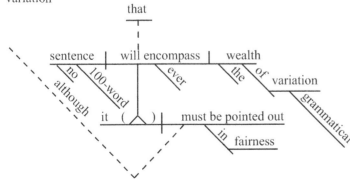

Step 4: that the English language has to offer

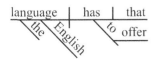

Step 5: If one sets out to write a 100-word sentence that has even a modicum of grammatical complexity

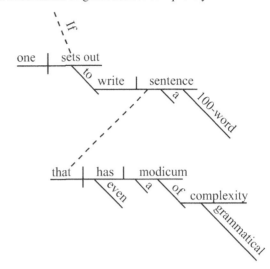

Step 6: that consists of more than a six-word introduction to 94 appositives

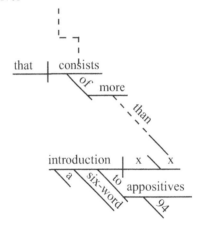

Step 7: or that is more sophisticated than a subject, a verb, and a series of fifteen infinitive phrases

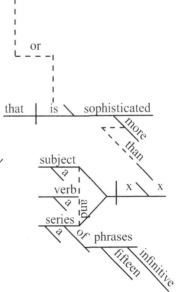

Sentence 3: If one sets out to write a 100-word sentence that has even a modicum of grammatical complexity, that consists of more than a six-word introduction to 94 appositives or that is more sophisticated than a subject, a verb, and a series of fifteen infinitive phrases, one will want to consider incorporating into the sentence several challenging constructions such as gerund phrases used as appositives, infinitive phrases used as objective complements, noun clauses used as adverbial objectives, and elliptical adverbial clauses used in equal and unequal comparisons, although it must in fairness be pointed out that no 100-word sentence will ever encompass the wealth of grammatical variation that the English language has to offer.

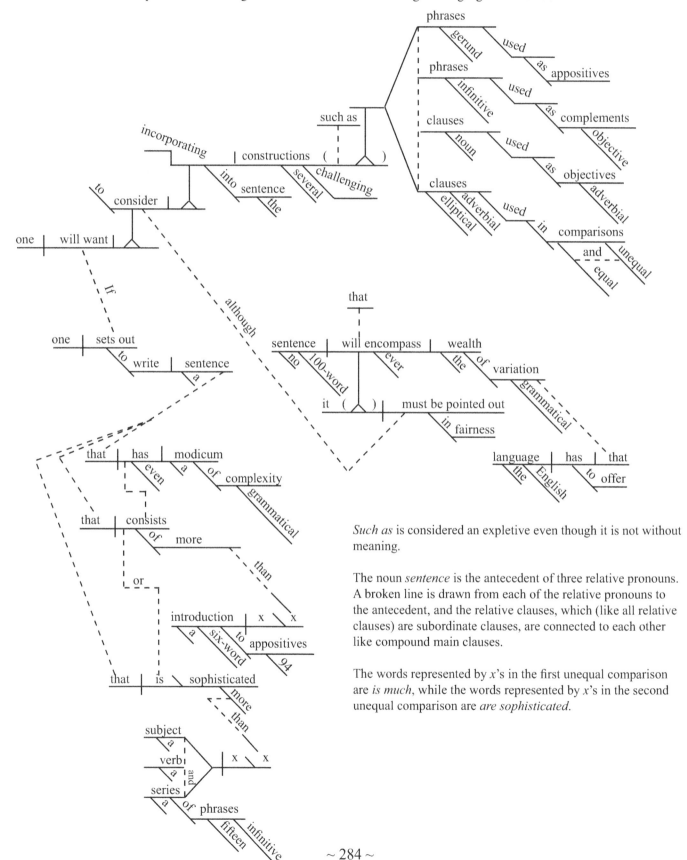

Such as is considered an expletive even though it is not without meaning.

The noun *sentence* is the antecedent of three relative pronouns. A broken line is drawn from each of the relative pronouns to the antecedent, and the relative clauses, which (like all relative clauses) are subordinate clauses, are connected to each other like compound main clauses.

The words represented by *x*'s in the first unequal comparison are *is much*, while the words represented by *x*'s in the second unequal comparison are *are sophisticated*.

~ 284 ~

Sentence 4: 114 Words

Step 1: he now sat, a week later, before a computer in Denver diligently checking weather forecasts

Step 4: which left forty or fifty pock marks on the hood, top, and trunk lid of his new Camry

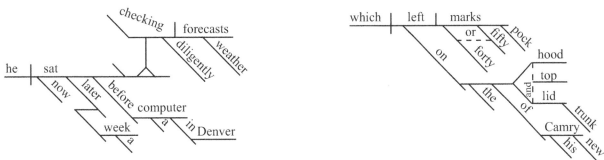

Step 2: (all of which promised multiple snowfalls over the next four days)

Step 5: looking and hoping for a window of departure that would allow him to return to St. Louis in time to feed, as promised, the pet raccoons of his neighbor

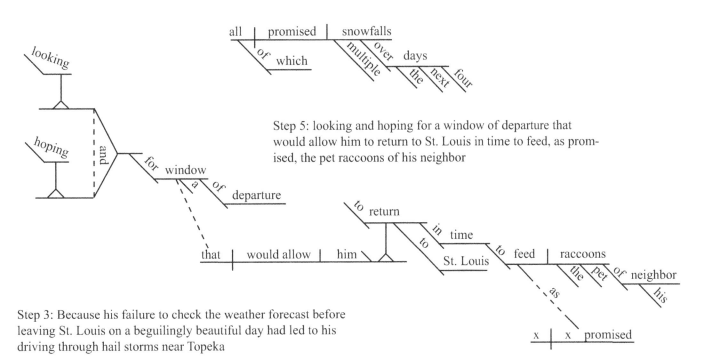

Step 3: Because his failure to check the weather forecast before leaving St. Louis on a beguilingly beautiful day had led to his driving through hail storms near Topeka

Step 6: who was vacationing comfortably aboard a cruise ship on the warm waters of the Caribbean Sea

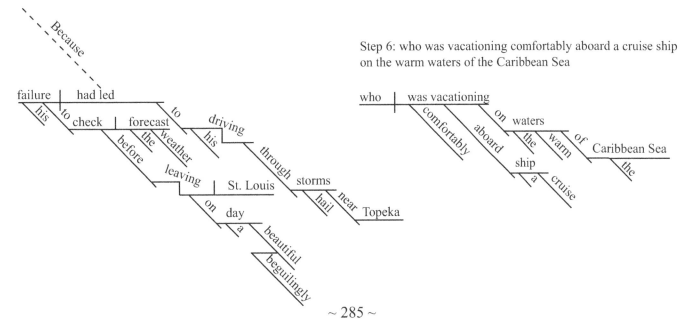

Sentence 4: Because his failure to check the weather forecast before leaving St. Louis on a beguilingly beautiful day had led to his driving through hail storms near Topeka, which left forty or fifty pock marks on the hood, top, and trunk lid of his new Camry, he now sat, a week later, before a computer in Denver diligently checking weather forecasts (all of which promised multiple snowfalls over the next four days), looking and hoping for a window of departure that would allow him to return to St. Louis in time to feed, as promised, the pet raccoons of his neighbor, who was vacationing comfortably aboard a cruise ship on the warm waters of the Caribbean Sea.

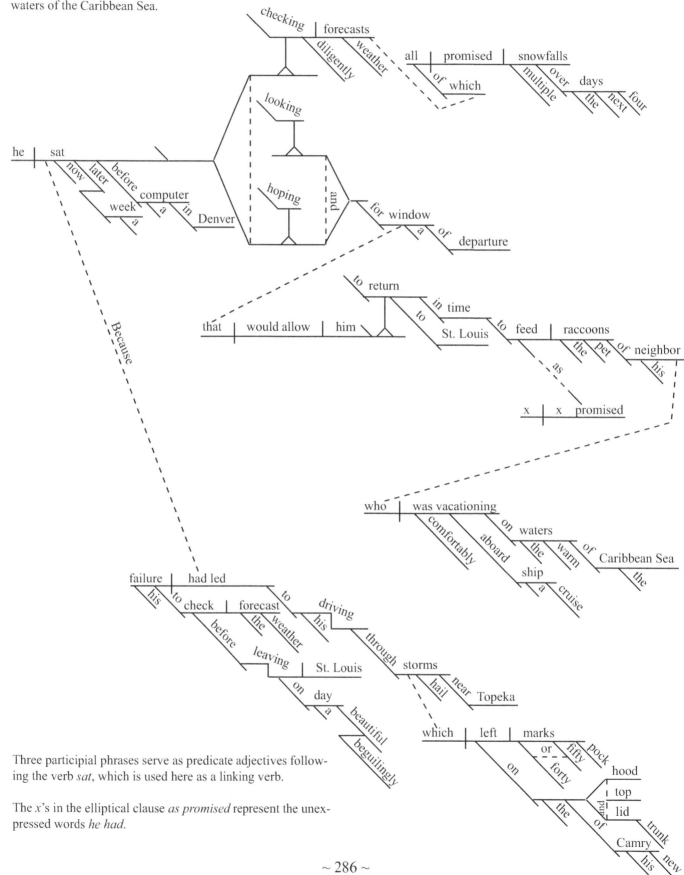

Three participial phrases serve as predicate adjectives following the verb *sat*, which is used here as a linking verb.

The *x*'s in the elliptical clause *as promised* represent the unexpressed words *he had*.

Sentence 5: 118 Words

Step 1: The sun had just slipped behind the clouds on the western horizon

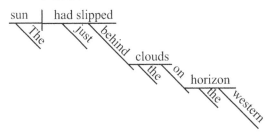

Step 2: and the south wind that had blown all day was beginning its nocturnal slumber

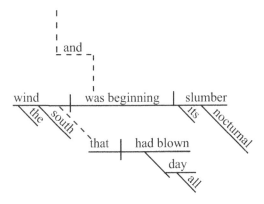

Step 3: when 12-year-old Christopher . . . urged his father's Arkansas Traveler out onto the lake and began casting and retrieving his favorite black-and-white River Runt

Step 4: dressed only in the short pants that were his everyday summer attire, skulling with his left hand

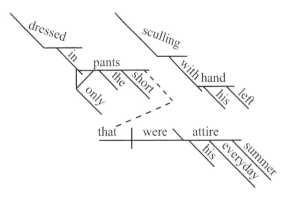

Step 5: as he moved the boat slowly toward an old stump around the bend

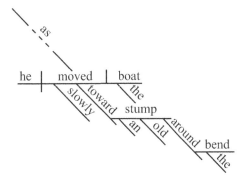

Step 6: where a week ago, at about this time of day, he had hooked and then lost the bass of his dreams

Step 7: a huge fish that he hoped, with a perfect cast and just the right lure action, to hook again

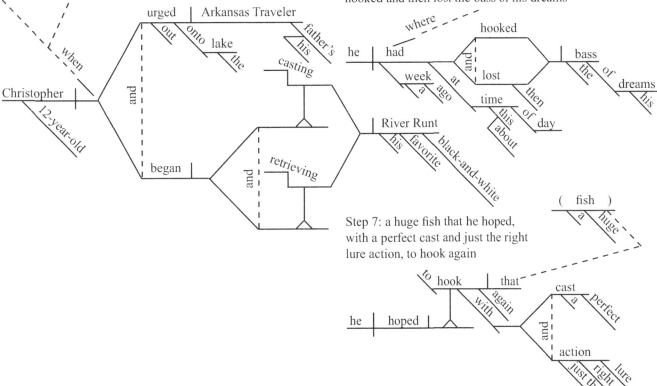

Sentence 5: The sun had just slipped behind the clouds on the western horizon, and the south wind that had blown all day was beginning its nocturnal slumber when 12-year-old Christopher, dressed only in the short pants that were his everyday summer attire, skulling with his left hand, urged his father's Arkansas Traveler out onto the lake and began casting and retrieving his favorite black-and-white River Runt as he moved the boat slowly toward an old stump around the bend, where a week ago, at about this time of day, he had hooked and then lost the bass of his dreams--a huge fish that he hoped, with a perfect cast and just the right lure action, to hook again.

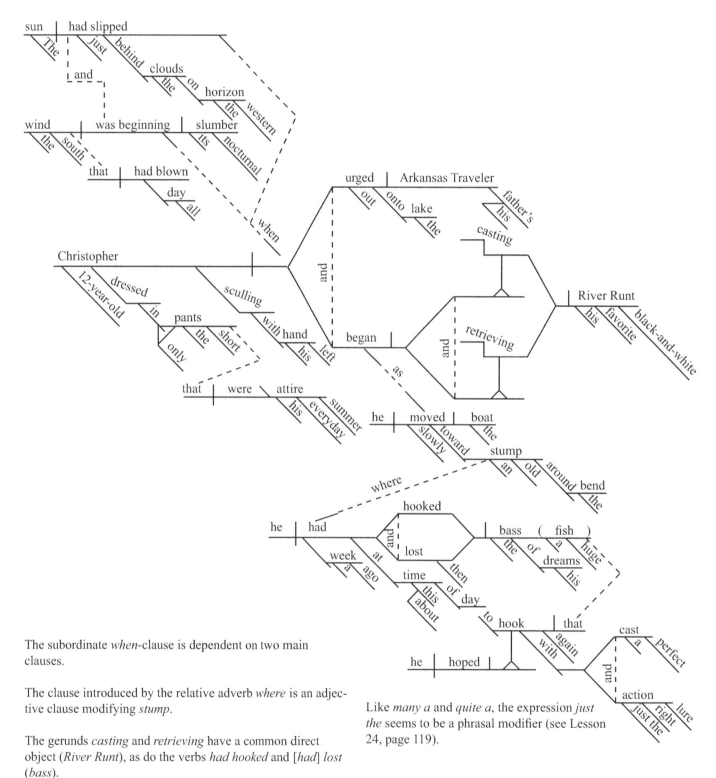

The subordinate *when*-clause is dependent on two main clauses.

The clause introduced by the relative adverb *where* is an adjective clause modifying *stump*.

The gerunds *casting* and *retrieving* have a common direct object (*River Runt*), as do the verbs *had hooked* and [*had*] *lost* (*bass*).

Like *many a* and *quite a*, the expression *just the* seems to be a phrasal modifier (see Lesson 24, page 119).

~ 288 ~

Sentence 6: 119 Words

Step 1: Jack . . . took hold of the beanstalk that had grown from the discarded bean and climbed it to the top

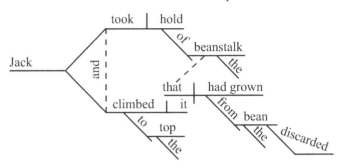

Step 2: Having sold the family cow for a magic bean, despite the fact that his mother needed and wanted cash for the cow

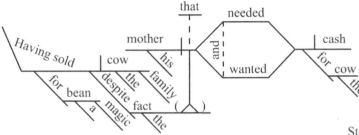

Step 3: who may have lacked prudence but was never without a sense of adventure

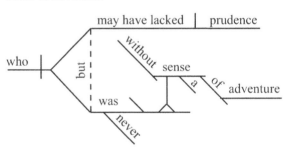

Step 4: where he discovered the giant who had stolen the family goose that laid golden eggs and, by waiting patiently and courageously for the giant to fall asleep, took back the goose

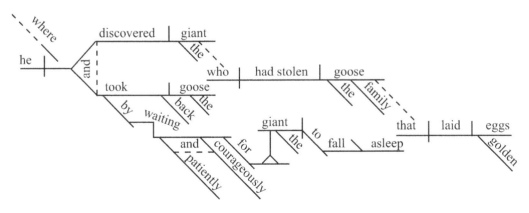

Step 5: whereupon he scampered down to earth with the giant in pursuit, and chopped down the beanstalk

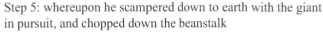

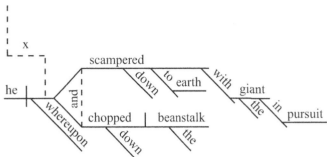

Step 6: which brought the life of the giant to an end and ensured his and his mother's future prosperity

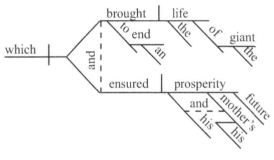

Sentence 6: Having sold the family cow for a magic bean, despite the fact that his mother needed and wanted cash for the cow, Jack, who may have lacked prudence but was never without a sense of adventure, took hold of the beanstalk that had grown from the discarded bean and climbed it to the top, where he discovered the giant who had stolen the family goose that laid golden eggs and, by waiting patiently and courageously for the giant to fall asleep, took back the goose; whereupon he scampered down to earth with the giant in pursuit, and chopped down the beanstalk, which brought the life of the giant to an end and ensured his and his mother's future prosperity.

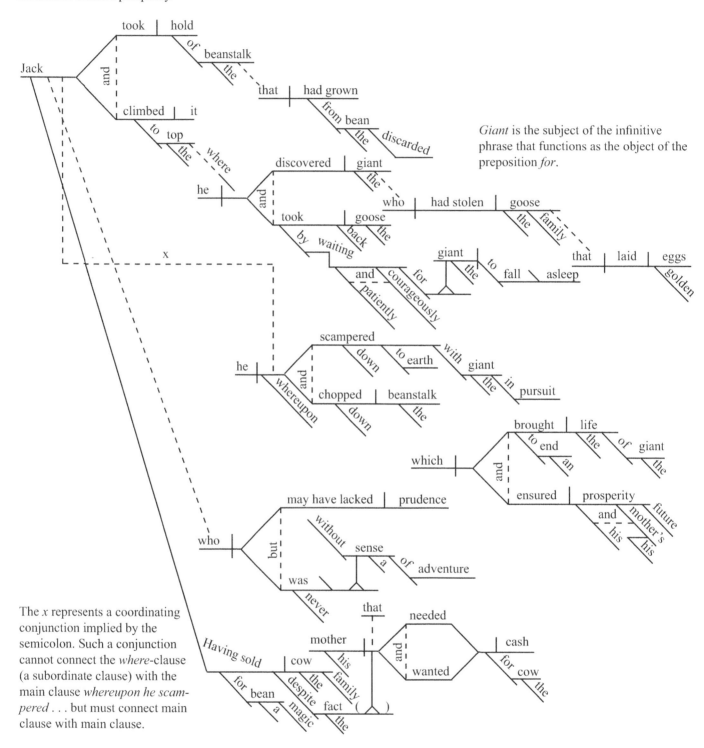

Giant is the subject of the infinitive phrase that functions as the object of the preposition *for.*

The *x* represents a coordinating conjunction implied by the semicolon. Such a conjunction cannot connect the *where*-clause (a subordinate clause) with the main clause *whereupon he scampered . . .* but must connect main clause with main clause.

The antecedent of the relative pronoun *which* is the clause *he chopped down the beanstalk.* Such an antecedent cannot be precisely identified in a Reed and Kellogg diagram. One simply places the relative clause near the antecedent.

The prepositional phrase *without a sense of adventure* serves as a predicate adjective.

Sentence 7: 131 Words

Step 1: the enterprising wolf found a ladder, climbed up on the roof, slid down the chimney, and landed right in a pot of boiling water

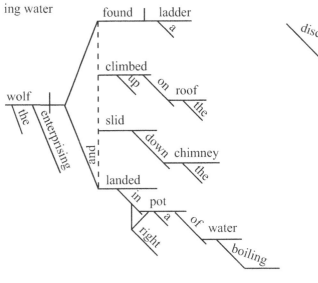

Step 2: where, to add insult to injury, he was serenaded in his final moments on earth by dancing pigs

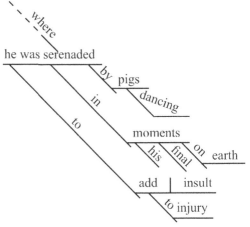

Step 3: who sang, "Who's afraid of the big bad wolf?"

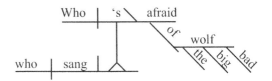

Step 4: Not at all discouraged when, having huffed and puffed and blown down the straw house of the youngest pig, he had allowed its inhabitant to flee to his older brother's house of sticks

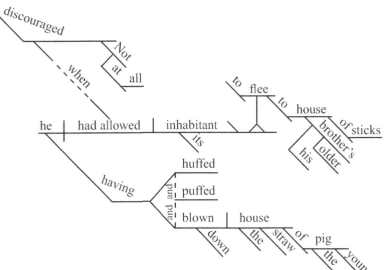

Step 5: nor when, having blown down the stick house, he had missed the two pigs

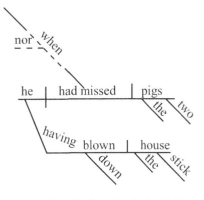

Step 6: who found refuge in the brick house of the oldest brother

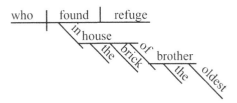

Step 7: nor when, having failed to blow down the house of bricks, he had had to endure the laughter of the succulent pigs

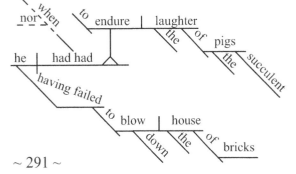

Sentence 7: Not at all discouraged when, having huffed and puffed and blown down the straw house of the youngest pig, he had allowed its inhabitant to flee to his older brother's house of sticks, nor when, having blown down the stick house, he had missed the two pigs, who found refuge in the brick house of the oldest brother, nor when, having failed to blow down the house of bricks, he had had to endure the laughter of the succulent pigs, the enterprising wolf found a ladder, climbed up on the roof, slid down the chimney, and landed right in a pot of boiling water, where, to add insult to injury, he was serenaded in his final moments on earth by dancing pigs, who sang, "Who's afraid of the big bad wolf?"

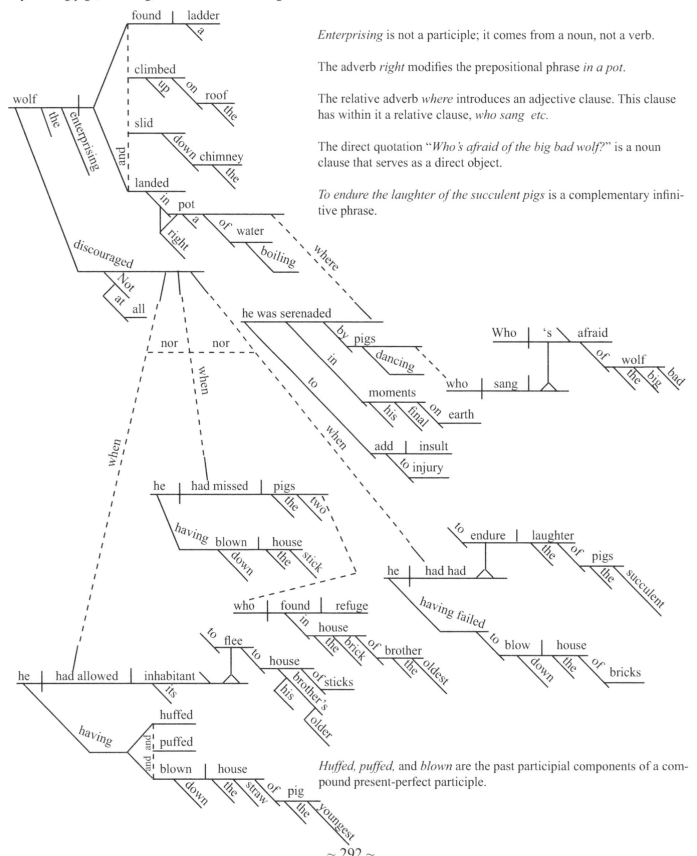

Enterprising is not a participle; it comes from a noun, not a verb.

The adverb *right* modifies the prepositional phrase *in a pot*.

The relative adverb *where* introduces an adjective clause. This clause has within it a relative clause, *who sang etc.*

The direct quotation "*Who's afraid of the big bad wolf?*" is a noun clause that serves as a direct object.

To endure the laughter of the succulent pigs is a complementary infinitive phrase.

Huffed, puffed, and *blown* are the past participial components of a compound present-perfect participle.

~ 292 ~

Sentence 8: 145 Words

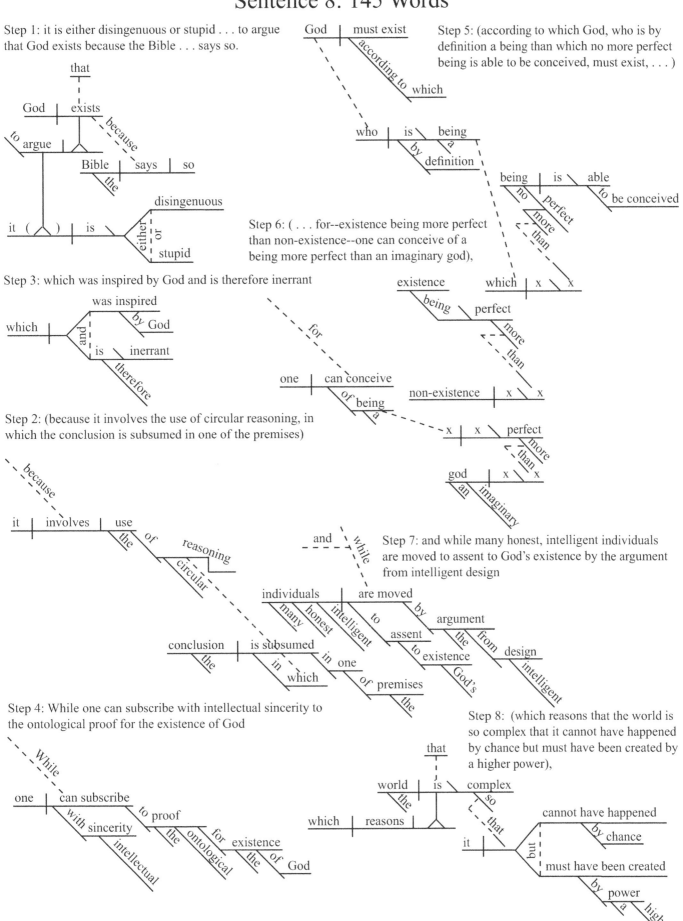

Step 1: it is either disingenuous or stupid . . . to argue that God exists because the Bible . . . says so.

that
God exists
to argue
because
Bible says so
the
it ( ) is either or disingenuous stupid

God must exist
according to which

Step 5: (according to which God, who is by definition a being than which no more perfect being is able to be conceived, must exist, . . .)

who is being
by a
definition

being is able
no perfect to be conceived
more than

Step 3: which was inspired by God and is therefore inerrant

which was inspired
and by God
is inerrant
therefore

Step 6: (. . . for--existence being more perfect than non-existence--one can conceive of a being more perfect than an imaginary god),

existence
being perfect
more than
non-existence x x
for
one can conceive
of being
a
x x perfect
more than x
god x x
an imaginary

Step 2: (because it involves the use of circular reasoning, in which the conclusion is subsumed in one of the premises)

because
it involves use
the of reasoning
circular
conclusion is subsumed
the in one
in which of premises
the

and while

Step 7: and while many honest, intelligent individuals are moved to assent to God's existence by the argument from intelligent design

individuals are moved
many honest intelligent to by argument
assent the from design
to existence intelligent
God's

Step 4: While one can subscribe with intellectual sincerity to the ontological proof for the existence of God

While
one can subscribe
with sincerity to proof
intellectual the ontological for existence
the of God

Step 8: (which reasons that the world is so complex that it cannot have happened by chance but must have been created by a higher power),

that
world is complex
the so
which reasons that
it but
cannot have happened
by chance
must have been created
by power
a higher

~ 293 ~

Sentence 8: While one can subscribe with intellectual sincerity to the ontological proof for the existence of God (according to which God, who is by definition a being than which no more perfect being is able to be conceived, must exist, for--existence being more perfect than non-existence--one can conceive of a being more perfect than an imaginary god), and while many honest, intelligent individuals are moved to assent to God's existence by the argument from intelligent design (which reasons that the world is so complex that it cannot have happened by chance but must have been created by a higher power), it is either disingenuous or stupid (because it involves the use of circular reasoning, in which the conclusion is subsumed in one of the premises) to argue that God exists because the Bible, which was inspired by God and is therefore inerrant, says so.

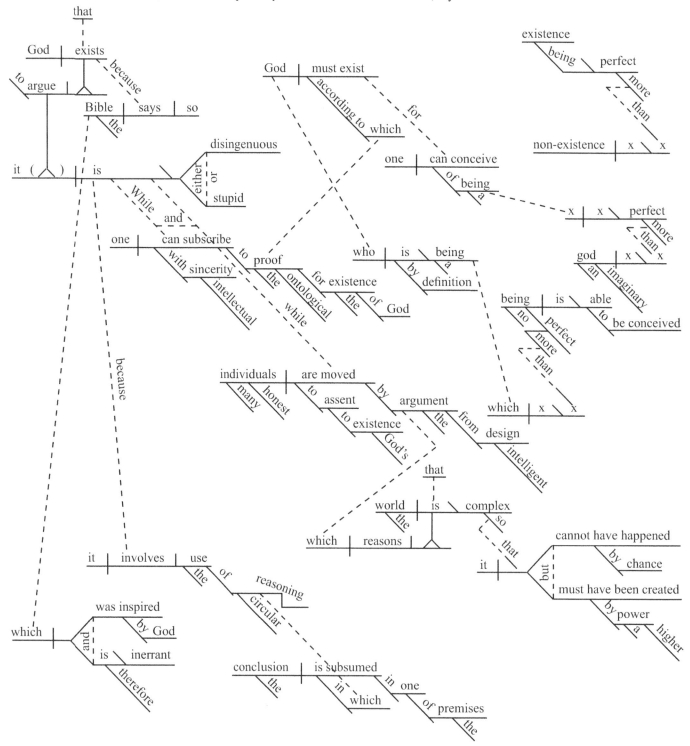

~ 294 ~

Sentence 9: 156 Words

Step 1: the young man realized that he would never become what his mother had wanted him to become, would never complete the course he had begun out of fear of damnation, but would follow his heart

Step 2: which even now was filling with the joy of living and the anticipation of the best that life has to offer a man: a wife and a family of his own

Step 3: As he knelt in the dimly lit convent church and thought about his classmates, who even at this moment were being ordained priests in the seminary chapel around the corner

Step 4: as he ruminated about the months of agonizing uncertainty that had culminated in his last-minute decision to rise above his fears and echew ordination

Step 5: as he imagined the surprise and disappointment of his peers upon their becoming aware that he was not among them

Step 6: and as he wondered how they would greet him when he returned to the seminary later that morning

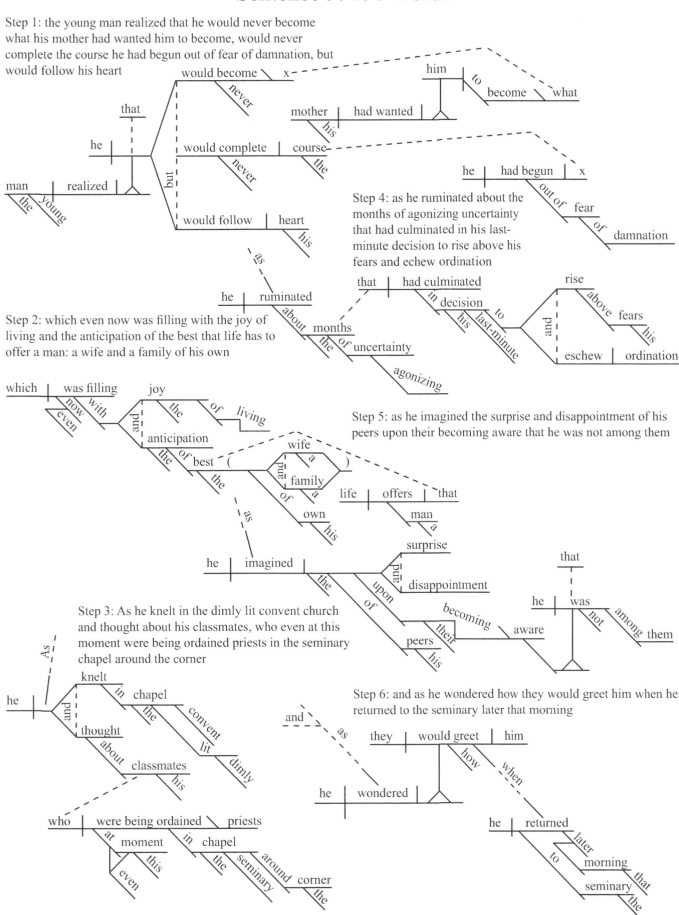

~ 295 ~

Sentence 9: As he knelt in the dimly lit convent chapel and thought about his classmates, who even at this moment were being ordained priests in the seminary chapel around the corner, as he ruminated about the months of agonizing uncertainty that had culminated in his last-minute decision to rise above his fears and eschew ordination, as he imagined the surprise and disappointment of his peers upon their becoming aware that he was not among them, and as he wondered how they would greet him when he returned to the seminary later that morning, the young man realized that he would never become what his mother had wanted him to become, would never complete the course he had begun out of fear of damnation, but would follow his heart, which even now was filling with the joy of living and the anticipation of the best that life offers a man: a wife and family of his own.

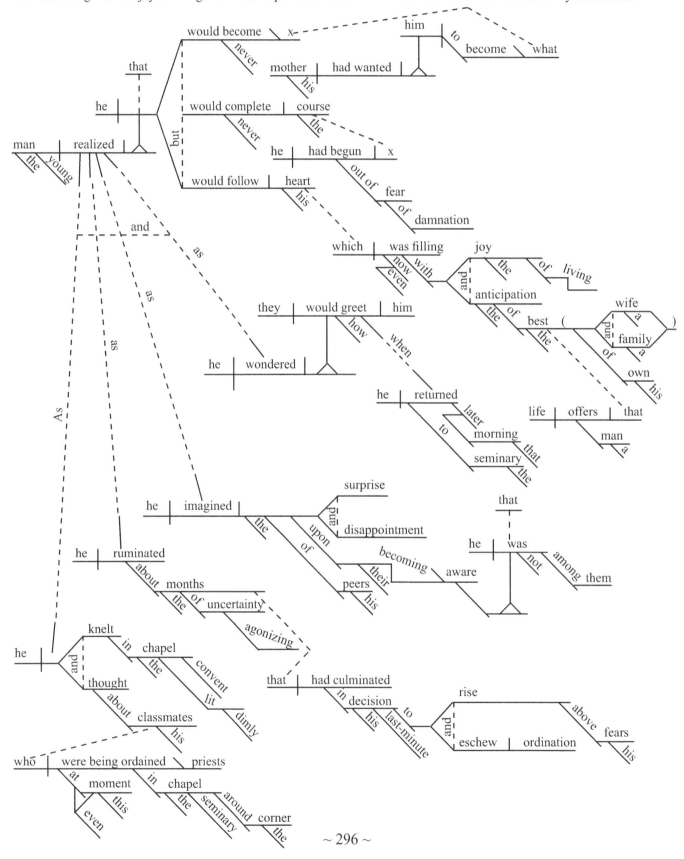

~ 296 ~

Sentence 10: 165 Words

Step 1: It is a fact greatly to be wondered at and abundantly to be praised that no man on his wedding day . . . has ever taken a second to consider that, some years hence, he may be standing at the bedside of his dying wife

Step 2: his mind enraptured by his bride's beauty and filled with thoughts of love

Step 2: (upper right)
Step 3: whose breathing has become erratic and for whom death is only minutes away

Step 5: whose cancer has made it necessary for her to receive all nourishment intravenously for the past five months

Step 6: after which he waits a minute, two minutes for another breath

Step 7: knowing that none will follow and that he has lost the greatest treasure he has ever had and can ever expect to have

Step 4: and yet, 41 years after his wedding, a grieving husband watches as his wife, the mother of his three children, the anchor of their family, . . . takes a final deep breath

Step 8: --the woman to whom (you may have guessed) this book has been gratefully and lovingly dedicated

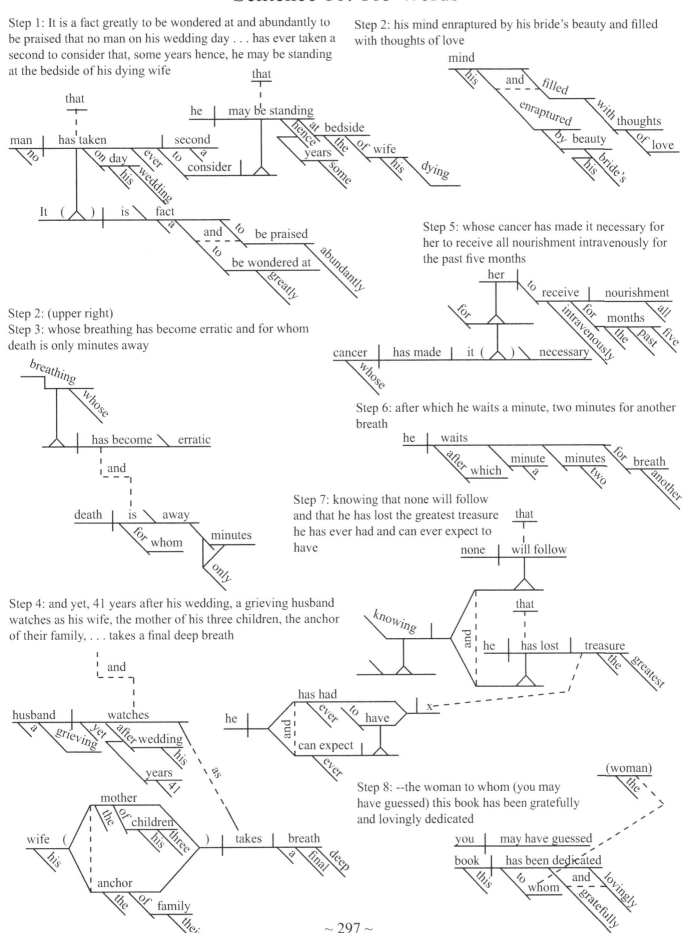

Sentence 10: It is a fact greatly to be wondered at and abundantly to be praised that no man on his wedding day, his mind enraptured by his bride's beauty and filled with thoughts of love, has ever taken a second to consider that, some years hence, he may be standing at the bedside of his dying wife, whose breathing has become erratic and for whom death is only minutes away, and yet, 41 years after his wedding, a grieving husband watches as his wife, the mother of his three children, the anchor of their family, whose cancer has made it necessary for her to receive all nourishment intravenously for the past five months, takes a final deep breath, after which he waits a minute, two minutes for another breath, knowing that none will follow and that he has lost the greatest treasure he has ever had and can ever expect to have--the woman to whom (you may have guessed) this book has been gratefully and lovingly dedicated.

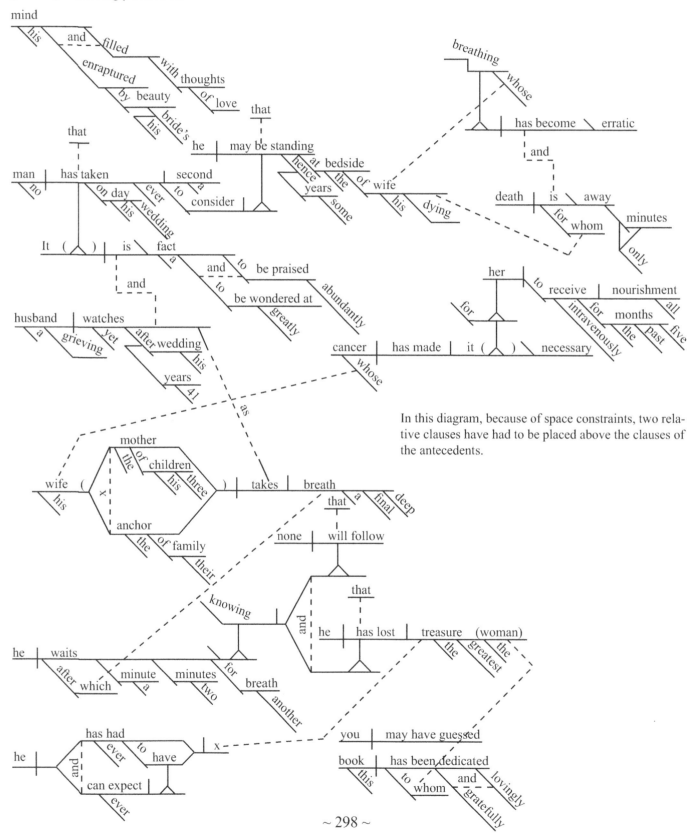

In this diagram, because of space constraints, two relative clauses have had to be placed above the clauses of the antecedents.

Tree-Diagram Solutions

Lesson 3

1.

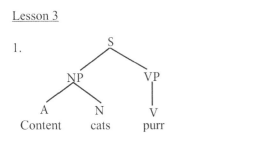

S
NP — VP
A — N — V
Content   cats   purr

2.

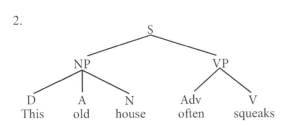

S
NP — VP
D — A — N — Adv — V
This   old   house   often   squeaks

Lesson 4

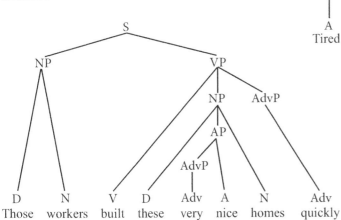

S
NP — VP
VP → NP AdvP
AP → AdvP
D — N — V — D — Adv — A — N — Adv
Those   workers   built   these   very   nice   homes   quickly

Trifurcation, used provisionally in #3 (2), #4, #5, #9, and #11, is inconsistent with the binary structure of tree diagramming. Details will become clear later.

Lesson 5

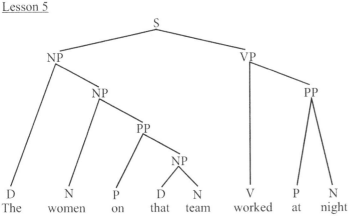

S
NP — VP
NP — PP
D — N — P — D — N — V — P — N
The   women   on   that   team   worked   at   night

Notice the use of NP → D NP.

Lesson 6

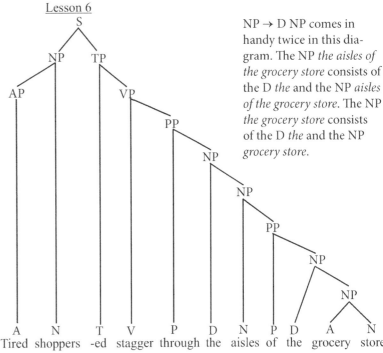

S
NP — TP
AP
VP — PP — NP — NP — PP — NP — NP
A — N — T — V — P — D — N — P — D — A — N
Tired   shoppers   -ed   stagger   through   the   aisles   of   the   grocery   store

NP → D NP comes in handy twice in this diagram. The NP *the aisles of the grocery store* consists of the D *the* and the NP *aisles of the grocery store*. The NP *the grocery store* consists of the D *the* and the NP *grocery store*.

Lesson 7

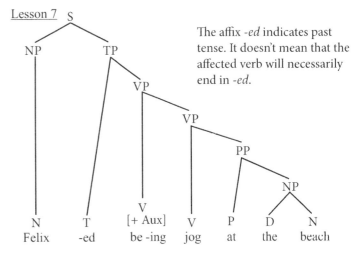

S
NP — TP
VP — VP — PP — NP
N — T — V — V — P — D — N
Felix   -ed   be -ing   jog   at   the   beach
[+ Aux]

The affix *-ed* indicates past tense. It doesn't mean that the affected verb will necessarily end in *-ed*.

Lesson 8

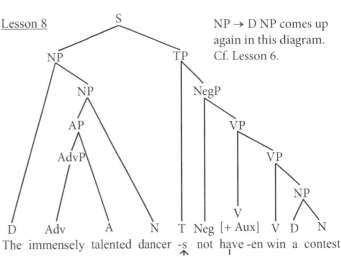

S
NP — TP
NP — NegP
AP — VP
AdvP — VP — NP
D — Adv — A — N — T — Neg — V — V — D — N
The   immensely   talented   dancer   -s   not   have   -en   win   a   contest
[+ Aux]

NP → D NP comes up again in this diagram. Cf. Lesson 6.

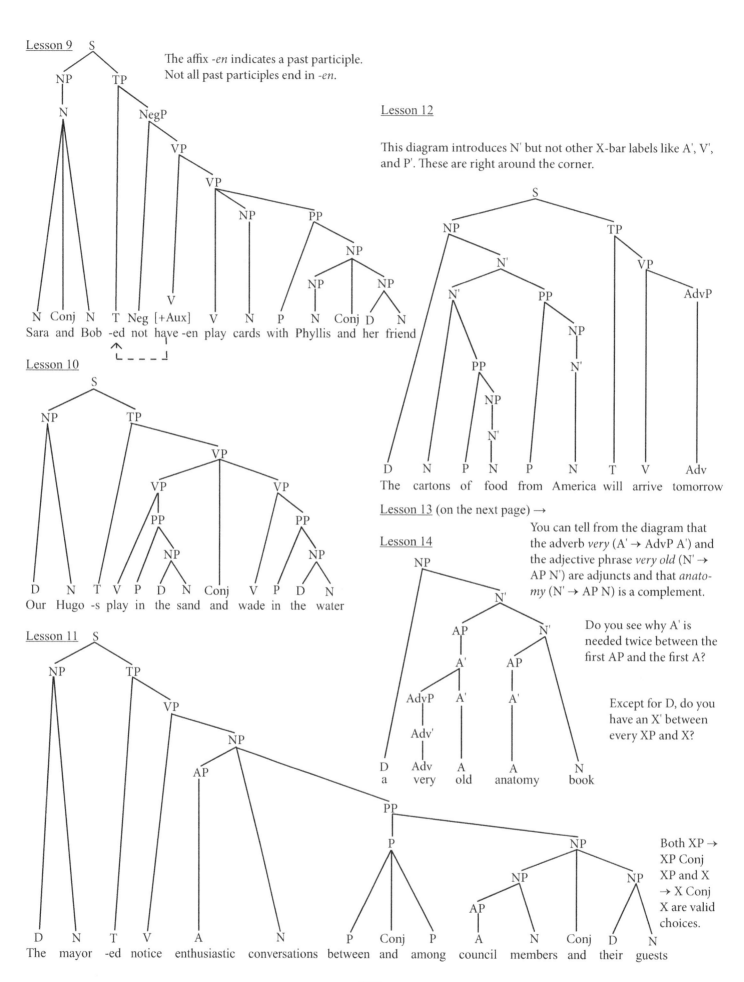

Lesson 9

The affix *-en* indicates a past participle.
Not all past participles end in *-en*.

Sara and Bob -ed not have -en play cards with Phyllis and her friend

Lesson 10

Our Hugo -s play in the sand and wade in the water

Lesson 11

The mayor -ed notice enthusiastic conversations between and among council members and their guests

Lesson 12

This diagram introduces N' but not other X-bar labels like A', V', and P'. These are right around the corner.

The cartons of food from America will arrive tomorrow

Lesson 13 (on the next page) →

Lesson 14

You can tell from the diagram that the adverb *very* (A' → AdvP A') and the adjective phrase *very old* (N' → AP N') are adjuncts and that *anatomy* (N' → AP N) is a complement.

Do you see why A' is needed twice between the first AP and the first A?

Except for D, do you have an X' between every XP and X?

a very old anatomy book

Both XP → XP Conj XP and X → X Conj X are valid choices.

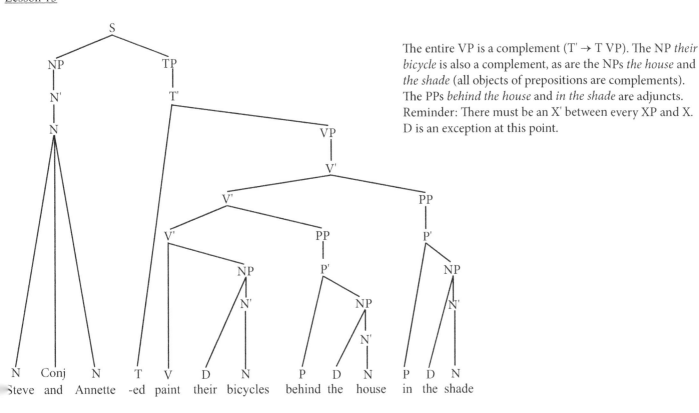

The entire VP is a complement (T' → T VP). The NP *their bicycle* is also a complement, as are the NPs *the house* and *the shade* (all objects of prepositions are complements). The PPs *behind the house* and *in the shade* are adjuncts. Reminder: There must be an X' between every XP and X. D is an exception at this point.

Lesson 15

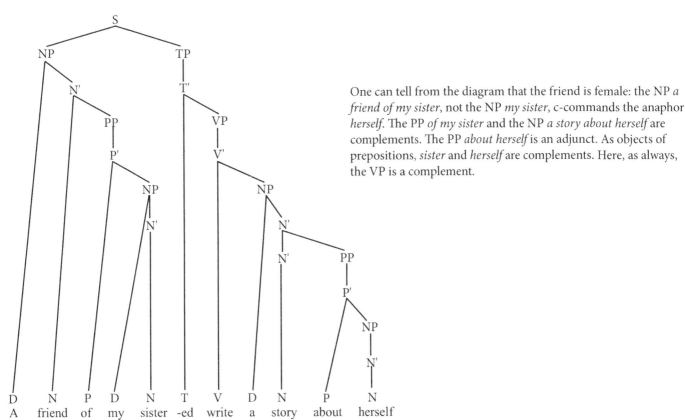

One can tell from the diagram that the friend is female: the NP *a friend of my sister*, not the NP *my sister*, c-commands the anaphor *herself*. The PP *of my sister* and the NP *a story about herself* are complements. The PP *about herself* is an adjunct. As objects of prepositions, *sister* and *herself* are complements. Here, as always, the VP is a complement.

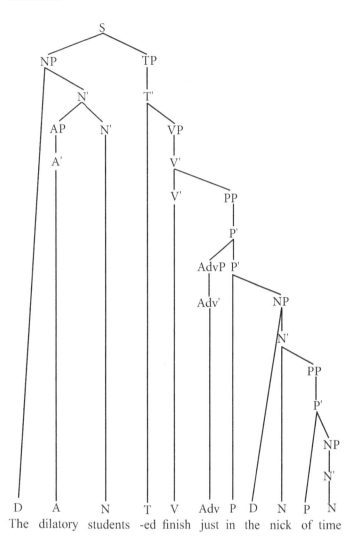

The complementizer phrase *that we moved* is a complement. In traditional grammar, it's a noun clause that functions as a direct object.

Be sure you can read from the diagram that the adjective *dilatory* and the prepositional phrase *just in the nick of time* are adjuncts, while the noun phrase *the nick of time*, the prepositional phrase *of time*, and the single-word noun phrase *time* are complements.

Lesson 18

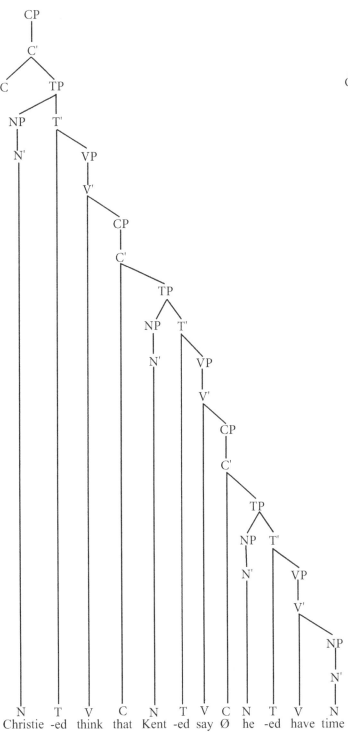

Both CPs are complements (V' → V CP). Note that the TPs introduced by the complementizers (one expressed and one unexpressed) are also complements (C' → C TP).

Lesson 19

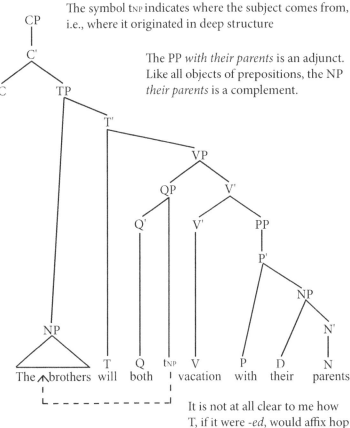

The symbol t_NP indicates where the subject comes from, i.e., where it originated in deep structure

The PP *with their parents* is an adjunct. Like all objects of prepositions, the NP *their parents* is a complement.

It is not at all clear to me how T, if it were *-ed*, would affix hop onto V since Q intervenes.

Lesson 20

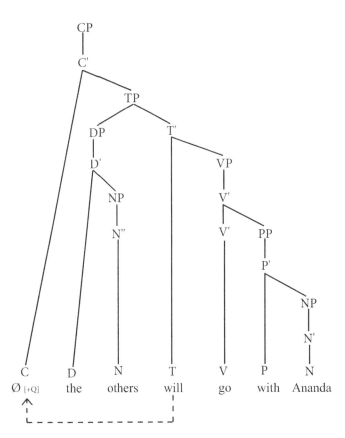

Lesson 21

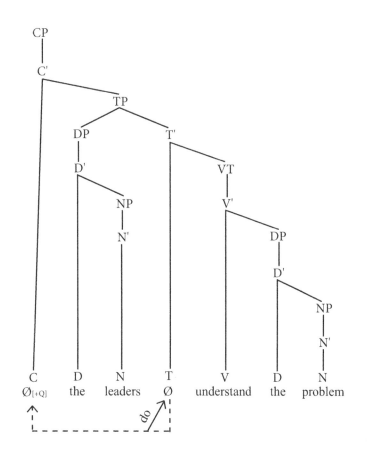

Lesson 22

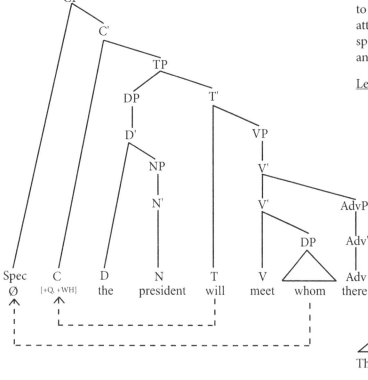

Lesson 23

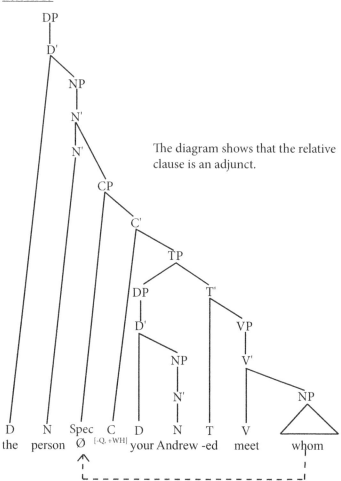

The diagram shows that the relative clause is an adjunct.

Only phrases can undergo WH-movement. *Wh*-phrases move to spec of C, attracted by [+WH] of C. The notion that [+WH] attaches to C is supported by the fact that some languages have special complementizers that express [+Q, +WH], [+Q, -WH], and [-Q, -WH].

Lesson 24

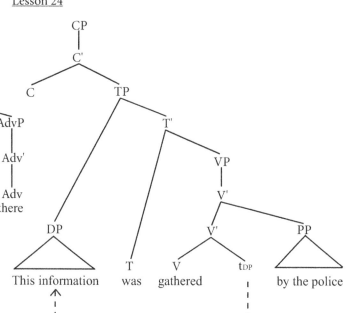

Made in the USA
Las Vegas, NV
30 March 2024